COMPUTER TEST BANK

PRENTICE HALL

America: Pathways
to the Present

Code 070

Prentice Hall
Englewood Cliffs, New Jersey
Needham, Massachusetts

COMPUTER TEST BANK

PRENTICE HALL America: Pathways to the Present

ISBN 0-13-830555-2

1 2 3 4 5 6 7 8 9 10   98 97 96 95 94

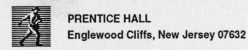

PRENTICE HALL
Englewood Cliffs, New Jersey 07632

Contents

ABOUT THE COMPUTER TEST BANK

The PRENTICE HALL America: **Pathways to the Present Computer Test Bank** provides you with a sophisticated tool for creating quizzes, chapter tests, midterms, and finals tailored to your individual classroom needs.

Available for DOS/IBM Systems and the Macintosh

You may order your easy-to-use software for the PRENTICE HALL **America: Pathways to the Present Computer Test Bank** in either a DOS-based or a Macintosh format. Just fill out the order form on the next page, designating which format you prefer, and mail the postage-paid order form to Prentice Hall. You will receive your disks together with complete installation and operating instructions in just a few weeks. (Individuals ordering the DOS disks will receive complete software on both 5 1/4" and 3 1/2" disks.)

Flexible Test Making

The PRENTICE HALL **America: Pathways to the Present Computer Test Bank** allows you to create tests easily and conveniently. You can select or add exactly the questions you want for each test. You can design tests for students of different ability levels, or you can select or add questions based on content you emphasized in class. You can use the

Computer Test Bank to create different tests for different classes or alternate versions of the same test. The **America: Pathways to the Present Test Bank** also allows you to tailor tests to meet your state and local course requirements and to build the appropriate content, skills, and critical thinking into your testing program. And there is no need to cut and paste the map, graph, or chart that students need to answer a test item. When you select a test item linked to an illustration, the Computer Test Bank will automatically print the illustration along with the question.

You can view all the test questions in your America: Pathways to the Present Computer Test Bank on-screen at your computer, or you may prefer to examine the available questions by looking at the printouts of the computer files in this book.

Help Is Just a Phone Call Away

Stuck at any point? Simply call our toll-free HELP Hotline for continuous and reliable support. The phone number for the hotline will be enclosed with your disks.

If you need more information about receiving the disks for your PRENTICE HALL **America: Pathways to the Present Computer Test Bank**, call Customer Service at 1-800-848-9500 or contact your Prentice Hall Sales Representative.

COMPUTER TEST BANK ORDER FORM

For Macintosh and IBM disks for the *PRENTICE HALL America: Pathways to the Present* Computer Test Bank

TO ORDER:
Complete this form,
(Please print)
Tear out, Fold, Tape,
and Mail.

We have already paid the postage for you.

PLEASE CHECK WHICH TYPE OF DISK YOU WANT.

PLEASE CHECK ONLY <u>ONE</u> TYPE OF DISK.

ITEM# (ISBN)	DESCRIPTION	CHECK HERE
0-13-830530-7	Macintosh 3 1/2-inch Computer Disks for the *Prentice Hall America: Pathways to the Present Computer Test Bank* (User's Guide included)	☐
0-13-830480-7	IBM Computer Disks for the *Prentice Hall America: Pathways to the Present Computer Test Bank* (Includes both 3 1/2- and 5 1/4-inch disks and User's Guide)	☐

SHIP TO:

SCHOOL _____   PHONE _____

SCHOOL ADDRESS _____

CITY _____ STATE _____ ZIP _____

NAME _____

For Internal use _____

Three Cultures Collide
(Before and After the 1400s)

Test Bank Questions

Complete each of the following sentences by selecting the appropriate term from the choices listed in parentheses.

1. In the 1400s most Europeans explained the contrasts among the wealthy, middle class, and working poor as part of a (division of labor, hierarchy).

2. The faith which follows the teachings of Muhammad is (Islam, Guinea).

3. The (lineage, kinship network) of a Native American family included grandparents, aunts, uncles, cousins, and those who had married into the family.

4. A male-dominated social organization is called a (clan, patriarchal society).

5. Native Americans passed their history and beliefs from generation to generation by way of (oral traditions, artifacts).

6. (Askia Muhammad, Christopher Columbus) ruled over the kingdom of Songhai.

7. The Muslim holy book is called the (Ozette, Koran).

8. The area of encounter among the people of the Americas, Africa, and Europe is known as the (West Indies, Atlantic World).

Write the letter of the correct ending.

9. Hunting vast herds of buffalo is an example of how Native Americans
   A) practiced a nomadic way of life.
   B) relied on kinship networks.
   C) adapted to their natural environment.
   D) set up patriarchal societies.

10. In Native American cultures, most social, religious, and political services were provided by
   A) a group of elected officials.
   B) the youngest members of the clan.
   C) the women.
   D) the extended family.

Test Bank Questions

Write the letter of the correct ending.

11. According the the fifteenth-century European view of the world,
    A) only women could own land.
    B) the church was the most important social unit in society.
    C) all people, except the enslaved, had equal rights.
    D) the wealthy had power over the poor.

12. All of the following were true of most European households in the 1400s EXCEPT that
    A) individual interests were encouraged.
    B) kinship was highly valued.
    C) the primary purpose of the household was production.
    D) the household operated as a patriarchy.

13. Unlike European traders, Native American groups traded goods in order to
    A) support their families.   B) make friends.
    C) avoid social obligations.   D) increase their wealth.

14. Queen Isabella and King Ferdinand sought to
    A) drive Muslims from the Spanish Christian kingdoms.
    B) prevent Europeans from trading with West Africans.
    C) prevent slavery on the Iberian peninsula.
    D) halt trade with Native Americans.

15. Most European Christians in the 1400s believed that
    A) the spread of Islam would promote Christianity.
    B) the Americas were not a part of God's divine plan.
    C) the end of the world was fast approaching.
    D) priests and bishops should sell indulgences.

16. In the 1400s, the West African forest kingdom of Benin was
    A) a small farming community.   B) an isolated society.
    C) large and wealthy.   D) unstable and unorganized.

17. In the late 1400s the empire of Songhai
    A) cut off all business with European traders.
    B) thrived as a major trading power.
    C) was destroyed by Muslim invaders.
    D) began to decline as a result of corrupt government.

Test Bank Questions

Write the letter of the correct ending.

18. One way life in West Africa differed from life in Europe in the 1400s was that
    A) ownership of land was a major source of wealth.
    B) slavery played a major role in the economy.
    C) disease was rare.
    D) overpopulation resulted in widespread starvation.

19. The greatest immediate effect of the European arrival in the Americas was
    A) the conversion of the majority of Native Americans to Christianity.
    B) a decline in the Native American population as a result of widespread disease.
    C) a mass migration of Native Americans from North to South America.
    D) a decline in trading among Native American cultures.

20. Europeans sought to conquer the Americas largely because they wanted to
    A) study and document Native American cultures and religions.
    B) convert America's natural resources into tradeable goods.
    C) capture Native Americans for sale as slaves in Europe.
    D) protect the Americas from invasion by Asians.

21. One effect of the Atlantic slave trade on West Africa was
    A) the establishment of sugar plantations.
    B) the destruction of many societies.
    C) European settlement.
    D) lasting peace.

Test Bank Questions

Use the map of migration to America to answer the following questions.

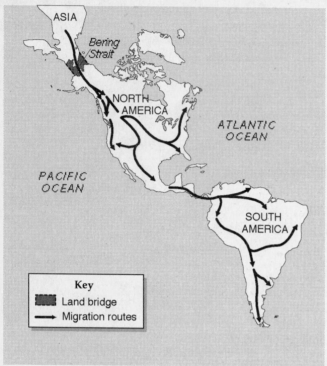

22. (a) From what part of the world did early peoples migrate to what is now Alaska?
    (b) How far south did early peoples migrate?

23. To which regions of what is today the United States did early peoples migrate?

24. How do you think archaeologists have been able to recreate these patterns of migration?

Answer the following questions.

25. How were the religious beliefs of Native Americans, European Christians, and some West Africans alike in the 1400s? How did religious beliefs differ?

26. Christopher Columbus wrote in his diary, "Gold is most excellent. Gold constitutes treasure, and he who possesses it may do what he will in the world...." How was this belief consistent with European thinking in the 1400s?

27. From a European point of view, why was West Africa the logical choice as a source of slave labor?

Test Bank Questions

Complete each of the following sentences by selecting the appropriate term from the choices listed in parentheses.

28. The Koran is the holy book of (Islam, Benin).

29. For Native Americans, the family was a (kinship network, hierarchy).

30. Native Americans relied on (artifacts, oral tradition) as a way of preserving their history and spiritual beliefs.

31. A social organization in which the father is the head of the household is called a (patriarchal society, clan).

32. (Division of labor, Natural order) is the assigning of specific tasks to certain groups or individuals.

33. Early followers of the prophet (Muhammad, Ferdinand) were called Muslims.

Write the letter of the correct answer.

34. Which was true of the early peoples who migrated from Asia?
    A) They maintained contact with other groups of peoples across the Atlantic.
    B) They could not survive the harsh Alaskan climate.
    C) They developed distinct languages and customs.
    D) They all settled in coastal areas.

35. Which of the following does NOT illustrate how Native Americans adapted to their natural environment?
    A) The Shoshoni lived as hunter-gatherers.
    B) Some groups developed a fishing and food storage technology.
    C) Many cultures used plants to make medicines and poison.
    D) They held religious ceremonies to prevent misfortune.

36. What was universally true of Native American societies throughout the Americas?
    A) Societies depended greatly upon growing corn.
    B) Families provided most social needs.
    C) Native Americans lived together in large groups.
    D) Buffalo became the most important resource.

37. On which subject did Native American and European attitudes differ in the 1400s?
    A) importance of family
    B) importance of trade
    C) ownership of land
    D) value of religious ceremony

Test Bank Questions

Write the letter of the correct answer.

38. Which of the following was true of land in fifteenth-century Europe?
    A) Farming played a minor role in Europe's economy.
    B) By law, farmers owned the land they tilled.
    C) Most landowners could barely afford to pay laborers.
    D) Land ownership was equated with wealth.

39. What belief did Native American, European, and West African societies share?
    A) An important social unit was the family.
    B) Slavery was an abomination.
    C) All people should have equal rights.
    D) Land could not be traded or owned.

40. Which of the following did NOT trouble most European Christians in the 1400s?
    A) the spread of Islam
    B) corruption in the Catholic church
    C) the reign of Queen Isabella
    D) fear of disease

41. What did the kingdoms of Guinea have in common with Songhai?
    A) Most people followed Islam.
    B) Arabic was commonly spoken.
    C) Trade was vital to the economy.
    D) Kinship networks were unnecessary.

42. Which statement accurately describes Songhai under the rule of Askia Muhammad?
    A) Citizens were not taxed.
    B) Teaching the Koran was prohibited.
    C) Christians were persecuted.
    D) Paid officials administered laws and kept the peace.

43. What was the major reason for the practice of slavery in Africa?
    A) a lack of livestock   B) a shortage of labor
    C) a shortage of land   D) widespread disease

44. How did the arrival of the Europeans in the Americas affect Native Americans?
    A) Native American groups banded together to form strong empires.
    B) European diseases decimated American populations.
    C) Native Americans learned to farm.
    D) Native Americans established their first trading system.

Test Bank Questions

Write the letter of the correct answer.

45. How did Columbus's encounter with the Americas impact Europe?

A) European nations were at peace with one another for the first time in centuries.

B) American diseases ravaged European populations.

C) Europe became the world's wealthiest continent.

D) Native American traditions forever changed European culture.

46. What major role did West Africans play in the European settlement of the Americas?

A) They taught the Europeans farming methods for tropical climates.

B) They supplied the labor needed to cultivate cash crops.

C) They supplied the firearms needed to control rebellious Native Americans.

D) They were the largest consumers of American products.

Use the map of migration to America to answer the following questions.

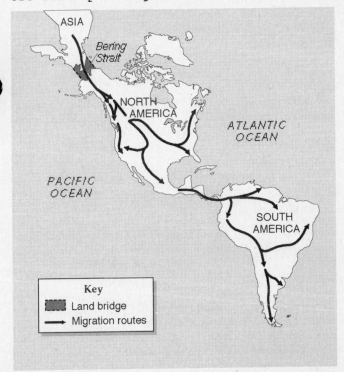

47. What geographic feature made it possible for early peoples to migrate from Asia to North America?

48. In what directions did most waves of migrants travel?

49. Why do you think migrating peoples did NOT travel north?

Test Bank Questions

Use the map of migration to America to answer the following questions.

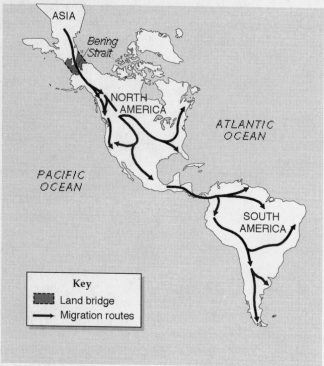

50. What evidence exists that enables archaeologists to recreate patterns of migration?

Answer the following questions.

51. What are some ways in which Native American and West African cultures were alike? Describe three similarities.

52. During their return voyage to Spain, Columbus and his crew encountered a dangerous storm at sea. In desperation, the entire crew fell to their knees and prayed loudly for God to save them. How do you think Native Americans aboard the ship viewed this religious ritual? Explain.

53. Historian Alfred W. Crosby once remarked, "The Columbian exchange of peoples, plants, products, and diseases, and ideas [was] the most important event in human history since the end of the Ice Age...." What evidence would you use to support Crosby's statement?

Test Bank Answer Key

[1] hierarchy

[2] Islam

[3] kinship network

[4] patriarchal society

[5] oral traditions

[6] Askia Muhammad

[7] Koran

[8] Atlantic World

[9] C

[10] D

[11] D

[12] A

[13] B

[14] A

[15] C

[16] C

[17] B

[18] B

[19] B

[20] B

[21] B

[22] (a) Asia
(b) to the southernmost tip of South America

[23] Northwest coast, Northeast, Southeast, Midwest Plains

[24] Archaeologists have been able to recreate these migration patterns by studying artifacts and by using dating techniques to determine when people arrived in various regions.

Test Bank Answer Key

[25] Native Americans, European Christians, and West Africans shared a belief that the most powerful forces in the world were spiritual and that ceremony and prayer must be performed in order to prevent misfortune. Unlike Native Americans and West Africans who believed that spirits existed in both animate and inanimate objects, European Christians believed in a single, all-powerful God who had a divine plan for the entire world.

[26] Gold, which could be exchanged for money and other goods, equaled wealth in the 1400s. Columbus' statement that whoever possessed great wealth could do as one pleased was consistent with the hierarchical system in Europe in which the wealthy had power over all those beneath them.

[27] Europeans had already established trading posts in West Africa and were familiar with the slave trade that existed among many African countries. In addition, West Africa was easily accessible by sea.

[28] Islam

[29] kinship network

[30] oral tradition

[31] patriarchal society

[32] Division of labor

[33] Muhammad

[34] C

[35] D

[36] B

[37] C

[38] D

[39] A

[40] C

[41] C

[42] D

[43] B

[44] B

[45] C

Test Bank Answer Key

[46] B

[47] A "land bridge" connected Asia with what is today Alaska.

[48] They moved southward from Alaska and eastward.

[49] They did not move north because the area was covered by glaciers.

[50] Archaeologists have been able to recreate migration patterns by studying artifacts and by using dating techniques to determine when people arrived in various regions. Also, archaeologists know what areas of the American continents were covered with glaciers, thus preventing migration to those areas.

[51] Both Native Americans and West Africans used oral tradition to preserve their history and beliefs, viewed kinship networks as the most important social unit, relied on ceremony and prayer to ward off misfortune, and developed networks of trade routes that linked their many societies.

[52] The Native Americans probably respected this religious ritual, since their own religion taught that spiritual forces controlled events on earth. Like Europeans, Native Americans believed that religious rituals and ceremonies warded off misfortune.

[53] The voyage of Columbus established a permanent exchange among Native Americans, Europeans, and Africans and brought tremendous changes to these cultures. The diseases that Europeans brought to the Americas decimated Native American populations. Gold and silver from the Americas made Europe the richest continent on earth. In Africa, manioc from America became a staple food, and entire societies were wiped out by the slave trade.

European Settlement and Native American Resistance (1519-1689)

Test Bank Questions

Match the terms below with the following descriptions. Write the letter of the correct answer. You will not use all the terms.

a. presidio
b. religious toleration
c. colony
d. conquistador
e. sachem
f. joint-stock company
g. indentured servant
h. Great Migration
i. hidalgo
j. enclosure movement
k. encomienda system
l. congregacion
m. Reformation

1. leader of a Native American group

2. Spanish term for conqueror

3. religious movement that led to the establishment of Protestant churches

4. idea that people of different faiths should live together in peace

5. eviction of tenant farmers to turn fields into pasture

6. person who contracted to work for a master for a set period of time

7. land area settled by immigrants who remain subjects of parent country

8. association of investors who each contribute money to the costs of an enterprise

9. settled village where Native Americans farmed and worshiped like Catholic Europeans

10. Spanish gentleman who led expeditions against Muslims

Write the letter of the correct ending.

11. The encomienda system illustrates how the Spanish

    A) forced Native Americans to participate in Spanish culture.

    B) tried to prevent the development of social classes in the Americas.

    C) learned to respect Native American cultures.

    D) decimated Native American societies.

Test Bank Questions

Write the letter of the correct ending.

12. The Spanish established presidios in Florida and New Mexico in order to
    A) help other Europeans adjust to Native American culture.
    B) protect Spanish fleets and spread Christianity.
    C) train Native Americans for duty in the Spanish military.
    D) treat Native Americans suffering from smallpox and other diseases.

13. The Pueblo Revolt of 1680 is an example of how
    A) the English encouraged Native Americans to rebel against Spanish rule.
    B) some Native Americans resisted Spanish rule.
    C) the Spanish allowed Native Americans to govern local affairs.
    D) disputes over land divided Native Americans.

14. Early English settlers believed that successful settlements depended upon
    A) the practice of religious tolerance toward Native Americans.
    B) the teaching of Native American cultures to Europeans.
    C) the complete destruction and remaking of Native American cultures.
    D) a peaceful blending of Native American and European cultures.

15. The Virginia colony survived largely because the English colonists
    A) worked cooperatively for the good of the colony.
    B) developed lasting friendships with Native Americans.
    C) began growing tobacco for sale.
    D) were well cared for by the Virginia Company.

16. After Bacon's Rebellion, the Virginia colony
    A) became a relatively classless society.
    B) was largely controlled by small farmers.
    C) was governed by an elite group of wealthy planters.
    D) became more dependent on trade with Native Americans.

17. The French and Dutch fur trade depended on all of the following EXCEPT
    A) forming strong trading ties with Native Americans.
    B) preserving forests, streams, and other natural habitats.
    C) converting Native Americans to Christianity.
    D) shipping goods via natural water routes.

Test Bank Questions

Write the letter of the correct ending.

18. Unlike the early French and Dutch settlers, the Puritans
    A) developed good relations with Native American groups.
    B) learned to respect Native American customs.
    C) transformed the American landscape into farmland.
    D) promoted religious toleration.

19. The main goal of Native Americans in King Philip's War was to
    A) stop the spread of English settlements.
    B) capture European weapons and farm tools.
    C) end the French exploitation of Native American trade routes.
    D) seize farm animals and crops to feed their starving populations.

20. As a result of King Philip's War,
    A) Native Americans became stereotyped as violent and cruel.
    B) Native American and European societies became interdependent.
    C) the Puritans lost control of New England.
    D) a powerful Native American society was established.

Use the time line to answer the following questions.

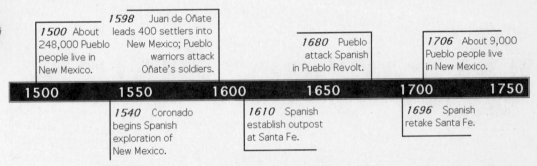

21. (a) How many years does the time line cover?
    (b) How many years after Coronado began his exploration of New Mexico did the Spanish begin settling the region?

22. How did the Pueblo people react to the Spanish settlement of New Mexico?

23. Based on the information in the time line, what was one result of the Pueblo Revolt?

Answer the following questions.

24. Discuss three reasons why it was virtually impossible for European American and Native American societies to peacefully coexist.

25. In your opinion, which pattern of interaction with Native Americans was the greatest threat to the Native American way of life--that of the Spanish, the English, or the French? Support your answer.

Test Bank Questions

Complete each sentence below by selecting the correct word from the list. You will not use all the words.

a. congregacion
b. Great Migration
c. hidalgo
d. enclosure movement
e. Reformation
f. sachem
g. religious toleration
h. encomienda system
i. joint-stock company
j. presidio
k. colony
l. indentured servant

26. A Spanish expedition to promote Chistianity and acquire wealth often was led by a young Spanish gentleman, or _____.

27. Native Americans who lived in a _____ farmed and worshipped like Spanish Catholics.

28. The Puritans who settled the Massachusetts Bay Colony did not believe in the principle of _____.

29. Metacom was the _____ of the Pokanokets.

30. A typical Spanish settlement in North America consisted of a fort, or _____.

31. In 1606, 104 adventurers created a(n) _____ to sponsor an English colony in the Americas.

32. In the early 1500s, the _____ brought bitter divisions to European Christians.

33. During the _____, English landowners evicted tenant farmers and turned fields into pastures.

34. A great wave of European immigrants journeyed across the Atlantic Ocean during the _____.

35. Under the _____, Native Americans were forced to work for the profit of an individual Spaniard.

Write the letter of the correct ending.

36. When the Spanish conquered Native American societies, one of their main objectives was to
    A) learn the Native American way of life.
    B) blend Native American and Spanish culture.
    C) destroy completely Native American cultures.
    D) develop trade relations with Native Americans.

37. In an effort to protect their empire and treasure fleets from other Europeans, the Spanish established
    A) congregacions.
    B) the encomienda system.
    C) presidios.
    D) joint-stock companies.

Test Bank Questions

Write the letter of the correct ending.

38. Many Spanish settlement efforts failed as a result of
    A) the establishment of more appealing French settlements.
    B) Native American rebellions and English attacks.
    C) uncooperative Franciscans and poorly trained soldiers.
    D) the Great Migration.

39. All of the following describe early life in Jamestown EXCEPT:
    A) The efforts of the Virginia Company saved the colony from near failure.
    B) Native Americans supplied the starving settlers with food and water.
    C) Disease caused thousands of deaths.
    D) Many settlers would not participate in hard physical work.

40. One result of the tobacco boom in Virginia was
    A) the rise of a classless society.
    B) a large migration of indentured servants to the colony.
    C) lasting cooperation between the English and Native Americans.
    D) rivalry between Dutch and English settlers over European trade.

41. Bacon led a rebellion against the colonial government of Jamestown to protest
    A) the government's refusal to protect settlers from Native Americans.
    B) the unequal distribution of land and power in Virginia.
    C) export duties on tobacco.
    D) the West African slave trade.

42. The early French and Dutch colonists were most interested in
    A) pushing Native American groups west.
    B) transforming the American countryside into towns and farmlands.
    C) conquering and remaking Native American cultures.
    D) forming trading ties with Native American hunters and trappers.

43. The Puritans migrated to New England in order to
    A) escape religious persecution.
    B) find gold and other sources of wealth.
    C) establish Catholic missions.
    D) experiment with new ways of life.

Test Bank Questions

Write the letter of the correct ending.

44. King Philip's War was an example of how
    A) French and English colonists fought for control of the Northeast.
    B) Native Americans fought to defend their way of life.
    C) European colonists tried to spread Christianity.
    D) Native Americans sympathized with the French.

45. One long-term effect of King Philip's War was
    A) an alliance between French and English colonists.
    B) the end of the Great Migration.
    C) the economic dependency of New Englanders on New England.
    D) the beginning of self-government in New England.

Use the time line to answer the following questions.

1500 About 248,000 Pueblo people live in New Mexico.

1598 Juan de Oñate leads 400 settlers into New Mexico; Pueblo warriors attack Oñate's soldiers.

1680 Pueblo attack Spanish in Pueblo Revolt.

1706 About 9,000 Pueblo people live in New Mexico.

1500   1550   1600   1650   1700   1750

1540 Coronado begins Spanish exploration of New Mexico.

1610 Spanish establish outpost at Santa Fe.

1696 Spanish retake Santa Fe.

46. (a) Into what intervals is the time line divided?
    (b) How many years of peace were there between major Pueblo attacks on the Spanish?

47. For how many years after the Pueblo Revolt were the Spanish kept out of Santa Fe?

48. What effect did the Spanish arrival in New Mexico have on the Pueblo population?

Answer the following questions.

49. Compare how the French fur traders and the English settlers in New England impacted Native American groups.

50. Wilma Mankiller, the first female Chief of the Cherokee Nation of Oklahoma, once said, "Without a doubt, the darkest pages in American history are those that chronicle the story of the taking of the Americas from indigenous people." What evidence could Mankiller use to support her statement?

Test Bank Answer Key

[1] e

[2] d

[3] m

[4] b

[5] j

[6] g

[7] c

[8] f

[9] l

[10] i

[11] A

[12] B

[13] B

[14] C

[15] C

[16] C

[17] C

[18] C

[19] A

[20] A

[21] (a) 250 years
     (b) fifty-eight years later

[22] The Pueblo people attacked Oñate's soldiers and later launched the Pueblo Revolt.

[23] The Spanish were forced out of Santa Fe.

Test Bank Answer Key

[24] As a result of cultural differences and the European attitude of cultural superiority, Native Americans and Europeans distrusted and feared each other. European desires to exploit Native American labor and wealth provoked Native Americans to defend their societies and their way of life. European farms and villages encroached on Native American lands, diminishing their food supply of wild game and vegetation, and in turn, threatening their very survival.

[25] The English were the greatest threat to the Native American way of life because they wanted to destroy and remake Native American culture in their own image. Their pattern of settlement also destroyed Native American hunting grounds.

[26] c

[27] a

[28] g

[29] f

[30] j

[31] i

[32] e

[33] d

[34] b

[35] h

[36] B

[37] C

[38] B

[39] A

[40] B

[41] B

[42] D

[43] A

[44] B

[45] C

Test Bank Answer Key

(a) 50 year intervals
[46] (b) 82 years

[47] 16 years

[48] The Spanish arrival reduced significantly the Pueblo population in New Mexico.

[49] The French fur trade caused great strife among Native American groups eager to trade for European products and led to wars among Native American groups for control of hunting grounds. English farming methods, which destroyed valuable hunting grounds, brought the Native Americans into conflict with the English colonists themselves.

[50] Mankiller could note that European diseases decimated Native American populations; the Spanish forced Native Americans to work in the encomienda system; some Native Americans were sold into slavery; English settlements forced Native Americans off their lands; and conflicts such as the Pueblo Revolt and King Philip's War cost the lives of thousands of Native Americans and European colonists.

The Maturing of Colonial Societies (1689-1754)

Test Bank Questions

Use each term below in a sentence which shows the meaning of the term.

1. mercantilism

2. balance of trade

3. cousinocracy

4. low country

5. Middle Passage

Write the letter of the correct ending.

6. English mercantilists believed that the colonies should

    A) buy ships from England.

    B) sell raw materials only to England.

    C) manufacture their own goods.

    D) sell products from all nations.

7. Trade flourished between the colonies and Great Britain in the early 1700s largely as the result of

    A) the British policy of salutary neglect.

    B) Britain's tight control over colonial legislatures.

    C) passage of the Navigation Act.

    D) the Glorious Revolution.

8. In the late 1600s and early 1700s, colonial society and government were dominated by

    A) a few wealthy manufacturers.

    B) prominent slave traders.

    C) a small group of male landowners.

    D) religious leaders.

9. Both William Byrd and Benjamin Franklin worked hard at

    A) succeeding in business.

    B) improving the status of colonial women.

    C) blending European and African American cultures.

    D) winning acceptance as "gentlemen."

Test Bank Questions

Write the letter of the correct ending.

10. In colonial America, most women
    A) were prohibited from managing family business affairs.
    B) exercised unlimited power in their homes.
    C) were legally inferior to men.
    D) owned land.

11. In the early 1700s, most enslaved Africans in South Carolina and Georgia
    A) bought their freedom.
    B) had regular contact with European American culture.
    C) preserved their cultural traditions.
    D) worked primarily as artisans.

12. Enslaved people in Virginia and Maryland in the early 1700s
    A) resorted to substitute kin.
    B) enjoyed legal rights such as ownership of land.
    C) cultivated tobacco and worked at a variety of other economic tasks.
    D) found it difficult to maintain close family ties.

13. British colonists began to move westward in the mid-1700s largely because
    A) there was no longer enough land to support expanding populations.
    B) slave rebellions were common occurrences in the British colonies.
    C) farming was becoming much less profitable in the East.
    D) Native Americans were willing to trade western land for European goods.

14. In the early 1750s, colonists in western Pennsylvania and Virginia vied with the French and Native Americans for control of
    A) the Fall Line.   B) the low country.
    C) the forks of the Ohio River.   D) Canada.

15. The Great Awakening is best described as
    A) a total rejection of Puritan ideas.
    B) the shift of many New Englanders to the Quaker faith.
    C) a series of religious revivals in the British colonies.
    D) the conversion of thousands of Native Americans to Christianity.

Test Bank Questions

Use the map of triangular trade routes in the 1700s to answer the following questions.

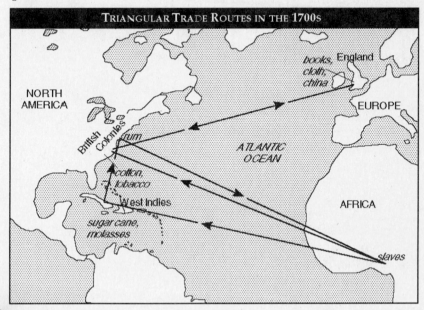

TRIANGULAR TRADE ROUTES IN THE 1700S

16. Name three areas involved in one of the routes shown.

17. In what ways did the colonies and England benefit from triangular trade?

18. What role did enslaved Africans play in the triangular trade route that passed through the West Indies?

Answer the following questions.

19. Compare the economies of the Southern, Middle, and New England colonies in the 1700s. How were they alike? How did they differ?

20. What problems were created as a result of the prosperity and population growth of the British colonies?

21. Your text states that the British colonies in North America "were not societies that valued or expected equality." What examples can you cite to support this conclusion?

Match the terms below with the following descriptions. Write the letter of the correct answer. You will not use all the terms.

a. gentry
b. mercantilism
c. forks of the Ohio River
d. salutary neglect
e. Middle Passage
f. balance of trade
g. cousinocracy
h. Great Awakening
i. low country
j. triangular trade

22. relationship that exists between a nation's exports and imports

Test Bank Questions

Match the terms below with the following descriptions. Write the letter of the correct answer. You will not use all the terms.

a. gentry
b. mercantilism
c. forks of the Ohio River
d. salutary neglect
e. Middle Passage
f. balance of trade
g. cousinocracy
h. Great Awakening
i. low country
j. triangular trade

23. British policy of the early 1700s that allowed the American colonies great freedom in governing themselves

24. strategic area where the Allegheny and Monongahela rivers meet

25. economic system designed to increase a nation's wealth, largely through the accumulation of bullion

26. political control exercised by families related by blood or marriage

27. coastal plain region of South Carolina and Georgia

Write the letter of the correct answer.

28. Which of the following greatly improved Great Britain's balance of trade in the late 1600s and early 1700s?
    A) The colonies provided Britain with raw materials.
    B) England shipped raw materials to the colonies.
    C) The colonies shipped England gold and silver.
    D) The colonies manufactured goods for sale in England.

29. Which of the following was true of colonial American society?
    A) It was divided into two classes--Americans of European descent and African Americans.
    B) It was based on the principle of inequality.
    C) It was based on the principle of economic opportunity for all.
    D) All citizens had the same political rights.

30. Which of the following statements best describes colonial "gentlemen"?
    A) They had a strong work ethic and engaged in physical labor.
    B) They strove to be refined, well-mannered, and respected.
    C) They despised slavery and worked to abolish it.
    D) They had little interest in European affairs.

31. For which of the following is Eliza Lucas Pinckney remembered?
    A) creating employment opportunities for artisans
    B) managing her father's plantations and promoting indigo
    C) working to improve the legal status of colonial women
    D) blending the customs of African and European origin

Test Bank Questions

Write the letter of the correct answer.

32. Which of the following was NOT true of conditions on the Middle Passage?
    A) Enslaved Africans sometimes staged mutinies.
    B) Africans were usually in chains.
    C) Young children were treated better than adult men and women.
    D) Many Africans died of disease.

33. Why were enslaved Africans in the low country more likely to preserve their traditions than those in other regions?
    A) They had no sense of kinship.
    B) They had little contact with European Americans.
    C) Relatively few slaves had come directly from Africa.
    D) They had more leisure time than did enslaved people on tobacco plantations.

34. What was the major work of enslaved African Americans who lived in Virginia and Maryland?
    A) cultivating tobacco   B) shipbuilding
    C) growing rice   D) cultivating indigo

35. Which of the following was a result of a land shortage in the British colonies?
    A) British colonists pushed westward into Native American lands.
    B) The slave trade was ended.
    C) Colonists began to fear starvation and rebellion.
    D) Britain limited immigration to the colonies.

36. What effect did the Great Awakening have on religious life in the colonies?
    A) It strengthened traditional Puritan teachings.
    B) It de-emphasized the importance of clergy and energized people to speak out for themselves.
    C) It enhanced the political and spiritual authority of ministers.
    D) It reinforced the social order in the colonies.

37. In what way did Quakers differ from Puritans?
    A) They believed in the doctrines of a single church.
    B) They practiced religious tolerance.
    C) They were farmers.
    D) They had fled persecution in England.

Test Bank Questions

Use the map of triangular trade routes in the 1700s to answer the following questions.

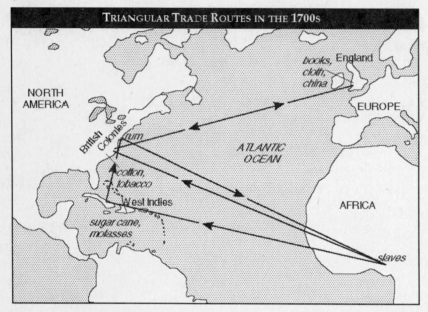

38. What areas were involved in a triangular trade route?

39. What raw materials shown on the map were imported by England?

40. What were two destinations of enslaved Africans and what crops did they cultivate in each place?

Answer the following questions.

41. The Europeans who settled in the British colonies equated land ownership with privilege and power. What problems did this principle create within the colonies? What problems did it create between the colonies and other groups?

42. Compare the lives of enslaved Africans who lived in the Northern, Middle, and Southern Colonies in the 1700s. How were their lives different? How were they alike?

43. How were the ecnomies of Great Britain and its colonies interdependent in the late 1600s and early 1700s?

Test Bank Answer Key

[1] According to the theory of <u>mercantilism</u>, a nation should try to obtain and keep as much bullion as possible.

[2] A nation must export more goods than it imports to maintain a favorable <u>balance of trade</u>.

[3] The colony of Virginia was run by a <u>cousinocracy</u>, about one hundred families who were related by blood or marriage.

[4] Planters found the <u>low country</u>, the coastal plain of South Carolina and Georgia, excellent for growing indigo and rice.

[5] During the <u>Middle Passage</u>, the part of the triangular trade that went between Africa and the Americas, many enslaved Africans perished.

[6] B

[7] A

[8] C

[9] D

[10] C

[11] C

[12] C

[13] A

[14] C

[15] C

[16] England, the British Colonies, Africa, or the West Indies

[17] The colonies obtained enslaved Africans to cultivate tobacco and cotton; England obtained raw material from the colonies in exchange for manufactured goods.

[18] Enslaved Africans were transported to the West Indies where they worked the sugar plantations producing sugar cane and molasses. These products were transported to the British colonies and exchanged for rum and firearms, which in turn could be traded for more slaves.

Test Bank Answer Key

[19] The economy of the Southern Colonies was based on the cultivation of staple crops such as rice and tobacco. Few cities or merchants existed in the South. Both commerce and agriculture were vital to the economy of the Middle Colonies, which included farmers who specialized in growing grains, merchants, traders, and artisans. Unlike merchants in the Middle Colonies, New England merchants depended heavily upon long-distance trade with England, West Africa, and the West Indies. Agriculture was less profitable in New England than it was in the Middle and Southern colonies, largely because farms were small and self-sufficient.

[20] The growth of the British colonies resulted in a land shortage, which created tensions between parents and children and posed a problem to American men who aspired to land ownership. As British colonists pushed westward in search of new land, tensions increased among colonists, Native Americans, and the French.

[21] Colonial American society was inherently unequal because only male property owners could vote and an elite gentry class dominated politics in every colony. Women were legally inferior to men and most colonists accepted slavery as a normal part of life.

[22] f

[23] d

[24] c

[25] b

[26] g

[27] i

[28] A

[29] B

[30] B

[31] B

[32] C

[33] B

[34] A

[35] A

[36] B

Test Bank Answer Key

[37] B

[38] England, Africa, the British Colonies, and the West Indies

[39] tobacco and cotton

[40] Enslaved Africans were transported to the West Indies to work on sugar plantations and to the Southern Colonies to work on tobacco and cotton plantations.

[41] Land ownership created a social hierarchy and promoted inequality within the colonies, since those who controlled the most land also dominated politics. As the population increased, a land shortage created tensions between parents and children and drove colonists westward. There they intruded upon Native American and French land claims, increasing tensions between English colonists and these groups.

[42] Enslaved Africans who lived in South Carolina and Georgia usually farmed large plantations, maintained strong kinship networks, and preserved many cultural traditions. By contrast, enslaved African Americans in Maryland, Virginia, and the Middle and Northern colonies blended their cultures with European culture and performed a wider variety of tasks, including shipbuilding, lumbering, and domestic service. In all colonies, enslaved Africans were the victims of harsh laws and often brutal treatment.

[43] Great Britain depended upon the colonies to buy its manufactured goods and to provide raw materials, such as tobacco and cotton, that it could sell to other nations. The colonies relied upon Great Britain to buy its raw materials and to sell them desired manufactured goods, such as cloth, china, and books.

The American Revolution (1754-1783)

Test Bank Questions

Match the terms below with the following descriptions. Write the letter of the correct answer. You will not use all the terms.

a. War for Independence
b. popular sovereignty
c. Treaty of Paris
d. Stamp Act
e. Intolerable Acts
f. social contract
g. Pontiac's Rebellion
h. minutemen
i. Treaty of Paris
j. American Revolution
k. Declaration of Independence
l. Tories
m. French and Indian War

1. series of struggles between the British and Native Americans in the Great Lakes region

2. British legislation punishing the colony of Massachusetts

3. military struggle that pitted the British and American colonists against the French and their Native American allies

4. colonists who remained loyal to King George

5. document in which George III renounced sovereignty over his thirteen former colonies

6. term used to describe the war between Britain and its North American colonies and the social and political changes that accompanied it

7. idea that ordinary people can and should govern themselves

8. document setting forth the basic principles of American government

9. agreement between the government and its citizens by which the people agree to support the government as long as it represents their best interests

Write the letter of the correct answer.

10. What was the outcome of the French and Indian War?
    A) The Native Americans surrendered the Great Lakes region.
    B) The British turned over all of Canada to the French.
    C) The British promised popular sovereignty in the colonies.
    D) The French surrendered all of Canada to the British.

Test Bank Questions

Write the letter of the correct answer.

11. Which statement best describes British-American relations after the French and Indian War?

A) The British began to treat Americans as equals.

B) The colonists became more dependent on Britain.

C) The colonists began to question British authority.

D) The British began to respect American culture.

12. After the French and Indian War, why did the British abandon their policy of salutary neglect?

A) They wanted to improve the colonial standard of living.

B) They wanted the colonists to help pay war debts.

C) They feared colonial merchants would begin trading with France.

D) They wanted to control trade with Native American societies.

13. Why did many colonists protest the Stamp Act?

A) The act threatened to disrupt trading patterns with overseas markets.

B) The act taxed the colonists without their consent.

C) The act increased the cost of British imports.

D) The act enabled the British to censor all written materials.

14. Which of the following caused many Americans to fear the British were taking away their freedoms?

A) repeal of the Sugar Act

B) passage of the Intolerable Acts

C) Pontiac's Rebellion

D) the Boston Tea Party

15. What did Paine's Common Sense and Jefferson's Declaration of Independence have in common?

A) Both supported the concept of popular sovereignty.

B) Both stated that the wealthy should have more rights than the poor.

C) Both stated that women should have the same rights as men.

D) Both supported the abolition of slavery.

16. Who carried out most of the fighting during the War for Independence?

A) young, relatively poor men   B) free African Americans

C) wealthy landowners and merchants   D) mercenaries

Test Bank Questions

Write the letter of the correct answer.

17. Which of the following was an American advantage during the War for Independence?

A) unity among American colonists

B) determination and perseverance

C) a strong navy

D) a well-organized army

18. Why were the Battle of Bunker Hill and Washington's attack on Trenton significant?

A) They were major victories for the Americans.

B) They bolstered the morale of American troops.

C) They encouraged France to support the American war effort.

D) They proved that the American army was well-disciplined.

19. Which of the following was NOT true of the War for Independence?

A) Inflation hurt economic development during the war.

B) African Americans served as soldiers in the war.

C) The war strengthened American-Native American relations.

D) British naval blockades upset American commerce.

Test Bank Questions

Use the map of British North America to answer the following questions.

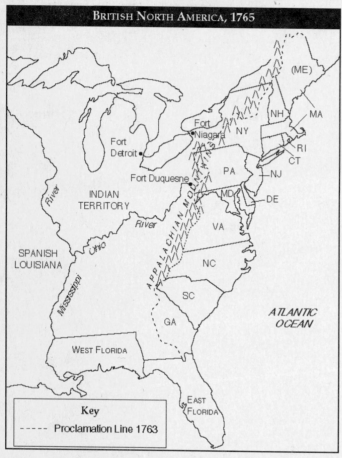

20. What strategic location, often the center of disputes before and during the French and Indian War, was located in Indian Territory in 1765?

21. Which group--the Native Americans or American colonists--seemed to benefit more from the Proclamation Act of 1763? Explain.

22. What geographic feature marked the eastern boundary of the Proclamation Line?

Answer the following questions.

23. Is the following statement from your text an accurate conclusion? <u>From the beginning, the American Revolution was more than a rebellion or a war for independence</u>. Give reasons to support your response.

24. Compare American and British advantages and disadvantages during the War for Independence.

Test Bank Questions

Answer the following questions.

25. How was the Native American shift in allegiance from the French and Indian War to the War for Independence consistent with their struggle to protect their way of life?

Complete each sentence below by selecting the correct word from the list. You will not use all the words.

a. American Revolution
b. French and Indian War
c. Tories
d. Intolerable Acts
e. Boston Tea Party
f. Pontiac's Rebellion
g. Stamp Act
h. Treaty of Paris
i. War for Independence
j. Proclamation of 1763
k. Declaration of Independence
l. Patriots

26. The British Parliament passed the _____ to prevent colonists from settling in the trans-Appalachian region.

27. During the _____, American colonists threw the cargoes of several British ships into the harbor.

28. The four sections of the _____ explained why the American colonies should cut their ties with Great Britain.

29. The _____ required colonists to pay a fee for all legal documents and printed materials.

30. The war between Britain and its thirteen colonies and the political and social changes that accompanied it are known as the _____.

31. The _____ pitted the British and American colonists against the French and their Native American allies.

32. During a series of struggles known as _____, the Ottawa, Potawatomis, and Hurons in the Great Lakes region rebelled against British rule.

33. The _____ granted the former American colonies complete sovereignty in 1783.

34. Colonists who remained loyal to King George III were called _____.

Write the letter of the correct ending.

35. As a result of the French and Indian War,
    A) Britain lost control of the trans-Appalachian region.
    B) Native Americans gained control of the Great Lakes region.
    C) France gained control of Florida.
    D) France gave all of Canada to Britain.

Write the letter of the correct ending.

36. After the French and Indian War, many colonists felt
    A) increasingly dependent on Britain.
    B) justified in seeking better and more equal treatment by the British.
    C) embarrassed by their poor military performance.
    D) angered by the lack of British involvement in colonial affairs.

37. The Sugar Act and the Stamp Act are examples of how the
    A) colonists eagerly sacrificed to pay their war debts.
    B) British tried to assert their authority over the colonies.
    C) British practiced salutary neglect in the colonies.
    D) British tried to stimulate colonial economies.

38. The Intolerable Acts led many Americans to believe that the British wanted to
    A) cut all ties with the colonies.
    B) take away their freedoms.
    C) anglicize American culture.
    D) stifle economic growth in the colonies.

39. Like the Declaration of Independence, Thomas Paine's Common Sense
    A) rejected the social contract theory.
    B) encouraged Americans to reject slavery.
    C) outlined American war strategy.
    D) promoted the idea of popular sovereignty.

40. The group that benefited most from the American Revolution was
    A) Native Americans.
    B) wealthy white women.
    C) free African Americans.
    D) poor white men.

41. Abigail Adams wrote that she hoped the Revolution would improve relationships between
    A) Americans and the British.
    B) colonists and Native Americans.
    C) slaveowners and enslaved Americans.
    D) husbands and wives.

42. One British disadvantage during the War for Independence was
    A) an undisciplined army.
    B) lack of naval support.
    C) an enemy that was widely scattered.
    D) limited resources.

Test Bank Questions

Write the letter of the correct ending.

43. All of the following helped Americans win the War for Independence EXCEPT
    A) Baron von Steuben's training of American troops.
    B) George Washington's bold leadership.
    C) support of Native American groups.
    D) financial and military aid from France.

44. American war morale improved as a result of the
    A) capture of Charlestown.
    B) surprise attack on British troops at Trenton.
    C) defeat of the Iroquois in western New York.
    D) publication of Common Sense.

Test Bank Questions

Use the map of British North America to answer the following questions.

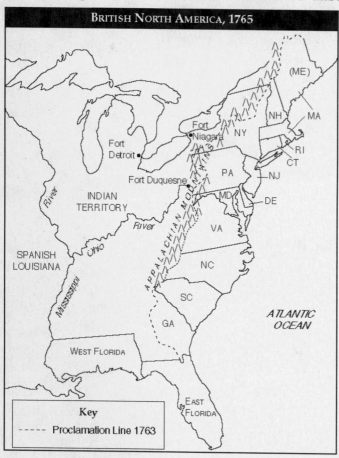

BRITISH NORTH AMERICA, 1765

45. What strategic rivers were located in Indian Territory in 1765?

46. In 1765, how did the size of Indian Territory compare to the land area of the thirteen colonies?

47. Use information from the map to draw conclusions about why colonists resented the Proclamation Act of 1763.

Answer the following questions.

48. In what way was the British treatment of Native Americans after the French and Indian War similar to their treatment of American colonists?

49. How did Britain's enforcement of the policies of mercantilism create problems in the American colonies?

Test Bank Questions

Answer the following questions.

50. Former President Calvin Coolidge once said, "Nothing in the world can take the place of persistence.... Persistence and determination alone are omnipotent." Based on what you have learned about the War for Independence, do you agree or disagree with Coolidge? Explain.

Test Bank Answer Key

[1] g

[2] e

[3] m

[4] l

[5] c

[6] j

[7] b

[8] k

[9] f

[10] D

[11] C

[12] B

[13] B

[14] B

[15] A

[16] A

[17] B

[18] B

[19] C

[20] the forks of the Ohio River, or Fort Duquesne

[21] The Native Americans seemed to benefit more--they were allowed nearly twice as much land as the colonists and did not have to confront colonists settling in their territory.

[22] the Appalachian Mountains

[23] The conclusion is accurate. The Revolution was also a movement to create a new American society based on equality and democracy. The basic principles of the new American government and society were set forth in the Declaration of Independence.

Test Bank Answer Key

During the War for Independence, the British had a strong military, the world's richest economy, and the support of many Tories and Native Americans. However, the war was fought thousands of miles from Great Britain on unfamiliar terrain, the enemy was spread out and difficult to locate, and many of the British at home sympathized with the colonists. By contrast, the Americans had a poorly trained army, disunity throughout the colonies, and opposition from Loyalists and Native Americans. American advantages included familiar fighting

[24] ground and the determination and perseverance of Patriot soldiers.

During the French and Indian War, Native Americans supported the French because, unlike the British, the French were not interested in transforming Native American culture. During the War for Independence, however, most Native Americans sided with the British against the colonists because most colonists favored westward

[25] expansion, which threatened the Native American way of life.

[26] j

[27] e

[28] k

[29] g

[30] a

[31] b

[32] f

[33] h

[34] c

[35] D

[36] B

[37] B

[38] B

[39] D

[40] D

[41] D

[42] C

[43] C

Test Bank Answer Key

[44] B

[45] the Mississippi and Ohio rivers

[46] Indian Territory was more than double the size of the thirteen colonies.

[47] The act restricted colonists to the region between the Appalachian Mountains and the Atlantic Ocean and prohibited settlement in such desireable regions as the Ohio River Valley.

[48] The British attitude toward Native Americans and toward American colonists was one of arrogance and superiority. The British regarded both groups as inferior, existing to serve British interests, and undeserving of equal rights. As a result, the British sparked anger, resentment, and rebellion on the part of both groups.

[49] Mercantilism encouraged British attitudes of supremacy over American colonists, which created resentment among the Americans. As the British applied mercantilistic principles by exerting greater control over colonial affairs, Americans feared the loss of freedoms and began to rebel.

[50] Agree. During the War for Independence, the British had the world's most prosperous economy and a powerful military. The British also had thousands of allies in the colonies. By contrast, the Patriot army was small, disorganized, and poorly trained. Sheer persistence and determination, however, enabled the Patriots to outlast the British and eventually win the war.

The Constitution of the United States (1781-1789)

Test Bank Questions

Match the terms below with the following descriptions. Write the letter of the correct answer. You will not use all the terms.

a. Virginia Plan
b. administration
c. executive branch
d. Electoral College

e. unicameral legislature
f. Three-fifths Compromise
g. faction
h. judicial branch

i. Bill of Rights
j. legislative branch
k. New Jersey Plan
l. Articles of Confederation
m. cabinet
n. Great Compromise
o. system of checks and balances

1. part of government that makes laws

2. amendments to the constitution that guarantee individual freedoms to American citizens

3. heads of the major departments of the executive branch

4. part of government that carries out the laws

5. device for selecting the President of the United States

6. proposal supported by James Madison that called for a bicameral legislature with proportionate representation

7. government structure in which each branch has the ability to limit the powers of the others

8. President's term in office

9. special interest group

10. legislature with only one group of representatives

Write the letter of the correct answer.

11. Which of the following was NOT a weakness of the Articles of Confederation?

    A) Unanimous approval was required to amend a law.

    B) Congress lacked coercive power.

    C) The judicial branch was too powerful.

    D) Congress lacked the power to tax.

Test Bank Questions

Write the letter of the correct answer.

12. What issue did the Great Compromise resolve?

A) representation in the legislature

B) popular sovereignty

C) abolition of slavery

D) the veto power of the executive

13. Which was a major concern of the Nationalists in the 1780s?

A) The states were selling too much land to foreign countries.

B) The military had too much power.

C) The national government was too weak.

D) The people had too little power in state legislatures.

14. How did the Nationalists regard Shay's Rebellion?

A) as proof that only a strong national government could prevent social disorder

B) as an example of how governments abuse their powers

C) as a demonstration of Americans' commitment to democracy

D) as proof that the states had too little power

15. Which issue divided delegates at the Constitutional Convention?

A) whether the national government should have a judicial branch

B) whether Congress should have the power to tax

C) whether the Articles of Confederation should be abandoned or amended

D) whether state governments should be strengthened

16. Which of the following most accurately describes the Constitution that was drafted in 1787?

A) It created a strong executive and judiciary, but a weak legislature.

B) It created a republican government that granted the people complete power over their own affairs.

C) It created a loose alliance of states.

D) It both protected a restricted popular sovereignty.

17. Which of the following ensured that the President would not gain dictatorial powers?

A) the Electoral College   B) the system of checks and balances

C) the Elastic Clause   D) the cabinet

Test Bank Questions

Write the letter of the correct answer.

18. Why did the Anti-Federalists oppose the Constitution?
    A) They thought it gave the people too much power.
    B) They thought the federal government was too strong.
    C) They felt the executive branch was too weak.
    D) They did not believe the Articles of Confederation needed to be reformed.

19. Which of the following was added to the Constitution in order to gain the approval of the Anti-Federalists?
    A) the Three-fifths Compromise   B) the national court system
    C) the Bill of Rights   D) the Preamble

20. Which of the following best describes Alexander Hamilton?
    A) He believed that governmental power could accomplish great things.
    B) He believed that power was best left in the hands of the people.
    C) He was deeply committed to human rights.
    D) He feared the federal government would interfere with American liberty.

21. How did President Washington want citizens to view the new government of the United States?
    A) as a weak central government backed by strong state governments
    B) as a kingship
    C) as a limited republic led by the people
    D) as a powerful democracy

Test Bank Questions

Use the map of the Electoral Vote to answer the following questions.

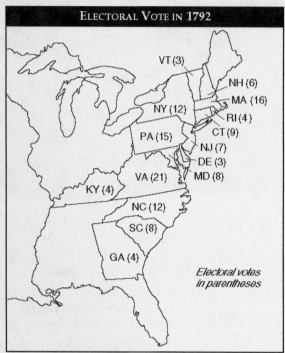

22. Which state had the most electoral votes in 1792? The least?

23. How many representatives did New York have in the Senate? In the House of Representatives?

24. At the Constitutional Convention, why did states such as New Jersey favor a plan by which all states would have an equal vote in a unicameral Congress?

Answer the following questions.

25. Discuss the powers of state governments and the national government under the Articles of Confederation. How did these powers change after the Constitution was adopted?

26. What are three questions that an Anti-Federalist would have asked about the proposed Constitution? Explain how your questions reveal Anti-Federalist concerns.

27. What are three features of the Constitution that might have appeased those who feared a strong central government? Explain.

Test Bank Questions

Complete each sentence below by selecting the correct word from the list. You will not use all the words.

a. Electoral College
b. judicial brance
c. cabinet
d. administration
e. Virginia Plan
f. legislative branch
g. Bill of Rights
h. executive branch
i. system of checks and balances
j. Three-fifths Compromise
k. bicameral legislature
l. Great Compromise
m. Articles of Confederation
n. unicameral legislature

28. The _____, favored by the large states, called for a legislature with representation in proportion to its population.

29. The _____ guarantees that the individual freedoms of American citizens will be protected.

30. The President appoints the _____, the heads of the major departments of the executive branch.

31. The power of the President to veto acts of Congress is an example of the _____.

32. The _____ is the part of government that judges whether laws have been broken.

33. A(n) _____ consists of two houses, or groups of representatives.

34. Under the _____, all enslaved people were to be counted as part of a state's population.

35. The candidate who receives the majority of votes in the _____ becomes President of the United States.

36. The _____ is the part of government that makes the laws.

37. Under the _____, the United States government consisted of a Continental Congress that both passed and enforced laws.

Write the letter of the correct ending.

38. One major weakness of the Articles of Confederation was that
    A) they could not be amended.
    B) the states were given too many votes in Congress.
    C) the executive branch had more power than the legislative branch.
    D) Congress did not have any coercive power.

39. In the 1780s the Nationalists organized to
    A) strengthen the power of the states.
    B) promote the need for a stronger central government.
    C) fight against taxation.
    D) protect the principle of popular sovereignty.

Test Bank Questions

Write the letter of the correct ending.

40. The Nationalists viewed Shay's Rebellion as proof that
    A) taxation would solve the nation's economic problems.
    B) the nation was on the brink of social disorder.
    C) farmers needed government protection.
    D) governments tend to act against the people's wishes.

41. One issue that divided the Constitutional Convention was whether
    A) slaves should be able to vote.
    B) representation in the legislature should be based on population.
    C) the national government should have a judicial branch.
    D) Congress should have the power to tax.

42. The system of checks and balances ensures that
    A) state legislatures will share power with the Congress.
    B) no one branch of government will gain too much power.
    C) the President will be elected directly by the people.
    D) the Senate will not be manipulated by the people.

43. The Constitution that was drafted in 1787
    A) ensured that total power rested with the people.
    B) created a loose alliance of states.
    C) both preserved and limited popular sovereignty.
    D) gave the states greater power than the national government.

44. The Anti-Federalists opposed the Constitution because they thought it
    A) gave the federal government too much power.
    B) provided no way to change the Constitution.
    C) gave the state governments too much power.
    D) created a weak federal court system.

45. The Anti-Federalists agreed to support the Constitution after the Federalists added the
    A) Bill of Rights.   B) Elastic Clause.
    C) Preamble.   D) system of checks and balances.

46. Unlike Thomas Jefferson, Alexander Hamilton
    A) feared a strong federal government.
    B) supported the Constitution.
    C) believed that a strong government could do great things.
    D) was a staunch supporter of human rights.

Test Bank Questions

Write the letter of the correct ending.

47. President Washington hoped that citizens would view the new
     government as

     A) weak and nonthreatening.   B) powerful and impressive.
     C) close to the people.   D) modest and pratical.

Use the map of the Electoral Vote to answer the following questions.

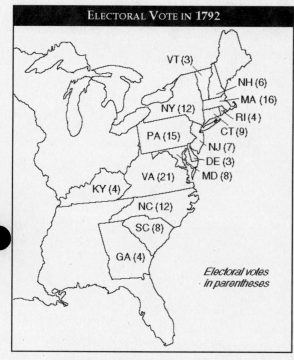

ELECTORAL VOTE IN 1792

VT (3)
NH (6)
MA (16)
NY (12)
RI (4)
CT (9)
PA (15)
NJ (7)
DE (3)
MD (8)
VA (21)
KY (4)
NC (12)
SC (8)
GA (4)

Electoral votes
in parentheses

48. What states do you think supported the New Jersey Plan and why?

49. If you had been running for President in 1792, in which three states
     would you have campaigned most vigorously? Explain.

Answer the following questions.

50. What problems did Nationalists see with the Articles of Confederation?

51. What were two major issues that divided the delegates at the
     Constitutional Convention and how were they resolved?

52. What were some major differences between the Articles of
     Confederation and the Constitution?

Test Bank Answer Key

[1]   j

[2]   i

[3]   m

[4]   c

[5]   d

[6]   a

[7]   o

[8]   b

[9]   g

[10] e

[11] C

[12] A

[13] C

[14] A

[15] C

[16] D

[17] B

[18] B

[19] C

[20] A

[21] D

[22] Virginia; Delaware and Vermont

[23] 2, 10

[24] New Jersey wanted to have as much voting power as heavily populated states, such as Virginia.

Test Bank Answer Key

[25] Under the Articles of Confederation, the states were very powerful and had almost complete control over their own affairs. By contrast, the national government was very weak and had no power to tax and no coercive mechanisms. After the Constitution was adopted, many powers--such as the power to tax--were shared by state and national authorities, while other powers shifted from the states to the national government. For example, only Congress could coin money, deal with other nations, regulate commerce, declare war, and raise an army and a navy.

[26] How does the Constitution protect individual rights? How can we be sure that the executive will not become a tyrannical dictator? What kinds of powers will be reserved for state governments? What protection do state governments have against the power of the federal government? The Anti-Federalists were concerned that the federal government would become too strong and threaten individual freedoms.

[27] Features of the Constitution that might have appeased those who feared a strong central government include the Bill of Rights, the system of checks and balances, and the creation of the House of Representatives. The Bill of Rights assured those who feared a tyrannical government that basic individual liberties would be protected, while the system of checks and balances limited the powers of the three branches. The House of Representatives, whose members were elected every two years, was directly responsible to the people.

[28] e

[29] g

[30] c

[31] i

[32] b

[33] k

[34] j

[35] a

[36] f

[37] m

[38] D

[39] B

[40] B

Test Bank Answer Key

[41] B

[42] B

[43] C

[44] A

[45] A

[46] C

[47] B

[48] States with small populations such as Vermont, New Hampshire, Rhode Island, Delaware, and Georgia, would have supported the New Jersey plan.

[49] A candidate would campaign in Virginia, Massachusetts, and Pennsylvania, because those states had the greatest number of electoral votes.

[50] Nationalists thought the Articles of Confederation made the national government too weak and the people too powerful. In their opinion, a strong national government was needed to prevent social disorder, to solve the nation's problems, and to command the respect of foreign nations.

[51] Delegates to the Constitutional Convention were divided over how representation in the legislature should be determined--some delegates wanted representation to be based on state population, while others wanted each state to have equal representation, regardless of size. Another divisive issue was the question of how enslaved people should be counted in a state's population. These issues were resolved by the Great Compromise, which called for a bicameral legislature that combined both views, and the Three-fifths Compromise, which allowed three-fifths of the slave population to be counted.

[52] Major differences centered on the powers of the state governments and the national government. Under the Articles of Confederation, the states were very powerful and had almost complete control over their own affairs. By contrast, the national government was very weak and lacked the power to tax as well as coercive powers. Under the Constitution, power was divided between the states and the national government. However, the national government was strengthened and given such power as coining money, dealing with other nations, regulating commerce, declaring war, and raising an army and a navy.

The Origins of American Politics (1789-1820)

Test Bank Questions

Complete each of the following sentences by selecting the appropriate term from the choices listed in parentheses.

1. A tax on foreign goods imported into the country is called (an excise, a tariff).

2. Under the (Alien and Sedition Acts of 1798, Embargo of 1807), the President gained the right to imprison or deport foreign residents and to severely limit criticism of government officials.

3. The (Treaty of Ghent, XYZ Affair) angered most Americans and strained relations between France and the United States.

4. General (Andrew Jackson, John Marshall) became a national hero during the War of 1812.

5. (Handsome Lake, Tenskwatawa), a Seneca leader, urged Native Americans to embrace many aspects of European American culture.

6. In 1803 the (Missouri Compromise, Louisiana Purchase) more than doubled the size of the United States.

7. In the early 1800s (Little Turtle, Tecumseh), a Shawnee war chief, organized a Native American movement to resist United States expansion into the Indiana Territory.

8. The principle of (judicial review, precedent) enables federal courts to declare laws unconstitutional.

9. During the (Battle of New Orleans, Battle of Tippecanoe) the overconfident British suffered heavy losses at the hands of American gunners.

10. In 1814 New Englanders called for constitutional amendments to increase the region's political power during the (Whiskey Rebellion, Hartford Convention).

Write the letter of the correct ending.

11. The Federalists lost the support of many Americans in the 1790s when they
    A) broke off diplomatic relations with Britain.
    B) supported the French Revolution.
    C) ignored the Whiskey Rebellion.
    D) launched Hamilton's economic program.

Test Bank Questions

Write the letter of the correct ending.

12. Unlike the Federalists, Jeffersonian Republicans
    A) favored the creation of a national bank.
    B) were pro-British.
    C) objected to the interference of the national government in the economy.
    D) supported most forms of taxation.

13. Jefferson and Madison drafted the Virginia and Kentucky Resolutions to protest
    A) Gabriel Prosser's Rebellion.
    B) the XYZ Affair.
    C) the Alien and Sedition Acts.
    D) the appointments of midnight judges.

14. The election of Thomas Jefferson as the third President proved that
    A) the French Revolution was an extension of the American Revolution.
    B) Americans could peacefully transfer power from one party to another.
    C) violent revolts and civil war had no place in a democracy.
    D) the Constitution had many weaknesses.

15. The case of Marbury v. Madison was significant because it
    A) marked the creation of the first political party in the United States.
    B) decreased the power of the Supreme Court.
    C) established the power of judicial review.
    D) increased the power of the Jeffersonian Republicans.

16. President Jefferson's popularity declined when he
    A) used the national government to aid westward expansion.
    B) broke the Jay Treaty with Great Britain.
    C) imposed the Embargo of 1807 to end harassment of American ships.
    D) increased the national debt by approving the Louisiana Purchase.

17. Handsome Lake and Tenskwatawa were alike in that they encouraged Native Americans to
    A) honor their traditions.
    B) make peace with the United States.
    C) leave their reservations.
    D) adopt European American customs and styles.

Test Bank Questions

Write the letter of the correct ending.

18. The pan-Indian movement was an attempt to
    A) unite and empower Native American groups.
    B) destroy Native American traditions.
    C) assimilate Native Americans into European American culture.
    D) gain support for the Treaty of Fort Wayne.

19. In 1812 Congress declared war on Great Britain largely because the British
    A) would not honor the Treaty of Ghent.
    B) had declared war on France.
    C) continued to smuggle goods into New England.
    D) harassed American merchant ships.

20. The Panic of 1819 began when
    A) New England suffered tremendous losses in trade after the War of 1812.
    B) Congress created the Second Bank of the United States.
    C) London banks demanded repayment of loans to American banks.
    D) foreigners stopped investing in the United States.

21. The Missouri Compromise settled the question of whether
    A) slavery should be allowed in future states.
    B) the territories should be represented in Congress.
    C) slavery should be declared unconstitutional.
    D) the territories should pay taxes.

Test Bank Questions

Use the map of the War of 1812 to answer the following questions.

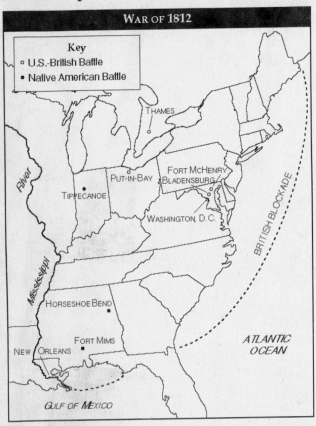

22. Why was it important to the United States to buy New Orleans from France?

23. During the War of 1812, how extensive was the British blockade?

24. What were the sites of Native American resistance during the War of 1812?

Answer the following questions.

25. Many historians have described Thomas Jefferson as favoring a strict construction of the Constitution. Explain whether the President's authorization of the Louisiana Purchase was consistent or inconsistent with his view of the Constitution.

26. Why were both John Adams and Thomas Jefferson unpopular Presidents when they left office? What conclusion can you draw about American attitudes toward the role of government in the late 1700s and early 1800s?

Test Bank Questions

Answer the following questions.

27. What issue dominated the election of 1800 and drove a wedge between Federalists and Jeffersonian Republicans? What was significant about the outcome of this presidential election?

Match the terms below with the following descriptions. Write the letter of the correct answer. You will not use all the terms.

a. Hartford Convention
b. XYZ Affair
c. Embargo of 1807
d. excise
e. Whiskey Rebellion
f. Louisiana Purchase

g. tariff

h. Panic of 1819
i. Missouri Compromise
j. Treaty of Ghent
k. pan-Indian movement
l. reservation
m. Marbury v. Madison

n. Alien and Sedition Acts of 1798

28. Native American resistance to the expansion of the United States

29. document that ended the War of 1812

30. area in which Native Americans were forced to live after losing their homelands

31. legislation halting trade with Europe

32. Supreme Court ruling that established the power of judicial review

33. meeting of New England delegates to promote constitutional amendments to increase the region's political power

34. measures that granted the President the power to deport or imprison foreign residents and that made it illegal to criticize government officials

35. tax on goods manufactured within a country

36. meeting during which French secret agents asked American diplomats for a bribe and a loan

37. first great U.S. depression

Write the letter of the correct answer.

38. Which of the following did NOT result in bitter opposition to the Federalists?
    A) the suppression of the Whiskey Rebellion
    B) Hamilton's economic program
    C) the Jay Treaty with Great Britain
    D) Washington's refusal to seek a third term

Test Bank Questions

Write the letter of the correct answer.

39. Which of the following best describes Jeffersonian Republicans?
    A) They preferred a loose construction of the Constitution.
    B) They objected to the national government's interference in local and state affairs.
    C) They favored Federalist policies.
    D) They wanted to restore monarchy in the United States.

40. How did Jefferson and Madison respond to the Alien and Sedition Acts?
    A) They published numerous accusations against the midnight judges.
    B) They drafted the Kentucky and Virginia Resolutions.
    C) They declared their support for Gabriel Prosser's rebellion.
    D) They resigned from President Adam's cabinet.

41. What was significant about the election of President Jefferson in 1800?
    A) It led to European investment in the United States.
    B) It underlined the weaknesses of the Constitution.
    C) The election unified Americans under a single faction.
    D) It was a victory for the democratic transfer of power.

42. Which of the following was President Jefferson's main goal during his first term?
    A) to decrease the influence of the national government on people's lives
    B) to slow the westward expansion of the United States
    C) to pay off the national debt
    D) to stabilize the nation's economy

43. Which was a result of the Embargo of 1807?
    A) President Jefferson's popularity declined.
    B) British–American relations improved.
    C) France sold its North American land holdings to the United States.
    D) The British and French economies collapsed.

44. Which of the following best describes Tenskwatawa and Tecumseh?
    A) They opposed organized resistance to the U.S. government.
    B) They called for total rejection of European American culture.
    C) They promoted the expansion of the United States as a positive development.
    D) The promoted assimilation of Native Americans into European American culture.

Test Bank Questions

Write the letter of the correct answer.

45. Which was one consequence of the Battle of Tippecanoe?
    A) The federal government slowed expansion in the Northwest Territory.
    B) Tecumseh gained control of the Indiana Territory.
    C) The pan-Indian movement lost momentum.
    D) The British and Native American military alliance was dissolved.

46. Why did the United States declare war on Great Britain in 1812?
    A) Britain had refused to comply with the Embargo of 1807.
    B) Britain had repeatedly harassed American trading ships.
    C) Britain had declared war on France, an ally of the United States.
    D) Britain had tried to gain control of the Mississippi River.

47. Which was an effect of the Panic of 1819?
    A) Congress created the Second Bank of the United States.
    B) The Federalist party made a strong comeback as a national political force.
    C) Congress severely restricted westward expansion.
    D) Many Americans considered increasing the government's role in the economy.

48. Which issue was resolved by the Missouri Compromise?
    A) the acquisition of new territories in the West
    B) the location, size, and political structure of reservations
    C) the admittance of territories as slave states and free states
    D) the constitutional rights of African American slaves

Test Bank Questions

Use the map of the War of 1812 to answer the following questions.

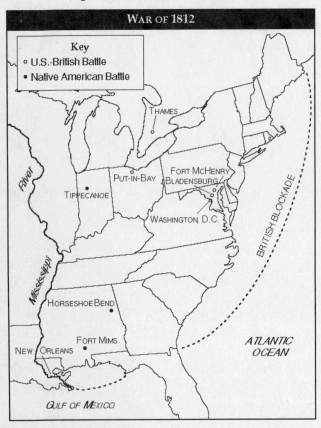

49. What were the sites of the battles between the Americans and the British during the War of 1812?

50. Why do you think the British wanted to capture New Orleans during the War of 1812?

51. Why was the British blockade so effective in stopping American trade?

Answer the following questions.

52. Compare the presidencies of John Adams and Thomas Jefferson. How did their approaches to national government differ?

53. What problems did the federal government face as a result of westward expansion in the late 1700s and early 1800s?

54. Thomas Jefferson once said, "In matters of style, swim with the current; in matters of principle, stand like a rock." Did Jefferson "swim with the current" in matters of presidential style? Explain your answer.

Test Bank Answer Key

[1]   a tariff

[2]   Alien and Sedition Acts of 1798

[3]   XYZ Affair

[4]   Andrew Jackson

[5]   Handsome Lake

[6]   Louisiana Purchase

[7]   Tecumseh

[8]   judicial review

[9]   Battle of New Orleans

[10] Hartford Convention

[11] D

[12] C

[13] C

[14] B

[15] C

[16] C

[17] A

[18] A

[19] D

[20] C

[21] A

[22] New Orleans is located at the mouth of the Mississippi River--a vital trade route for Americans who settled in the western part of the nation.

[23] The British fleet blockaded most of the American coast from Maine to Georgia, to New Orleans.

[24] Tippecanoe, Fort Mims, and Horseshoe Bend

Test Bank Answer Key

[25] President Jefferson's approval of the Louisiana Purchase was inconsistent with his view as a strict constructionist because the Constitution did not allow for land purchases west of the Mississippi River. A strict constructionist would have argued that the government should not exercise any power not granted to it in the Constitution.

[26] Adams angered many Americans by raising taxes to support a larger military and by passing the Alien and Sedition Acts of 1798. Jefferson lost the support of many Americans when he passed the Embargo of 1807, forbidding European trade. Americans opposed the direct interference of the national government in their lives and the infringement of their freedoms.

[27] The election of 1800 focused on the nature of the national government. Americans chose between the Federalist candidate, who supported a powerful government committed to order, and Jefferson, who favored a weaker government committed to liberty. By choosing Jefferson, the people proved that they could peacefully change the course of their government.

[28] k

[29] j

[30] l

[31] c

[32] m

[33] a

[34] n

[35] d

[36] b

[37] h

[38] D

[39] B

[40] B

[41] D

[42] A

[43] A

[44] B

Test Bank Answer Key

[45] C _____

[46] B _____

[47] D _____

[48] C _____

[49] Thames, Put-in-Bay, Washington, D.C., Fort McHenry, Bladensburg

[50] By taking New Orleans, the British would gain control of the Mississippi River--a vital trade route.

[51] The British fleet blockaded most of the Atlantic coast from Maine to Georgia and the Gulf coast to New Orleans.

[52] Adams favored a strong national government that would preserve order and stability. He increased taxes to support a larger army and navy, and used the power of the national government to quiet government critics. Unlike Adams, Jefferson favored strong local and state governments. He decreased the influence of the national government on people's lives by reducing taxes and downsizing the federal bureaucracy and armed forces.

[53] The westward expansion of the United States worsened relations with Native Americans and resulted in riots, bloodshed, and organized Native American resistance--the pan-Indian movement. In addition, the annexation of new territories increased tensions over the issue of slavery and challenged the role of the national government in states' affairs.

[54] No; Jefferson changed the style of the presidency to reflect his belief that the President was merely the first among equals. To create the impression of a democratic style of government, Jefferson personally answered the door of the White House, asked to be called "Mr. President," and refused to deliver speeches to Congress.

Life in the New Nation (1783-1830)

Test Bank Questions

Match the terms below with the following descriptions. Write the letter of the correct answer. You will not use all the terms.

a. Noah Webster
b. Richard Allen
c. John Ross
d. Eli Whitney

e. Samuel Slater
f. Susanna Haswell Rowson
g. Robert Fulton
h. Benjamin Rush

1. New Englander who invented the cotton gin

2. writer of the popular moralizing novel <u>Charlotte Temple</u>

3. writer who promoted education and stressed the importance of a standard national language

4. minister who founded the African Methodist Episcopal Church

5. British textile worker who constructed the first water-powered spinning mill in the United States

Write the letter of the correct answer.

6. Why might Free Frank and Lucy be called persisters?
   A) because they migrated west and founded a new settlement
   B) because they opened their own business
   C) because they bought their freedom
   D) because they had a large family

7. Which statement best describes population trends in the United States from 1780 to 1830?
   A) The population grew older and gradually decreased in size.
   B) Mass immigration from Europe resulted in overpopulation.
   C) High birth rates caused a population explosion.
   D) The Native American population grew faster than the white population.

8. Why did most young women in the Northeast attend school in the early 1800s?
   A) to become religious instructors at churches
   B) to learn how to be good mothers and wives
   C) to learn important farm skills
   D) to become skilled in a specific academic field, such as mathematics

Test Bank Questions

Write the letter of the correct answer.

9. How did Native American migration differ from that of Americans of European descent?

   A) Most Native Americans migrated to reclaim their homelands, not to explore.

   B) Americans of European descent wanted to migrate, but Native American migration was forced.

   C) Most Native Americans migrated south instead of west.

   D) Wherever they migrated, Native Americans did not enslave Africans.

10. What was one effect of the invention of the cotton gin in 1793?

    A) Laws called black codes were passed.

    B) The demand for slave labor increased.

    C) Thousands of southern plantation owners went bankrupt.

    D) Migration from the South to undeveloped lands in the West declined.

11. Which of the following did NOT contribute to the communication revolution in the late 1700s and early 1800s?

    A) The system of interchangeable parts was invented.

    B) The federal government improved public postal services.

    C) Steam power reduced the cost of transportation and commerce.

    D) Canals helped link the eastern and western regions of the nation.

12. How did constant migration change the lives of many Americans in the early 1800s?

    A) Friendship often replaced family ties as the primary link between people.

    B) The divorce rate declined.

    C) Suicide and alcoholism decreased.

    D) Most men were no longer interested in dueling or behaving like "gentlemen."

13. Which of the following best describes the experience of most working-class women in the early 1800s?

    A) They often married the man of their parents' choice.

    B) They usually rejected marriage in favor of working.

    C) They endured long, formal courtships.

    D) Establishing households was a matter of necessity, not usually romantic love.

Test Bank Questions

Write the letter of the correct answer.

14. How was the Second Great Awakening similar to the First Great Awakening?

   A) It united most denominations into a single group.

   B) It was an evangelical movement.

   C) It appealed almost exclusively to the upper class.

   D) It stressed the importance of rituals and good deeds.

15. Why did so many Americans join the Methodist church in the late 1700s and early 1800s?

   A) It was the only church that promoted multiracial worship.

   B) Methodists promoted the belief that anyone could achieve salvation.

   C) Methodists encouraged women to become ministers and church leaders.

   D) People enjoyed the lack of organization and ritual in the Methodist church.

16. What role did women play in church communities in the early 1800s?

   A) Women formed clubs and societies both to help and convert others.

   B) Women took turns drafting and preaching weekly sermons.

   C) Women often assumed leadership roles within the church.

   D) Most denominations did not allow women to actively participate in the church community.

Test Bank Questions

Use the map of the main roads and turnpikes to answer the following questions.

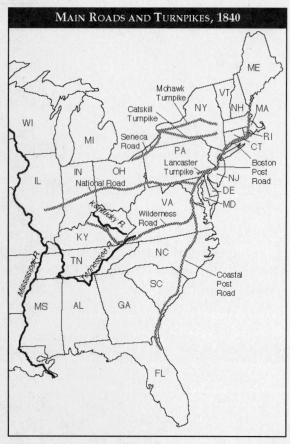

MAIN ROADS AND TURNPIKES, 1840

17. If you were migrating west from Virginia to Kentucky, what route would you travel? In what river valley might you settle?

18. If you wanted to visit relatives in South Carolina, what route would you travel from your home in New England?

19. How do you think the building of the National Road affected the economic development of western lands? Why?

Answer the following questions.

20. How did the constant migration that characterized the late 1700s and early 1800s affect people in the new republic?

21. In what ways were African American pioneers discriminated against?

Test Bank Questions

Complete each sentence below by selecting the correct word from the list. You will not use all the words.

a. Samuel Slater   e. Susanna Haswell Rowson
b. John Ross   f. Richard Allen
c. Noah Webster   g. Robert Fulton
d. Eli Whitney   h. Charles Wilson Peale

22. The African Methodist Episcopal Church was founded by _____ .

23. _____ promoted education and a standard national language.

24. In 1794 _____ published a popular moralizing novel entitled <u>Charlotte Temple</u>.

25. _____ invented the cotton gin in 1793.

26. Working from memory alone, _____ duplicated the British spinning mill and helped bring the Industrial Revolution to the United States.

Write the letter of the correct ending.

27. The great increase in the United States population during the period before 1830 was mostly a result of

    A) an increase in the African slave trade.

    B) immigration from Asia.

    C) an increase in the birth rate.

    D) immigration from Europe.

28. In the Adams–Onís Treaty of 1819, the United States

    A) acquired Native American lands.

    B) made Kentucky a slave state.

    C) made Illinois a free state.

    D) gained possession of Florida.

29. In the late 1700s and early 1800s, laws called black codes

    A) required all settlers to post security bonds to settle in the Northwest.

    B) made indentured servitude illegal.

    C) kept African Americans in free territories in a subordinate position.

    D) prevented Native American groups from becoming independent nations.

30. Republican women were expected to

    A) join the Female Missionary Society.

    B) be involved in local politics.

    C) serve society as educated mothers and wives.

    D) serve as their husbands' business partners.

Test Bank Questions

Write the letter of the correct ending.

31. Steam power and canal-building were important for all of the following reasons EXCEPT:

    A) They lessened the need for slave labor.

    B) They reduced the cost of transportation and commerce.

    C) They encouraged settlement and development of more western regions.

    D) They linked the economies of eastern and western regions.

32. Migration from southern states to undeveloped western regions increased as a result of the

    A) the application of the system of interchangeable parts.

    B) Adams-Onís Treaty.

    C) decline of the African slave trade.

    D) invention of the cotton gin.

33. Unlike working-class women in the early 1800s, most middle-class women

    A) established households out of necessity.

    B) allowed their parents to arrange the marriage.

    C) chose a career instead of marriage.

    D) engaged in long courtships.

34. Many historians believe that suicide and drunkenness increased in the early 1800s partly because

    A) dueling had become a popular pastime.

    B) the number of marriages had decreased.

    C) friendship had become more important than family ties.

    D) economic successes were limited.

35. The evangelical movement that occurred in the early 1800s

    A) was highly democratic.

    B) excluded lower class and non-white groups.

    C) promoted good works and rituals as the way to salvation.

    D) appealed most to successful businessmen.

36. The most popular Christian denomination in the late 1700s and early 1800s was the

    A) Catholic Church.

    B) Church of Jesus Christ of Latter-Day Saints.

    C) Methodist Church.

    D) Disciples of Christ.

Test Bank Questions

Write the letter of the correct ending.

37. The First and Second Great Awakenings were alike in that they
    A) promoted the belief that all people could experience salvation.
    B) promoted social equality between men and women.
    C) renounced camp meetings.
    D) encouraged most denominations to unite.

Use the map of the main roads and turnpikes to answer the following questions.

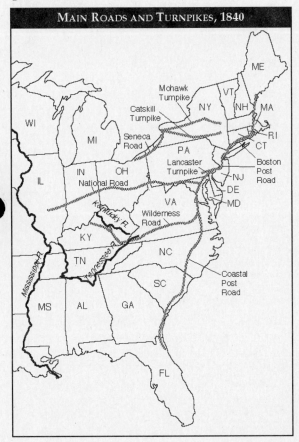

38. In 1840, what route would you have traveled from your home in Florida to visit relatives in Connecticut?

39. What regions of the country benefited most from the building of the Mohawk Turnpike and the Seneca Road?

40. By 1840, what roads linked eastern and western regions of the United States?

Test Bank Questions

Answer the following questions.

41. How did revolutions in transportation and communication affect the United States in the late 1700s and early 1800s?

42. Many middle-class women in the early 1800s believed that young working-class women lacked self-control and virtue because they married so quickly and at such a young age. Explain whether this view was accurate or inaccurate.

Test Bank Answer Key

[1] d

[2] f

[3] a

[4] b

[5] e

[6] A

[7] C

[8] B

[9] B

[10] B

[11] A

[12] A

[13] D

[14] B

[15] B

[16] A

[17] the Wilderness Road; Tennesee or Kentucky river valley

[18] Boston Post Road and Coastal Post Road

[19] It stimulated the economic growth of the region by making migration and transportation of goods easier and less expensive.

[20] In the late 1700s and early 1800s, constant migration put a tremendous strain on both men and women and made the early republic a country of strangers. Many men resorted to heavy drinking and dueling, either in free-for-all fights or with formal rules, and women exercised more independence and caution in selecting a husband. Many women became active members in the church community, where they overcame their loneliness by forming social clubs and outreach organizations.

Test Bank Answer Key

[21] In the late 1700s and early 1800s, many Americans of European descent, fearing that African American settlers might take their land and jobs, passed black codes to keep African Americans in a subordinate position or from taking up residence in the territories. African Americans faced discrimination even at worship--few churches supported multiracial services, and sometimes African Americans were asked to sit in the church balcony.

[22] f

[23] c

[24] e

[25] d

[26] a

[27] C

[28] D

[29] C

[30] C

[31] A

[32] D

[33] D

[34] D

[35] A

[36] C

[37] A

[38] Coastal Post Road to Boston Post Road

[39] the Great Lakes region and New York State

[40] the Wilderness Road and the National Road

[41] Revolutions in transportation and communication helped link the eastern and western regions of the United States. Steamboats and canals made shipping goods easier, faster, and cheaper, and an efficient postal service made information available to large numbers of people throughout the nation. As a result, many Americans found it more profitable and less of a social strain to settle and develop western lands.

Test Bank Answer Key

Middle-class women held an inaccurate view of working-class women as "fallen" women who lacked self-control. Most working-class women needed to marry quickly, either because their parents would not or could not financially support them. While working-class women enjoyed the freedom of choosing their own spouse, they often married for
[42] practical, not romantic or passionate reasons.

The Market Revolution (1815-1845)

Test Bank Questions

Complete each sentence below by selecting the correct word from the list. You will not use all the words.

a. capitalism
b. commodity
c. American System
d. Panic of 1837
e. Maysville Road Veto
f. Market Revolution
g. McCulloch v. Maryland

h. household economy
i. Tariff of Abominations
j. Monroe Doctrine
k. Trail of Tears
l. spoils system
m. second American party system

1. Thousands of Americans lost their jobs and poverty increased during the _____.

2. The face-off between National Republicans and Jacksonian Democrats is referred to as the _____.

3. During the _____ more Americans began purchasing rather than making goods, and money began to replace trading.

4. In a _____ people's business consists mainly of supplying their own goods and services.

5. The _____ warned European governments not to interfere with nations in the Americas.

6. An economic system in which manufacturing is controlled by individuals and private corporations competing for profit is called _____.

7. The Adams administration proposed the _____ under which the government would support internal improvements.

8. Under President Jackson, patronage became known as the _____.

9. Southerners claimed that the _____ which imposed taxes on imports, only benefited northern manufacturers.

10. The Cherokee referred to their forced westward migration as the _____.

Write the letter of the correct ending.

11. In the early 1800s, most banks
    A) were unable to loan money.
    B) were regulated by the federal government.
    C) were controlled by the states.
    D) did not have the money to back up their transactions.

Test Bank Questions

Write the letter of the correct ending.

12. All of the following changes occurred during the Market Revolution EXCEPT

A) more Americans became entrepreneurs.

B) work became a commodity.

C) families became more self-sufficient.

D) capitalism began to flourish.

13. One reason for the growth of cities in the early 1800s was that

A) farming was no longer profitable.

B) urban centers were needed to process and market farm products.

C) farmland in the West had become difficult to obtain.

D) working conditions had improved in northern cities.

14. In the early 1800s, most cities in the Northeast

A) had adequate sewage systems.

B) were unable to support the growing population.

C) provided excellent social services.

D) consisted of mostly middle-class neighborhoods.

15. Unlike the North, the South in the early 1800s was

A) expanding rapidly.   B) predominantly an industrial society.

C) mostly rural.   D) crowded and bustling.

16. In the early 1800s, northern factory owners and southern slaveowners were alike in that they

A) had little concern for their workers' welfare.

B) were absentee owners.

C) provided their workers with housing and medical care.

D) often developed personal relationships with their workers.

17. In the election of 1824, John Quincy Adams

A) received a majority of votes in the Electoral College.

B) won the popular vote.

C) won a landslide victory over Andrew Jackson.

D) was elected President by the House of Representatives.

18. Unlike the Jacksonian Democrats, the National Republicans thought the national government should

A) encourage the development of American industries.

B) have less control over Americans' lives.

C) reduce the tariff on foreign goods.

D) stop interfering with the economy.

Test Bank Questions

Write the letter of the correct ending.

19. One effect of the termination of the Bank of the United States was the
    A) Maysville Road Veto.
    B) American System.
    C) Panic of 1837.
    D) Market Revolution.

20. President Jackson ignored a Supreme Court decision when he
    A) upheld the spoils system.
    B) ordered the removal of the Cherokee people.
    C) terminated the national bank.
    D) sponsored the Force Bill in 1833.

21. When South Carolina nullified the Tariff of 1828, President Jackson
    A) forced South Carolina to comply but reduced some import duties.
    B) declared that all states had the right to nullify corrupt laws.
    C) applauded the action as a step toward greater liberty.
    D) repealed the measure.

Test Bank Questions

Use the cartoon of King Andrew to answer the following questions.

KING ANDREW THE FIRST

Constitution
of the
United States

22. What image in the cartoon shows that President Jackson wanted to limit the power of the Congress?

23. What image in the cartoon depicts Jackson as a dictator?

24. Which group--the Whigs or Jacksonian Democrats--probably promoted this cartoon? Explain.

Answer the following questions.

25. Do you think the Market Revolution improved or worsened the lives of most Americans who lived in the Northeast in the early 1800s? Explain your reasoning.

26. In the early 1800s, many Americans viewed President Jackson as a "hero to the common man." In light of his actions as President, do you think this was an accurate image? Explain.

27. Your text states that differences between the North and South in the early 1800s laid the foundation for serious conflict in the 1850s and 1860s. What were some of these differences?

Test Bank Questions

Match the terms below with the following descriptions. Write the letter of the correct answer. You will not use all the terms.

a. Monroe Doctrine   g. nullification
b. Panic of 1837   h. centralize
c. spoils system   i. capitalism
d. commodity   j. household economy
e. Tariff of Abominations   k. secede
f. Trail of Tears   l. capital

28. action of a state to override a law passed by Congress

29. term used to describe the forced migration of the Cherokee

30. economic system in which manufacturing is controlled by individuals and private corporations competing for profit

31. something that can be bought and sold

32. economic system in which people supply most of their own goods and services

33. to concentrate all production tasks in one place

34. wealth that can be used to produce goods and make money

35. U.S. policy to prevent European nations from interfering with nations in the Americas

36. to withdraw from an organization

37. severe depression marked by high unemployment and increased poverty

Write the letter of the correct answer.

38. What happened during the Market Revolution of the early 1800s?

   A) Families became more self-sufficient.

   B) Capitalism began to flourish.

   C) Work was no longer a commodity.

   D) The household economy began to dominate North American life.

39. Which of the following was LEAST important to southern plantation owners in the early 1800s?

   A) large amounts of land   B) access to markets

   C) slave labor   D) urban centers to process their crops

40. Which of the following best describes Mason Weems?

   A) As a writer, he was committed to truth and accuracy.

   B) He published the first do-it-yourself books and encouraged the development of a household economy.

   C) He was an entrepreneur who yearned to make money.

   D) He was a priest who denounced capitalism and greed.

Test Bank Questions

Write the letter of the correct answer.

41. What was one effect of the rapid growth of cities in the early 1800s?
    A) The gap widened between the rich and poor.
    B) Poverty declined sharply.
    C) The unemployment rate decreased.
    D) Social services improved dramatically.

42. Which of the following best describes employers in the early 1800s?
    A) They usually provided health care and retirement programs.
    B) They did not feel morally or socially obligated to their workers.
    C) They were very involved in their workers' personal lives.
    D) They often provided free housing and meals instead of wages.

43. How did many southern states react to the uprisings led by Vesey and Turner?
    A) They passed laws to restrict slave trade.
    B) They passed harsher slave laws.
    C) They condemned slaveowners who treated their slaves cruelly.
    D) They encouraged plantation owners to replace slaves with indentured servants.

44. How was John Quincy Adams elected President in 1824?
    A) He won the popular vote.
    B) He became President upon the death of President Harrison.
    C) He was elected by the House of Representatives.
    D) He was elected by the Electoral College.

45. How did Jacksonian Democrats differ from National Republicans?
    A) They thought the national government should control business.
    B) They supported a high tariff on foreign goods.
    C) They opposed government interference with the economy.
    D) They thought the national government should regulate the banks.

46. Which of the following contributed to President Jackson's reputation as the hero of the common man?
    A) McCulloch v. Maryland   B) the spoils system
    C) the American System   D) the Monroe Doctrine

47. What was President Jackson's opinion of the Bank of the United States?
    A) He thought the bank should be subject to taxation by states.
    B) He wanted to recharter the bank to prevent economic depression.
    C) He thought the bank was a "monster" institution.
    D) He supported the bank but thought it needed to be reformed.

Test Bank Questions

Write the letter of the correct answer.

48. How did President Jackson react to Georgia's seizure of Cherokee land?

A) He refused to get involved in the dispute.

B) He ordered the U.S. Army to force the Cherokee to migrate west.

C) He negotiated a compromise that gave one third of the land to Georgia.

D) He supported the Supreme Court ruling that Georgia's action was unconstitutional.

Use the cartoon of King Andrew to answer the following questions.

49. How can you tell that President Jackson probably frustrated Congress?

50. Did the cartoonist view Jackson as a "hero to the common man"? Explain.

51. Which political party most likely promoted this cartoon in the early 1830s? Explain.

Answer the following questions.

52. Why was a middle-class entrepreneur more likely to applaud the Market Revolution than was an urban factory worker?

Test Bank Questions

Answer the following questions.

53. Compare agriculture in the North with agriculture in the South in the early 1800s. How did farming affect the type of society that developed in each region?

54. Cite evidence to support the following conclusion from your text: "President Jackson worked to clear the path to success for white men."

Test Bank Answer Key

[1]   d

[2]   m

[3]   f

[4]   h

[5]   j

[6]   a

[7]   c

[8]   l

[9]   i

[10] k

[11] D

[12] C

[13] B

[14] B

[15] C

[16] A

[17] D

[18] A

[19] C

[20] B

[21] A

[22] the bill marked "VETO" in his hand

[23] He is shown as an absolute monarch trampling on the Constitution.

[24] The Whigs--named after the British party that had opposed the king--most likely promoted the cartoon to depict Jackson as a tyrant who threatened democracy.

The Market Revolution seemed to improve the lives of middle-class Americans and the wealthy by providing them with more luxuries and investment opportunities. The lives of working-class people, however, seemed to decline. Many workers were forced to live in dirty, crowded cities and work long hours at unrewarding jobs that offered low wages. In addition, poverty and disease increased during the Market [25] Revolution.

Some of Jackson's actions, such as his endorsement of the spoils system and his refusal to recharter the Bank of the United States, supported his image as a defender of the interests of the "common man." Other actions, however, such as his condemnation of South Carolina's nullification, may have shaken this view in the minds of those who believed that he was favoring the government over the people. Also, his support of the relocation of Native American groups to Oklahoma demonstrated his lack of compassion for and prejudice [26] against Native Americans.

The North was a section of farms, cities, banks, and factories, while the South consisted of farms and plantations that depended on slave labor to produce staple crops. As a result, the North and South had conflicting economic concerns and were affected differently by legislation. For example, while the Tariff of 1828 protected American industries in the North, it angered southerners because it increased [27] the prices they paid for goods.

[28] g _____

[29] f _____

[30] i _____

[31] d _____

[32] j _____

[33] h _____

[34] l _____

[35] a _____

[36] k _____

[37] b _____

[38] B _____

[39] D _____

[40] C _____

Test Bank Answer Key

[41] A

[42] B

[43] B

[44] C

[45] C

[46] B

[47] C

[48] B

[49] Jackson is holding a bill marked "VETO" in his hand.

[50] No, the cartoonist viewed Jackson as a dictator or monarch, not as a protector of the rights of ordinary citizens.

[51] The Whigs--who took their name from the British party that had opposed the king--probably promoted the cartoon to show their opposition to "King Andrew."

[52] During the Market Revolution, a middle-class entrepreneur could borrow money from a bank to start or expand a business, buy a house in the suburbs, and furnish the house with luxurious goods. Conversely, an urban factory worker was likely to live in a dirty, overcrowded tenement and to work for low wages under poor working conditions.

[53] In the North, farmers produced grains such as corn and wheat, which tended to spoil quickly. As a result, industrial areas developed in the North where factories employed workers to process and market farm products. In the South, farmers produced staple crops such as cotton, tobacco, and rice. Because these crops required little processing, they were shipped to markets outside of the South. Thus, the South remained a largely rural society. In addition, the South needed labor to grow crops like cotton, so slavery became an integral part of the southern society.

[54] President Jackson used the spoils system to ensure that his friends--Jacksonian Democrats--would hold powerful and well-paying jobs. In addition, he supported the relocation of Native American groups to open up more land for white, male landowners.

Religion and Reform (1815-1860)

Test Bank Questions

Match the terms below with the following descriptions. Write the letter of the correct answer. You will not use all the terms.

a. Horace Mann
b. Dorothea Dix
c. David Walker
d. Sojourner Truth
e. Samuel F.B. Morse
f. Harriet Tubman
g. Elizabeth Cady Stanton
h. Henry David Thoreau
i. Lucretia Mott
j. Frederick Douglass
k. Catharine Beecher
l. Charles Grandison Finney
m. William Lloyd Garrison

1.   former slave who became a leader of the underground railroad

2.   inventor and painter who attacked Catholicism

3.   African American writer whose essay Appeal encouraged the antislavery movement to become more aggressive

4.   Transcendentalist who wrote about his two years of solitary life at Walden Pond

5.   Massachusetts lawyer who sparked a movement for educational reform

6.   Presbyterian minister who emphasized the importance of individual conversion and personal choice in religious beliefs

7.   former slave and spokesperson at antislavery and women's rights meetings

8.   African American abolitionist and publisher of The North Star

9.   Boston school teacher who promoted legislation to improve conditions in prisons and poorhouses

10. teacher whose work A Treatise on Domestic Economy stressed the importance of a woman's role in the family

Write the letter of the correct answer.

11. Which of the following best describes the ideology of Transcendentalists?
    A) They believed that people's lives were predetermined by God.
    B) They did not believe in God or any kind of greater power.
    C) They believed that human beings had control over their fates.
    D) They encouraged individuals to rely on God.

Write the letter of the correct answer.

12. What did temperance societies have in common with the educational reform movement of the early 1800s?

    A) Both worked to fight crime and poverty.

    B) Both promoted solid moral values.

    C) Both promoted women's rights.

    D) Both promoted antislavery sentiments.

13. What happened to most experiments with utopian communities in the early 1800s?

    A) They fell prey to crime, poverty, and disease.

    B) They became successful models of American democracy.

    C) They were torn apart by selfishness and infighting.

    D) They were dissolved by the federal government.

14. Why did most African American abolitionists oppose colonization?

    A) They wanted to be completely free of United States control.

    B) They wanted to remain in the United States.

    C) They wanted the same rights as Native Americans.

    D) They wanted the same standard of living that they had enjoyed on southern plantations.

15. What was the purpose of the gag rule?

    A) to stop the activities of prohibitionists

    B) to expose the underground railroad

    C) to prevent the passage of antislavery legislation

    D) to discredit the woman suffrage movement

16. Who were the most ardent followers of William Lloyd Garrison?

    A) prohibitionists   B) educational reformers

    C) abolitionists   D) woman suffragists

17. Which was considered a controversial activity for women?

    A) offering advice to their husbands   B) teaching school

    C) lecturing in public assemblies   D) writing books

18. Which of the following had the greatest influence on woman suffragists in the 1840s?

    A) utopian communities

    B) the temperance and abolition movements

    C) the underground railroad

    D) the cult of domesticity and Transcendentalism

Test Bank Questions

Write the letter of the correct answer.

19. Which of the following best describes southern society in the 1830s and 1840s?

    A) Southern women enjoyed more equality and greater opportunities than most northern women.

    B) Many southerners, outraged at inhumane conditions in northern cities, pioneered prison and public school reforms.

    C) Many southern families continued to blend work and family activities and saw little need for reforms.

    D) The South became increasingly urban and industrial, and tensions with the North decreased.

20. To whom did the reform movements of the 1830s and 1840s appeal most?

    A) middle-class residents in the North

    B) settlers in the West

    C) working-class citizens

    D) white southerners

Use the chart of the South to answer the following questions.

THE SOUTH, 1850		
	All Slave States	**Cotton States**[1]
Number of slaveholding families	347,525	154,391
Number of families owning 1 to 9 slaves	255,258	104,956
Number of families owning 10 to 49 slaves	84,328	43,299
Number of families owning 50 or more slaves	7,939	6,144
White population	6,242,418	2,137,284
Free Negro population	238,187	34,485
Slave population	3,204,077	1,808,768

[1] South Carolina, Georgia, Florida, Alabama, Mississippi, Louisiana, Arkansas, and Texas

Source: *Century of Population Growth*, p. 136; J.D.B. De Bow, *Statistical View of the U.S.* (1854), pp. 45, 63, 82, 95, 99.

21. (a) How many families in the South had slaves?
    (b) How many slaves did the majority of these families have?

22. In 1850, how did the population of enslaved African Americans compare with the white population in the South?

23. Based on the information in the chart, how did the population of the cotton states compare with the population of all the states in the South?

Test Bank Questions

Answer the following questions.

24. In addition to the economic issues discussed in Chapter 8, what other issues increased tensions between middle-class northerners and southern whites in the 1830s and 1840s? Explain.

25. Compare the values and interests of most Catholic immigrants with those of northern evangelical Protestants in the North in the 1830s and 1840s.

Complete each sentence below by selecting the correct word from the list. You will not use all the words.

a. Harriet Tubman
b. Horace Mann
c. Lyman Beecher
d. Elizabeth Cady Stanton
e. Catharine Beecher
f. David Walker
g. Dorothea Dix

h. Harriet Beecher Stowe
i. Sojourner Truth
j. Samuel F.B. Morse
k. Henry David Thoreau
l. William Lloyd Garrison
m. Frederick Douglass

26. Lucretia Mott and _____ organized the first convention to discuss the question of women's rights.

27. Abolitionist _____ published an antislavery newspaper called The Liberator.

28. Under the leadership of _____, Massachusetts pioneered school reform.

29. Charles Grandison Finney and _____ were popular revivalists of the Second Great Awakening.

30. In his book Walden, _____ described his two years of solitary life.

31. _____ led hundreds of African Americans to freedom along the underground railroad.

32. Self-educated and a former slave, _____ became an eloquent spokesman for the American Anti-Slavery Society.

33. _____ worked to improve conditions in prisons and poorhouses.

34. In A Treatise on Domestic Economy, _____ stressed the importance of women to the welfare of the United States.

35. A former slave who never learned to read or write, _____ became a powerful spokesperson in the anti-slavery cause and an activist for women's rights.

Test Bank Questions

Write the letter of the correct ending.

36. Like the religious revivalists of the 1830s and 1840s, Transcendentalists believed that people should
    A) rely on God for all things.
    B) spread the teachings of the Bible.
    C) work toward self-improvement.
    D) have greater respect for traditional authority.

37. Reformers believed that temperance would help prevent all of the following EXCEPT
    A) moral decay.   B) illiteracy.
    C) employee absenteeism.   D) domestic violence.

38. Middle-class Americans who pioneered public school reforms
    A) focused on vocational training, such as farm or factory skills.
    B) promoted traditional religious beliefs.
    C) wanted schools to teach character and manners.
    D) wanted girls to receive the same education as boys.

39. Most African American abolitionists in the 1830s supported
    A) the education of enslaved peoples before freeing them.
    B) the immediate emancipation of all slaves.
    C) colonization in Liberia.
    D) migration of enslaved people to utopian communities.

40. Northern opponents of the antislavery movement advanced all of the following arguments EXCEPT
    A) "Freedom for African Americans is unconstitutional."
    B) "The antislavery movement will hurt trade between the North and South."
    C) "African Americans are socially inferior to whites, and should not live in our communities."
    D) "African Americans will steal jobs from white workers."

41. Southern politicians protected the institution of slavery by
    A) establishing the underground railroad.
    B) promoting compulsory education for slaves.
    C) abolishing utopian communities.
    D) passing the gag rule.

42. Seneca Falls, New York, is most closely associated with
    A) the antislavery movement.
    B) the women's rights movement.
    C) the temperance movement.
    D) Transcendentalism.

Test Bank Questions

Write the letter of the correct ending.

43. Cultural traditions and attitudes about a woman's role in the early 1800s were best reflected in the writings of
    A) Harriet Tubman.
    B) Lucretia Mott.
    C) Catharine Beecher.
    D) Sojourner Truth.

44. In the 1830s and 1840s, most working-class immigrants
    A) advocated women's rights and public school reforms.
    B) resented the major reform movements.
    C) dominated the temperance movement.
    D) embraced evangelical Protestant morality.

45. In the 1830s and 1840s, most southern whites
    A) defended their traditional way of life.
    B) were beginning to oppose slavery.
    C) promoted prison and public school reforms.
    D) encouraged industrial development in the South.

Use the chart of the South to answer the following questions.

THE SOUTH, 1850		
	All Slave States	Cotton States[1]
Number of slaveholding families	347,525	154,391
Number of families owning 1 to 9 slaves	255,258	104,956
Number of families owning 10 to 49 slaves	84,328	43,299
Number of families owning 50 or more slaves	7,939	6,144
White population	6,242,418	2,137,284
Free Negro population	238,187	34,485
Slave population	3,204,077	1,808,768

[1] South Carolina, Georgia, Florida, Alabama, Mississippi, Louisiana, Arkansas, and Texas

Source: *Century of Population Growth,* p. 136; J.D.B. De Bow, *Statistical View of the U.S.* (1854), pp. 45, 63, 82, 95, 99.

46. By 1850, how many free blacks were living in the South? In the cotton states?

47. (a) How did the number of slaves owned by families in the cotton states compare with the number owned by slaveholding families in all of the South?
    (b) What is one reason for this disparity in numbers?

48. Based on the information in the chart, by 1850, into what social classes was southern society divided?

Test Bank Questions

Answer the following questions.

49. Why do you think most reforms in the 1830s and 1840s occurred in the North rather than in the South? Give reasons to support your answer.

50. In what ways did the belief of middle-class evangelical Protestants influence the reform movements of the early 1800s?

Test Bank Answer Key

[1]   f

[2]   e

[3]   c

[4]   h

[5]   a

[6]   l

[7]   d

[8]   j

[9]   b

[10] k

[11] C

[12] B

[13] C

[14] B

[15] C

[16] C

[17] C

[18] B

[19] C

[20] A

[21] (a) 347,525
      (b) from 1 to 9 slaves

[22] The white population in the South was about double that of the enslaved African American population.

[23] In the cotton states, fewer families owned more slaves than did families in all the southern states.

Test Bank Answer Key

In the 1830s and 1840s, issues such as abolition, women's suffrage, prison reform, and public school reform increased tensions between the North and South. Southerners objected to abolitionism because their economy had become dependent on slave labor. Southerners opposed women's suffrage because it ran counter to their cultural traditions. Unlike the urban, industrial North, the rural, agricultural South did not see the need for prison reforms or for
[24] establishing public schools.

Most evangelical Protestants valued self-improvement, self-discipline, morality, hard work, and laws that restricted drinking and gambling. By contrast, most Catholic immigrants were working-class residents whose energies were consumed by making a living. They saw little need to change their ways, and enjoyed such
[25] pastimes as drinking, gambling, and organized sports.

[26] d

[27] l

[28] b

[29] c

[30] k

[31] a

[32] m

[33] g

[34] e

[35] i

[36] C

[37] B

[38] C

[39] B

[40] A

[41] D

[42] B

[43] C

[44] B

[45] A

[46] 238,187; 34,485

[47]
(a) Fewer families owned a greater number of slaves
    in the cotton states than in all of the South.
(b) Large numbers of laborers were needed to work on
    cotton plantations.

[48] The South was divided into four classes: wealthy plantation owners;
middle-class farmers; free blacks; and enslaved African Americans.

[49] As a result of the Market Revolution, the North had become a more
urban and industrial society with serious social problems. The South
had remained predominantly agricultural and rural and dependent on a
household economy. As a result, southerners did not recognize a need
for public schools, social reforms, or women's rights, and especially
opposed abolitionism, which posed a serious threat to their economy.

[50] Evangelical Protestants valued self-discipline, self-improvement, and
morality, the same goals that motivated such movements as temperance
and public school reform. They believed that the answer to the
question of national salvation lay in the work of individual
salvation.

Beyond the Mississippi (1800-1860)

Test Bank Questions

Complete each sentence below by selecting the correct word from the list.
You will not use all the words.

a. Jason Lee
b. Sam Houston
c. William Travis
d. William Clark
e. Joseph Smith
f. Kamiakin

g. Stephen Austin
h. Sacajawea
i. Antonio López de Santa Ana
j. Narcissa Prentiss Whitman
k. Brigham Young

1.   Meriwether Lewis and _____ led an expedition to explore the Louisiana Territory.

2.   In the 1840s, Mormon leader _____ led followers westward to the Great Salt Lake Basin.

3.   Under the leadership of _____, about 300 Americans founded a colony in the Mexican territory of Texas.

4.   _____ served as translator and guide for the American explorers of the Louisiana Territory.

5.   The dictatorship of General _____ encouraged many American settlers to fight for an independent Texas.

6.   Yakima chief _____ led Native Americans in a war against the United States in 1855.

7.   Christian missionary _____ was one of the first white women to cross the Continental Divide.

8.   In 1834 a Methodist minister named _____ built a mission school for Native Americans in the Willamette Valley.

9.   In 1830 _____ founded the Mormon religion.

10. _____ led Texan rebels at San Jacinto and became the first president of the Republic of Texas.

Write the letter of the correct ending.

11. The arrival of the horse encouraged many Native Americans to
     A) become nomads.
     B) stop trading.
     C) become farmers.
     D) establish permanent villages.

Write the letter of the correct ending.

12. In nomadic cultures, Native American women were
    A) influential leaders.
    B) aggressive warriors.
    C) skilled riders and horse thieves.
    D) homemakers producing food and tanning buffalo hides.

13. In the early 1800s, most nomadic Native Americans lived
    A) west of the Continental Divide.
    B) east of the Mississippi River.
    C) on the Great Plains.
    D) in Mexico.

14. In the early 1800s, the Spanish were most successful in
    A) colonizing most of Texas.
    B) establishing thriving missions in California.
    C) establishing small farms and towns throughout New Mexico.
    D) conquering Native Americans in present-day New Mexico.

15. In the 1830s, many Americans in Texas began to rebel against the Mexican government because they wanted
    A) protection from Native Americans.
    B) more trade with the United States.
    C) more political freedom.
    D) to abolish slavery in Texas.

16. During their fight for independence, many Texans were enraged and energized by what happened at
    A) Guadalupe Hidalgo.   B) the Alamo and Goliad.
    C) the Battle of Buena Vista.   D) Vera Cruz.

17. Those who made the greatest contribution to blazing the Oregon Trail were
    A) free blacks.   B) missionaries.
    C) land surveyors.   D) mountain men.

18. One myth about pioneers who journeyed along the Oregon Trail was that
    A) they endured dangerous and difficult traveling conditions.
    B) they often conducted trade with Native Americans.
    C) many were killed in raids led by hostile Native Americans.
    D) the majority were white settlers from midwestern states.

Test Bank Questions

Write the letter of the correct ending.

19. In the 1840s, the phrase <u>manifest destiny</u> referred to the idea that the United States would inevitably
    A) become the most powerful nation in the world.
    B) spread liberty throughout the world.
    C) possess the North American continent.
    D) abolish slavery.

20. One important result of the Mexican War was that
    A) the Republic of Texas became an independent nation.
    B) Mexico and the United States became permanent allies.
    C) the Rio Grande became the American-Mexican border.
    D) the United States gained control of the entire Oregon Country.

21. The Wilmot Proviso created controversy and conflict over whether
    A) the United States should annex Texas.
    B) the Mormons should be granted citizenship rights.
    C) Native Americans should be forced to live on reservations.
    D) slavery should be allowed in the western territories.

Test Bank Questions

Use the map of trails to the West to answer the following questions.

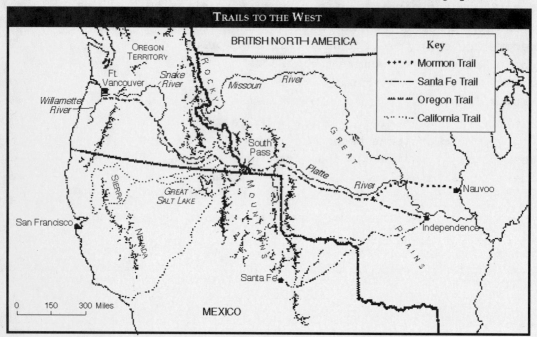

22. What two rivers would pioneers cross on the journey from Independence, Missouri, to the Oregon Country?

23. What route did the Mormons probably travel from Nauvoo to the Great Salt Lake?

24. How can you tell from the map that the journey to California was extremely difficult?

Answer the following questions.

25. Why might some Americans have felt that the Mexican War created more problems than it resolved?

26. Give evidence to support or refute the conclusion that by the end of the 1850s, "violence was the only possible outcome" in the clash between white Americans and nomadic Native Americans on the Great Plains.

104 Chapter 10

Test Bank Questions

Match the terms below with the following descriptions. Write the letter of the correct answer. You will not use all the terms.

a. Great Plains
b. the Alamo
c. Santa Fe
d. Rio Grande
e. Continental Divide
f. Oregon Trail

g. Goliad
h. Independence
i. Monterey
j. Willamette Valley
k. Snake River
l. Nueces River

27. capital of the California territory

28. path through the Rocky Mountains to settlements in the West

29. ridge of the Rocky Mountains that separates rivers that flow west from rivers that flow east

30. capital of New Mexico

31. vast grassland region that lies between the Mississippi River and Rocky Mountains

32. point at which pioneers traveling to California would turn southwest to follow the Humboldt River across the Sierra Nevada

33. site of Jason Lee's mission school in Oregon

34. fortress built on the ruins of a Spanish mission in San Antonio, Texas

35. town in western Missouri that marked the beginning of the 2,000-mile trek to Oregon

36. official American-Mexican border

Write the letter of the correct answer.

37. What was the purpose of the Lewis and Clark expedition in 1804?

    A) to conquer Native Americans in the West

    B) to establish Christian missions

    C) to establish colonies in Oregon

    D) to explore the Louisiana Territory

38. What impact did the arrival of the horse have on Native Americans?

    A) Farming replaced hunting.

    B) Many Native Americans became nomads.

    C) Trading declined.

    D) Men and women shared more responsibilities.

39. Which of the following did NOT contribute to the decline of agricultural Native American societies in the early 1800s?

    A) expansion by white settlers

    B) raids by nomadic Native Americans

    C) division of labor between men and women

    D) the spread of European diseases

Test Bank Questions

Write the letter of the correct answer.

40. What contribution did Stephen Austin make to Texas?
    A) He led the first organized group of American settlers into Texas.
    B) He helped make slavery legal in Texas.
    C) He led Texans in their fight for independence from Mexico.
    D) He blazed the Santa Fe Trail.

41. Which of the following contributed to the success of Spanish missions in California?
    A) Native American labor
    B) good living conditions and excellent medical care
    C) raids by nomadic Native Americans
    D) the priests' tolerance and understanding of other cultures

42. Which group actually lost rights when New Mexico became a part of the United States in 1848?
    A) landowners   B) the wealthy class
    C) women   D) Roman Catholics

43. Why did Narcissa Prentiss Whitman journey to Oregon in 1836?
    A) to teach Native Americans about Christianity
    B) to search for gold
    C) to join in the fur trade
    D) to practice medicine

44. Which statement best describes the relationship between emigrating pioneers and Native Americans in the 1840s?
    A) Native Americans and pioneers usually traded with each other.
    B) Native Americans and pioneers rarely interacted at all.
    C) Native Americans usually raided and destroyed the caravans.
    D) Nomadic Native Americans usually guided and protected the caravans.

45. What territory did the United States gain in the Treaty of Guadalupe Hidalgo?
    A) California and New Mexico   B) Texas
    C) Florida   D) the Oregon Country

46. What issue became a major problem for the United States government after the Mexican War?
    A) whether slavery should be allowed in the western territories
    B) whether Americans should migrate into Mexico's northern territories
    C) whether the United States should annex Texas
    D) whether Mormons should be allowed to settle Utah

Test Bank Questions

Write the letter of the correct answer.

47.   How did the gold rush affect Native Americans in California?

A) Many Native Americans became wealthy by panning for gold.

B) Native Americans were assimilated into white European culture.

C) Native American villages became boom towns.

D) Disease and forced labor devastated Native American societies.

Use the map of trails to the West to answer the following questions.

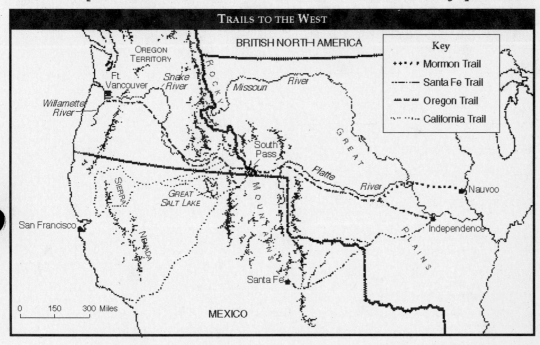

48.   (a) At what town did pioneers en route to Oregon probably stock up on supplies and form wagon caravans?
(b) Along what river would they travel to South Pass?

49.   Why were nomadic Native Americans on the Great Plains unwilling or unable to move farther west?

50.   Describe the journey from Independence to Fort Vancouver in Oregon.

Answer the following questions.

51.   Why do you think nomadic Native Americans were more successful than village societies in resisting domination by the United States government?

52.   Why was the annexation of Texas a difficult decision for the United States?

Test Bank Answer Key

[1] d

[2] k

[3] g

[4] h

[5] i

[6] f

[7] j

[8] a

[9] e

[10] b

[11] A

[12] D

[13] C

[14] B

[15] C

[16] B

[17] D

[18] C

[19] C

[20] C

[21] D

[22] the Platte and Snake rivers

[23] They probably traveled to the Platte River and followed the Oregon Trail to the California Trail to the Great Salt Lake.

[24] The journey covered a long distance, and pioneers had to cross mountain ranges and rivers.

Test Bank Answer Key

While the Mexican War ended the dispute over the southern border of Texas, it created a crisis over the extension of slavery into the territories acquired from Mexico. As growing numbers of Americans migrated west into newly acquired territories, relations between white settlers and Native American groups deteriorated and U.S. government officials were forced to consider solutions to the "Indian problem." In addition, the war led to decades of poor relations and [25] misunderstandings between Mexico and the United States.

Westward migration caused thousands of Americans to pour into what was originally promised to be "Indian Country." The slaughter of buffalo and the creation of farms and communities on the Plains threatened the Native Americans' way of life. Since nomadic groups refused to abandon their way of life and move to reservations and Americans refused to end their pursuit of land, violence became [26] inevitable.

[27] i _____

[28] f _____

[29] e _____

[30] c _____

[31] a _____

[32] k _____

[33] j _____

[34] b _____

[35] h _____

[36] d _____

[37] D _____

[38] B _____

[39] C _____

[40] A _____

[41] A _____

[42] C _____

[43] A _____

[44] A _____

Test Bank Answer Key

[45] A

[46] A

[47] D

[48] (a) at Independence
(b) Platte River

[49] There were mountains to the west and no great expanse of plains for the buffalo herds.

[50] The journey follows the Oregon Trail the entire route. It crosses the Great Plains, Rocky Mountains, and Snake River.

[51] Nomadic Native Americans were accustomed to living in many different areas and could adapt more easily when pushed from one territory to another. By moving frequently, they avoided some of the diseases that ravaged village societies. Finally, nomadic Native Americans were skilled fighters and warriors.

[52] Because slavery was allowed in the Republic of Texas, northerners feared that the addition of one more slave state would tip the balance of power in Congress to the South. In addition, many Americans worried that annexation would lead to war with Mexico, which did not officially recognize the independence of Texas.

The Coming of the Civil War (1848-1861)

Test Bank Questions

Complete each sentence below by selecting the correct word from the list. You will not use all the words.

a. John C. Breckinridge
b. Robert E. Lee
c. John Brown
d. Jefferson Davis
e. Stephen Douglas
f. George Fitzhugh
g. Abraham Lincoln
h. Charles Sumner
i. Harriet Beecher Stowe
j. William Henry Seward
k. Roger Taney

1. Senator _____ of Illinois introduced the Kansas-Nebraska Act in 1854.

2. The book <u>Uncle Tom's Cabin</u>, by _____, caused many white Americans to question slavery.

3. Abolitionist _____ led the attack on the federal arsenal at Harpers Ferry.

4. In the <u>Dred Scott</u> case, Chief Justice _____ upheld the right of slaveowners to take enslaved people anywhere in the United States.

5. In 1858 Republican nominee _____ opposed slavery on moral grounds in debates with Stephen Douglas.

6. In <u>Cannibals All!</u>, _____ attacked northern industrialists.

7. Vice President _____ was committed to an aggressive policy of expanding slavery in the territories.

8. Senator _____ of Massachusetts gave a powerful anti-slavery speech entitled "The Crime Against Kansas."

9. Because his antislavery position seemed too aggressive, _____ lost the 1860 Republican presidential nomination.

10. Senator _____ of Mississippi was elected president of the Confederate States of America.

Write the letter of the correct ending.

11. Unlike the South, the North in 1860
    A) was committed to capitalism.
    B) had a democratic form of government.
    C) was not prejudiced against African Americans.
    D) was becoming a thriving industrial society.

Test Bank Questions

Write the letter of the correct ending.

12. Many southern whites criticized northern capitalists for
    A) assuming personal responsibility for workers.
    B) exploiting their workers.
    C) trying to control workers' lives.
    D) refusing to hire African American workers.

13. Northerners objected to the Compromise of 1850 because it
    A) gave the South much greater power in Congress.
    B) made California a slave state.
    C) forced them to assist in the return of runaway slaves.
    D) allowed citizens in New Mexico and Utah to determine the legal status of slavery in their territories.

14. In the mid-1800s, nativists wanted to ensure that
    A) people born in the United States were better treated than immigrants.
    B) immigrants from all countries would receive equal treatment.
    C) immigrants would become United States citizens.
    D) Catholic immigrants would renounce "Papal Power."

15. The Republicans gained support in the late 1850s by
    A) opposing economic and political domination by the North.
    B) supporting both slavery and a strong national government.
    C) supporting the idea of popular sovereignty in the territories.
    D) opposing both slavery and Catholicism.

16. All of the following further divided proslavery and antislavery groups in Kansas in the 1850s EXCEPT
    A) the Lecompton constitution.
    B) the Kansas-Nebraska Act.
    C) membership in the Whig party.
    D) raids led by abolitionists.

17. In a popular speech in 1858, Abraham Lincoln insisted that
    A) the issue of slavery should be resolved independently by each state or territory.
    B) African Americans were entitled to full citizenship rights.
    C) compromise was possible between the North and South.
    D) the Union had to become all slave or all free.

18. Most southerners who wanted to expand slavery belonged to the
    A) Republican party.   B) American party.
    C) Democratic party.   D) Constitutional Union party.

Test Bank Questions

Write the letter of the correct ending.

19. In the 1860s, Delaware, Maryland, Kentucky, and Missouri were called the

A) Slave Power.   B) Border States.

C) Upper South.   D) Lower South.

20. In 1860 and 1861, seven southern states seceded from the Union in protest against the

A) election of Republican Abraham Lincoln as President.

B) federal government's refusal to punish John Brown.

C) Dred Scott decision.

D) brutal caning of Charles Sumner in the Senate.

21. President Lincoln summoned volunteer troops in response to the

A) illegal formation of the Confederate States of America.

B) secession of South Carolina.

C) surrender of Fort Sumter.

D) attack on Lawrence, Kansas, a center of free-soiler activity.

Use the graph of Union and Confederate Resources to answer the following questions.

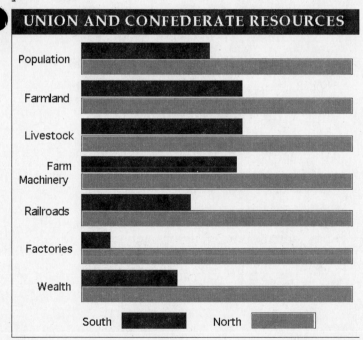

UNION AND CONFEDERATE RESOURCES

Population, Farmland, Livestock, Farm Machinery, Railroads, Factories, Wealth

South   North

22. Which region had a better transportation system? Which region was more industrial?

Test Bank Questions

Use the graph of Union and Confederate Resources to answer the following questions.

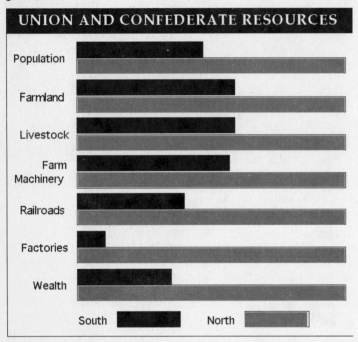

UNION AND CONFEDERATE RESOURCES

Population
Farmland
Livestock
Farm Machinery
Railroads
Factories
Wealth

South   North

23. How did agriculture in the South compare with that in the North?

24. Based on these graphs, do you think southern fears that the North would control the United States government were justified? Explain.

Answer the following questions.

25. Explain why northern whites who opposed slavery and southern whites who supported slavery both felt they were fighting to defend liberty.

26. In 1861, what alternatives did President Lincoln consider for dealing with the Confederate States of America? What were the pros and cons of each alternative?

27. In early 1861, President Lincoln said, "There is in my judgment but one compromise which would really settle the slavery question, and that would be a prohibition against acquiring any more territory." Explain whether or not you think Lincoln's compromise would have settled the "slavery question."

Test Bank Questions

Match the terms below with the following descriptions. Write the letter of the correct answer. You will not use all the terms.

a. American party
b. Fugitive Slave Act
c. Kansas-Nebraska Act
d. Lecompton constitution
e. Confederate States of America
f. Republican party
g. the Slave Power
h. the Union
i. naturalization
j. Border States
k. Constitutional Union party
l. Compromise of 1850

28. new nation created by the states of the Lower South when they seceded from the United States

29. proslavery laws drawn up to govern Kansas

30. proposal to admit California as a free state while allowing New Mexico and Utah to decide for themselves whether to legalize slavery

31. political organization that arose in the mid-1850s to oppose slavery

32. term used to describe the United States

33. process through which immigrants become United States citizens

34. term used by northerners in the mid-1800s to describe the South

35. law that ordered all citizens to assist in the return of runaway slaves

36. political group made up of southern Whigs and politicians from the Border States

37. political organization formed by nativists in 1854

Write the letter of the correct answer.

38. How did the book <u>Uncle Tom's Cabin</u> affect American society in the 1850s?

   A) It caused some slaveholders to allow slaves to buy their freedom.

   B) It convinced many northerners that enslaved people were property.

   C) It resulted in passage of laws protecting slaves from abusive owners.

   D) It turned many northern whites against slavery.

39. Against which group did the American party discriminate most?

   A) middle-class evangelical Protestants

   B) African Americans

   C) northern factory workers

   D) Irish Catholics

Test Bank Questions

Write the letter of the correct answer.

40. What did Senator Stephen Douglas propose in the Kansas-Nebraska Act?
    A) to allow slavery in Nebraska but not in Kansas
    B) to uphold the Missouri Compromise
    C) to rely on popular sovereignty to decide on the legal status of slavery in the territories
    D) to make Kansas and Nebraska slave states

41. Which of the following statements is true of both the North and the South in the mid-1800s?
    A) Industrial centers were vital to the economy of both regions.
    B) Both regions had capitalist economies.
    C) Both regions had strong communication systems.
    D) Cotton was the most important cash crop in both regions.

42. Which of the following statements would John C. Calhoun most likely have made?
    A) Slavery is morally wrong and a threat to liberty.
    B) Owning enslaved people as property is a constitutional right.
    C) The South should part ways with the North.
    D) The South should abandon slavery to save the nation.

43. What did Chief Justice Roger Taney decide in <u>Dred Scott v. Sandford</u>?
    A) Slave owners could not take slaves to free states or territories.
    B) The federal government should protect the slave owner, not the slave.
    C) The slave trade should be abolished in Washington, D.C.
    D) Slavery was unconstitutional.

44. Which principle did Abraham Lincoln profess during the 1858 senatorial debates with Stephen Douglas?
    A) Slavery should be prohibited in the South.
    B) Whites and African Americans should have social and political equality.
    C) White citizens could choose the kind of society they wanted.
    D) Slavery was a moral issue.

45. What was the greatest impact of John Brown's raid on Harpers Ferry?
    A) Northerners and southerners reached a temporary "cease-fire."
    B) The raid deepeded the division between North and South.
    C) The raid led to the breakdown of the Second American Party System.
    D) The federal government decided to let state governments resolve all slavery issues.

Test Bank Questions

Write the letter of the correct answer.

46. Why were southern states so upset with the election of Abraham Lincoln as President in 1860?
    A) He was committed to an aggressive policy of ending slavery.
    B) He had not campaigned fairly.
    C) He had not won any votes from the southern states.
    D) He had not won a majority in the Electoral College.

47. What stance did President Lincoln take toward secession?
    A) He offered a compromise to the states.
    B) He refused to recognize the Confederacy.
    C) He declared war on the states.
    D) He agreed to let the states secede.

48. What final challenge signaled the start of the Civil War?
    A) the creation of the Confederate States
    B) the formation of the Constitutional Union party
    C) the split in the Democratic party
    D) the bombardment of Fort Sumter

Test Bank Questions

Use the graph of Union and Confederate Resources to answer the following questions.

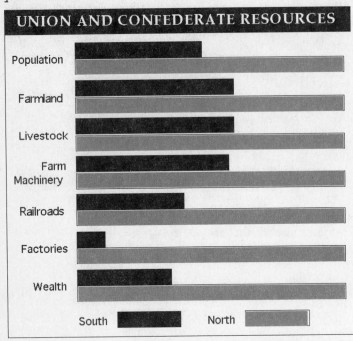

UNION AND CONFEDERATE RESOURCES

Population
Farmland
Livestock
Farm Machinery
Railroads
Factories
Wealth

South   North

49. In 1860, how did the population of the North compare with the population of the South?

50. Which region was more industrial? Which region was wealthier?

51. What information in the graph supports this statement from your text: "New technology had a heavier impact on the North than on the South"?

Answer the following questions.

52. Do you agree with President Lincoln's statement that the United States could not survive unless it became all free or all slave? Explain.

53. How was it possible that both northern abolitionists and southern slaveowners believed that they were defending the Constitution?

54. Based on the attitudes of most northern and southern whites toward African Americans in the mid-1800s, what do you think life would be like for enslaved people if slavery were abolished?

Test Bank Answer Key

[1] e

[2] i

[3] c

[4] k

[5] g

[6] f

[7] a

[8] h

[9] j

[10] d

[11] D

[12] B

[13] C

[14] A

[15] D

[16] C

[17] D

[18] C

[19] B

[20] A

[21] C

[22] the North; the North

[23] The North had more farmland, livestock, and farm machinery.

[24] Yes. The North, with a population almost double that of the South, had more electoral votes and more representatives in the House.

[25] Northern whites thought slavery violated the right to liberty of enslaved people. Southern whites felt that the abolition of slavery threatened their freedom to own property and their way of life.

Test Bank Answer Key

[26] Lincoln could have allowed the South to leave peacefully. This alternative would have prevented war, but would also have destroyed the Union. Lincoln could have attempted another compromise with the South, but there was no reason to think it would succeed when all others had failed. Finally, he could oppose secession, thereby risking a civil war to preserve the Union.

[27] Such a compromise might have helped quiet southern fears about the growing power of the North in Congress and relieve tension for a short period. Such a compromise, however, would not have permanently settled the slavery question. Abolitionists would have continued to oppose slavery on moral grounds and the rapid population growth in the North would have eventually given the North and those who opposed slavery domination of the Congress and the presidency.

[28] e

[29] d

[30] l

[31] f

[32] h

[33] i

[34] g

[35] b

[36] k

[37] a

[38] D

[39] D

[40] C

[41] B

[42] B

[43] B

[44] D

[45] B

[46] C

Test Bank Answer Key

[47] B

[48] D

[49] The population of the North was almost double that of the South.

[50] the North; the North

[51] The North had more railroads, factories, and farm equipment.

[52] Yes. In the mid-1800s, slavery had become a moral issue as well as a political one. Even if compromises could temporarily achieve a balance of power between North and South, the number of northern abolitionists was increasing at a much faster rate than that of southern slave owners.

[53] Northern abolitionists believed that the Constitution guaranteed freedom for all people. Because enslaved people were not free, the institution of slavery was a direct contradiction of the Constitution. By contrast, southern slaveowners felt that the abolition of slavery threatened the constitutional right of Americans to own property--in this case, slaves.

[54] Although enslaved people would be "free," they would still face widespread discrimination. Most northern and southern whites in the mid-1800s believed that African Americans were inferior and that the races should in no way be equal. Freed slaves would lack education and skills and many would probably have to continue working on plantations out of economic necessity. Theirs would be a long struggle for social, political, and economic equality.

The Civil War (1861-1865)

Test Bank Questions

Match the terms below with the following descriptions. Write the letter of the correct answer. You will not use all the terms.

a. greenbacks
b. contraband
c. siege
d. war of attrition

e. canisters
f. gunboats
g. draft

h. total war
i. Anaconda Plan
j. Thirteenth Amendment
k. writ of habeas corpus

l. Copperheads
m. Radical Republicans

1. General Scott's strategy to surround the Confederacy with Union forces and slowly squeeze it to death

2. bank notes guaranteed by the federal government

3. conflict in which a weaker army inflicts small, but continuous losses on its enemy

4. antiwar Democratic politicians

5. property seized from the enemy and forfeited to the government

6. small floating forts equipped with rifled cannons

7. legal means of forcing people to serve in the armed forces

8. court order that commands an officer to produce justification for holding a prisoner in jail

9. conflict in which opponents strike against soldiers, civilians, and the enemy's entire economic system

10. form of prolonged attack in which a city is surrounded and starved into surrender

Write the letter of the correct answer.

11. What tactic did both sides take in the early fighting of the Civil War?
    A) adopting guerilla-like tactics
    B) sending masses of soldiers to seize the enemy's capital
    C) fighting defensively to prevent invasion
    D) waging a war of attrition

Write the letter of the correct answer.

12. Which of the following was NOT a problem the Confederacy faced during the Civil War?

    A) lack of unity among states

    B) lack of a formal constitution

    C) lack of human resources

    D) lack of money

13. During the first two years of the war, what were the North's most significant victories?

    A) capturing the Confederate capital in the East

    B) destroying Confederate rail centers

    C) gaining river highways into the midwestern Confederate states

    D) cutting off the Upper South from the Lower South

14. How did the Republican-controlled Congress change the role of the federal government during the Civil War?

    A) The federal government assumed the responsibility of protecting basic civil liberties.

    B) The government loosened its control of industry.

    C) The government began to direct the economy.

    D) New laws limited the power of the federal government.

15. Whom did the Emancipation Proclamation free?

    A) enslaved people living in the territories

    B) enslaved people living in the Union states

    C) enslaved people living in areas rebelling against the Union

    D) all enslaved people living in the United States

16. What contribution did William Harvey Carney make during the Civil War?

    A) His bravery on the battlefield helped improve white attitudes toward African American soldiers.

    B) He and other abolitionists forced Lincoln to issue the Emancipation Proclamation.

    C) He was the first African American soldier to become a Union general.

    D) He helped set thousands of African Americans free by declaring them contraband.

17. Which of the following was a terrible blow to General Robert E. Lee and his Confederate troops?

    A) the battle of Fredericksburg   B) the battle of Manassas

    C) the battle of Shiloh   D) the battle of Gettysburg

Test Bank Questions

Write the letter of the correct answer.

18. How did the military struggle at Vicksburg differ from most other battles in the Civil War?

A) Soldiers were fighting over supplies, not territory.

B) It was directed against both civilians and soldiers.

C) Shells and canisters were used during the battle.

D) It became the most important Confederate victory.

19. What was the significance of Lincoln's Gettysburg Address?

A) It helped mend hostile relations between the North and South.

B) It stressed that freedom and equality were for all people.

C) It condemned the use of total war.

D) It declared that Americans would never again practice slavery.

20. Where did Robert E. Lee and Ulysses S. Grant discuss surrender terms?

A) the capitol at Jackson   B) the White House

C) Appomattox Court House   D) a fortress at Vicksburg

21. What was the significance of the presidential election of 1864?

A) The Copperheads supported Lincoln.

B) Voters showed their approval of Lincoln's stand on slavery.

C) Voters showed their approval of Lincoln's peace plan.

D) Voters showed their disapproval of Lincoln's war policy.

Test Bank Questions

Use the map of The War on the Rivers to answer the following questions.

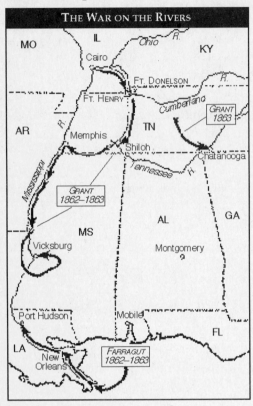

22. Name at least three rivers that were strategically important for the control of commerce and troops throughout the midwestern region of the Confederacy.

23. What strategy did Grant use to attack and capture Vicksburg?

24. How would Union control of the Mississippi River affect the economy of the Confederacy?

Answer the following questions.

25. At the start of the Civil War, why do you think many Americans favored the North to win?

26. What asssumptions did northerners and southerners each make at the start of the Civil War?

27. Name at least one social, economic, and political problem the South would face in the post-Civil War years. Give reasons for your response.

Test Bank Questions

Complete each sentence below by selecting the correct word from the list. You will not use all the words.

a. siege
b. greenback
c. draft
d. gunboats
e. contraband
f. total war
g. Anaconda Plan
h. Gettysburg Address

i. war of attrition
j. Emancipation Proclamation
k. writ of <u>habeas</u> <u>corpus</u>
l. Thirteenth Amendment
m. Internal Revenue Act of 1862
n. Pacific Railroad Act of 1862
o. canisters

28. President Lincoln's _____ redefined the ideas of freedom and equality in the United States.

29. Forts Donelson and Henry were bombarded by Union _____.

30. Both the North and South suspended the _____ so that Americans who objected to federal policies could be imprisoned.

31. President Lincoln issued the _____ to free enslaved people in areas rebelling against the U.S. government.

32. In a _____, a weaker army avoids direct confrontations and inflicts small but continuous losses on the enemy.

33. The Confederate government was the first to pass _____ laws to force people to serve in the armed forces.

34. The _____ had a powerful impact on the expansion of the United States.

35. Northern newspapers called General Scott's strategy of surrounding the Confederacy the _____.

36. During the Civil War, enslaved African Americans that were the property of the enemy were considered _____.

37. The _____ ended slavery in the United States.

38. During a _____, a city is surrounded and starved into surrender.

39. Striking not only against soldiers but also against civilians and the enemy's economic system is a _____.

Write the letter of the correct ending.

40. Given the technology of rifles and canisters, both the North and the South would have been better off

A) avoiding direct confrontation.

B) assembling forces for one major battle.

C) fighting a more aggressive, offensive war.

D) attacking the enemy's capital.

Test Bank Questions

Write the letter of the correct ending.

41. The early battles at Manassas and Shiloh proved that the
    A) war would not be over quickly.
    B) Confederacy had better trained soldiers than did the Union.
    C) the South had the support of Great Britain.
    D) Union forces were better organized.

42. In the first two years, the Union was most successful in
    A) capturing the Confederate capital.
    B) destroying Confederate railroad centers.
    C) capturing river highways in the western part of the Confederacy.
    D) splitting the Confederacy in two.

43. Like the central government of the Confederacy, the federal government of the United States
    A) clashed with independent-minded state governments.
    B) was practically bankrupt.
    C) denied its citizens some of their basic rights.
    D) seized control of the banks from private owners.

44. During the Civil War, a Republican-controlled Congress managed to
    A) establish a strong government-business relationship.
    B) stall westward expansionism.
    C) end high taxation and unfair draft laws.
    D) decrease the power of the national government.

45. The Radical Republicans wanted President Lincoln to
    A) emancipate the enslaved people of the South.
    B) break all political and economic ties with the South.
    C) begin peace negotiations with the Confederacy.
    D) provide jobs for freed slaves.

46. The Union forces finally captured Vicksburg, Mississippi, by
    A) forcing a direct confrontation.
    B) riding gunboats down the Yazoo River.
    C) digging a canal from one part of the Mississippi River to another.
    D) laying siege to the city.

47. General Ulysses S. Grant was most admired for
    A) his brilliant war strategy.
    B) caring for the welfare of his troops.
    C) opposing total war.
    D) his determination and persistence.

Test Bank Questions

Write the letter of the correct ending.

48. The reelection of President Lincoln in 1864 showed that most Americans
    A) approved of his stand against slavery.
    B) were tired of war.
    C) approved of his plans for peace.
    D) expected the war to last several more years.

49. On April 9, 1865, General Robert E. Lee agreed to the terms of the Confederate surrender
    A) at Appomattox Court House.
    B) at the capital of the Confederacy.
    C) in Washington, D.C.
    D) in Savannah.

Use the map of The War on the Rivers to answer the following questions.

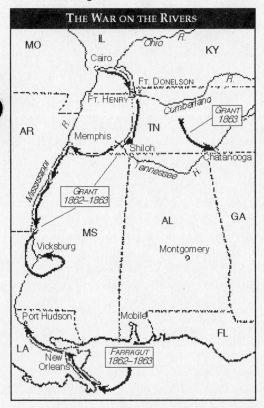

50. What two Confederate strongholds on the Mississippi River did Commodore Farragut and his Union sailors capture?

51. Why was the Union capture of Fort Henry and Fort Donelson a blow to the Confederacy?

Test Bank Questions

Use the map of The War on the Rivers to answer the following questions.

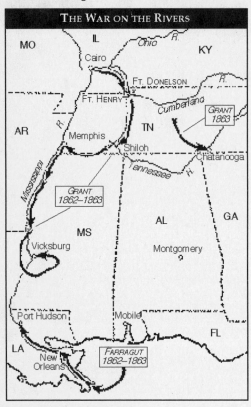

52. What impact would Union control of the Mississippi River have on the Confederacy?

Answer the following questions.

53. What advantages did the North have over the South during the Civil War?

54. How might the abolition of slavery create problems in both the North and the South following the Civil War?

55. Why did both Sherman and Grant engage in total war against the South? How did they justify this principle of war? What were the long-term consequences of this military strategy?

Test Bank Answer Key

[1] i

[2] a

[3] d

[4] l

[5] b

[6] f

[7] g

[8] k

[9] h

[10] c

[11] B

[12] B

[13] C

[14] C

[15] C

[16] A

[17] D

[18] B

[19] B

[20] C

[21] B

[22] Mississippi River, Cumberland River, and Tennessee River

[23] He sent his army south of the city, marched northeast, and attacked the city from the east.

[24] The economy would be destroyed with the loss of the cotton trade abroad.

Test Bank Answer Key

[25] The South faced the challenge of turning rebels into citizens and forging loyalty to a new government. Unlike the South, the North had a strong, well-organized federal government in power and did not have to create one while fighting a major war. The North was also a much wealthier region than the South, possessing more economic and human resources.

[26] Northerners and southerners both assumed the war would be short and an easy victory. They each underestimated the strength and determination of their opponent. They also assumed that the old ways of fighting a war--attacking the enemy's capital, gathering forces for one big, decisive battle--were still the most effective tactics.

[27] The South would face serious economic problems as a result of the destruction of crops, railroads, bridges, factories, and plantations. Socially, both white southerners and free African Americans would have to adjust to the change in their status as a result of the abolition of slavery. Politically, the South, firmly committed to states' rights, would find it difficult to share power with a strong federal government.

[28] h

[29] d

[30] k

[31] j

[32] i

[33] c

[34] n

[35] g

[36] e

[37] l

[38] a

[39] f

[40] A

[41] A

[42] A

[43] C

Test Bank Answer Key

[44] A

[45] A

[46] D

[47] D

[48] A

[49] A

[50] New Orleans and Port Hudson

[51] The Union gained access to two important river highways--the Cumberland and Tennessee rivers--into Confederate states.

[52] The western regions of the Confederacy would be cut off from the east, the southern states could no longer transport cotton and other goods to the Gulf of Mexico and abroad.

[53] Unlike the South, the North already had a strong federal government in power and did not have to try to create one in wartime. The North did not have the problem of turning rebels into citizens and forging a loyalty to a new government. The North was also much wealthier than the South and had more industry, people, and capital.

[54] In the North, Copperheads and others who had disapproved of abolishing slavery might become more hostile to African Americans. Fear of losing jobs to free African Americans could intensify racial fears and lead to discriminatory policies and riots. Abolition of slavery would create social and economic problems as the South tried to rebuild its economy without slave labor. Both white southerners and free African Americans would be forced to work out new social, political, and economic relationships.

[55] The goal of total war is to persuade the enemy not to continue fighting because defeat would result not only in military losses but in economic and civilian losses as well. Total war was justified on the ground that war itself was cruel, followed no rules, and could not be refined. During war, everything and everyone was subject to attack. Total war makes the peace process more vindictive and the healing process more difficult.

Reconstruction (1863-1877)

Test Bank Questions

Complete each sentence below by selecting the correct word from the list. You will not use all the words.

a. pardon
b. impeach
c. Reconstruction
d. Freedmen's Bureau
e. debt peonage
f. sharecropper

g. Crédit Mobilier
h. Ku Klux Klan
i. Fourteenth Amendment
j. Fifteenth Amendment
k. Millitary Reconstruction Act of 1867
l. United States Sanitary Commission

1. The _____ stated that everyone born or naturalized in the United States was a citizen and was entitled to equal protection under the law.

2. Congress established the _____ to provide aid to former slaves and to help them make the adjustment to freedom.

3. With the ratification of the _____, African Americans gained the right to vote.

4. As part of his Reconstruction policy, President Lincoln offered a _____ to any Confederate who would swear allegiance to the Union and accept the end of slavery.

5. A _____ is a farmer who grows a crop on land owned by someone else and gives the landowner a portion of the annual yield.

6. The _____ divided the South into five districts to be governed by northern generals.

7. Under the system of _____, planters forced former slaves to sign labor contracts.

8. After President Johnson tried to fire his Secretary of War, the House of Representatives voted to _____ him.

9. The most notorious example of postwar political and economic corruption was the _____ scandal.

10. Formed in 1861, the _____ helped local organizations provide medical aid and other assistance to soldiers.

Test Bank Questions

Write the letter of the correct ending.

11. The most important goal for freed African Americans was
    A) forming their own churches.
    B) participating in politics.
    C) owning land.
    D) traveling away from the plantation.

12. The story of White Hall Plantation illustrated how
    A) southern landowners were able to preserve the slave system in new forms.
    B) southern whites felt insulted by new attitudes among former slaves.
    C) most African Americans remained loyal to their former owners.
    D) the plantation system recovered its dominance in the southern economy.

13. President Lincoln's Reconstruction policy ensured
    A) southern endorsement of the Thirteenth Amendment.
    B) a fair redistribution of land.
    C) the rights of African Americans in the South.
    D) continued military rule in the South.

14. Southern state governments tried to weaken President Johnson's Reconstruction plan by
    A) refusing to hire African American workers.
    B) convening constitutional conventions.
    C) passing black codes.
    D) refusing to pay their war debts.

15. All of the following were passed by Congress to weaken southern resistance to Reconstruction EXCEPT the
    A) Fourteenth Amendment.   B) Military Reconstruction Act of 1867.
    C) Tenure of Office Act.   D) Civil Rights Act of 1866.

16. Carpetbaggers were northern Republicans who
    A) moved to the South.
    B) became Democrats.
    C) were poor tenant farmers.
    D) voted to impeach President Johnson.

17. Southern Republicans tried to improve economic conditions by
    A) compensating former slaveowners for loss of labor.
    B) enforcing a radical policy of land redistribution.
    C) raising cotton prices.
    D) increasing taxes for railroad and business development.

Test Bank Questions

Write the letter of the correct ending.

18. After Rutherford B. Hayes became President in 1877, he
    A) promised to regulate the railroads.
    B) removed federal troops from the South.
    C) pledged to promote women's rights.
    D) ended corruption in government.

19. At the end of the Civil War, industry in the United States
    A) was booming as a result of war profits and business leadership.
    B) was stifled by government regulation.
    C) had trouble adjusting to the postwar economy.
    D) was weakened by overproduction and lack of demand.

20. By the 1870s, African Americans in the North
    A) were close to achieving economic equality with white Americans.
    B) made significant strides toward social equality.
    C) still remained politically powerless.
    D) were members of various state legislatures.

21. During Reconstruction, the Supreme Court supported
    A) southerners' constitutional rights of private property.
    B) Lincoln's Reconstruction plan.
    C) congressional plans for Reconstruction.
    D) laws restricting the rights of freed people.

Test Bank Questions

Use the cartoon below to answer the following questions.

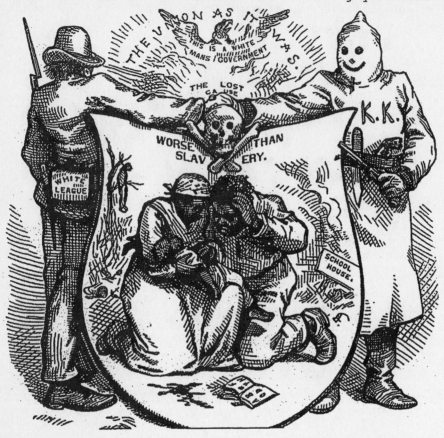

Source: Library of Congress

22. According to the cartoonist, what was the goal of the Ku Klux Klan?

23. What kinds of weapons did Klan members intend to use against freed people?

24. What actions did the KKK threaten to take to make the lives of freed people "worse than slavery"?

Answer the following questions.

25. Which Reconstruction policy do you think President Lincoln would have supported--that of President Johnson, or that of the Congress? Explain.

Test Bank Questions

Answer the following questions.

26. How did southern defiance to President Johnson's Reconstruction plan backfire and work against white southerners? Give examples to support your answer.

27. Compare the steps taken by Republicans in the North to improve economic conditions with those taken by Republicans in the South.

Match the terms below with the following descriptions. Write the letter of the correct answer. You will not use all the terms.

a. debt peonage
b. carpetbagger
c. impeach
d. sharecropper

e. Freedmen's Bureau

f. Reconstruction

g. Crédit Mobilier

h. Fourteenth Amendment
i. pardon
j. Fifteenth Amendment
k. United States Sanitary Commission
l. Military Reconstruction Act of 1867
m. scalawag
n. tenant farmer

28. farmer who grows a crop on someone else's land and gives the landowner a portion of the annual yield

29. official forgiveness of a crime

30. legislation that divided the South into five districts to be governed by northern generals

31. organization that provided aid to former enslaved people and helped them adjust to freedom

32. legislation stating that no citizen could be denied the vote because of race, color, or previous condition of servitude

33. legislation stating that all persons born or naturalized in the United States were citizens and no state could restrict their rights

34. act of formally charging an official with wrongdoing in office

35. system that kept former slaves dependent upon planters who had loaned them money in exchange for labor

36. dummy corporation created by stockholders to oversee the construction of the Union Pacific Railroad

37. northern Republican who moved to the South after the Civil War

Write the letter of the correct answer.

38. After the Civil War, why did so many freed people travel long distances?

   A) to assert their independence

   B) to escape white prejudice

   C) to find jobs in northern factories

   D) to reunite with their families

Test Bank Questions

Write the letter of the correct answer.

39. Which of the following was the most important goal of freed African Americans at the end of the Civil War?
    A) to participate in the political process
    B) to travel wherever they wanted
    C) to own property
    D) to start their own churches

40. Why did President Lincoln veto the Reconstruction plan proposed by Congress?
    A) He thought the plan was too moderate.
    B) He wanted to protect the rights of African Americans.
    C) He thought the plan was too severe.
    D) He thought the plan was unconstitutional.

41. How did southern state governments try to weaken President Johnson's Reconstruction policy?
    A) They ignored the orders of northern military officers.
    B) They enacted black codes to severely restrict the rights of freed people.
    C) They boycotted merchandise from the North.
    D) They refused to pay off their war debts.

42. What impact did southern resistance to Johnson's plan have on the United States government?
    A) It weakened the Senate.
    B) It increased the power of Radical Republicans in Congress.
    C) It drove a wedge between Congress and the Supreme Court.
    D) It increased the power of the President.

43. How did southern governments try to improve economic conditions in the South?
    A) by lowering taxes and paying off state debts
    B) by building more railroads and businesses
    C) by raising cotton prices
    D) by redistributing land

44. How did Rutherford B. Hayes become President in 1876?
    A) He made concessions to southern Democrats.
    B) His opponent was accused of political corruption.
    C) He won the popular vote by a very narrow margin.
    D) He won the electoral vote by a landslide.

Test Bank Questions

Write the letter of the correct answer.

45. How did the Ku Klux Klan affect the South during Reconstruction?
    A) It strengthened the African American fight for civil rights.
    B) It helped to hasten Reconstruction in the South.
    C) It enabled Radical Republicans to gain power in the South.
    D) It helped to reverse Reconstruction in the South.

46. Which of the following best describes industrial growth in the North by the end of the Civil War?
    A) Bribes and corruption led to the downfall of many industries.
    B) Government regulations stifled industrial growth.
    C) War profits fueled the growth of industries.
    D) Overproduction during wartime resulted in an economic depression.

47. What was the final outcome of Reconstruction?
    A) The nation made great strides toward social justice.
    B) African Americans gained strong political power in the North.
    C) Few legal and political freedoms were guaranteed to African Americans.
    D) The southern economy was rebuilt.

48. What position did the Supreme Court take during Reconstruction?
    A) It declared President Johnson's plan unconstitutional.
    B) It took no position on plans for Reconstruction.
    C) It went along with congressional plans for Reconstruction.
    D) It supported the rights of Confederate landholders.

Test Bank Questions

Use the cartoon below to answer the following questions.

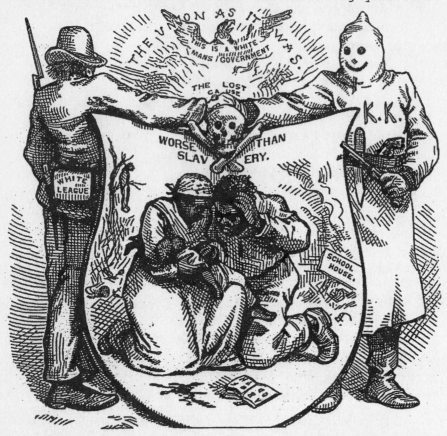

Source: Library of Congress

49. What type of government did the Ku Klux Klan favor?

50. What do you think was "the lost cause"?

51. In what two ways would freedom be worse then slavery?

Answer the following questions.

52. Why did the abolition of slavery tend to increase discrimination toward African Americans?

53. The text states that "Between 1862 and 1872, the United States granted over 100 million acres of federal land and millions of dollars to corporations." Why do you think the government aided industry, but was reluctant to help freed African Americans, farmers, and workers?

Test Bank Questions

Answer the following questions.

54. What problems did the Republican party have to overcome in the South to implement its plan for Reconstruction? How did the Republicans address these problems?

Test Bank Answer Key

[1] i

[2] d

[3] j

[4] a

[5] f

[6] k

[7] e

[8] b

[9] g

[10] l

[11] C

[12] B

[13] A

[14] C

[15] C

[16] A

[17] D

[18] B

[19] A

[20] C

[21] C

[22] to ensure that the government remains in the hands of white males (to restore white supremacy)

[23] pistols and knives

[24] They threatened terrorist acts such as burning school houses and lynching African Americans.

Test Bank Answer Key

Lincoln would have supported President Johnson's plan which paralleled his own plan for Reconstruction. Both presidential plans were moderate and forgiving of former Confederates. Lincoln rejected radical plans for Reconstruction as evidenced by his refusal to sign the Wade–Davis Bill passed in 1864.

[25]

As a result of southern defiance, the Radical Republicans gained more power in Congress. They passed harsher laws such as the Military Reconstruction Act, which allowed northern generals to govern military districts in the South, and pushed through constitutional amendments protecting the rights of African Americans. In addition, former slaveholders lost the right to be compensated for the loss of their slave labor.

[26]

In the South, white Republicans advocated "the gospel of prosperity" and argued that economic conditions would improve, not with land redistribution, but with the building of more railroads, banks, and businesses. Southern governments aided economic development with grants paid for by higher taxes. In the North, Republicans allied themselves with leading industrialists who had prospered during the Civil War. Corporations, especially railroad companies, used bribes and other forms of political corruption to get the federal land and funds they needed for their projects.

[27]

[28] d _____

[29] i _____

[30] l _____

[31] e _____

[32] h _____

[33] j _____

[34] c _____

[35] a _____

[36] g _____

[37] b _____

[38] D _____

[39] C _____

[40] C _____

[41] B _____

Test Bank Answer Key

[42] B

[43] B

[44] A

[45] D

[46] C

[47] C

[48] C

[49] a government run by white men

[50] the Civil War and the abolition of slavery

[51] Schools would be burned and freed African Americans would be lynched.

[52] Many white Americans could not accept freed African Americans who asserted their equality. For generations, southern whites had assumed that they shared some type of common relationship and affection with their enslaved workers. They were shocked and hurt when they saw this illusion shattered. In addition, many white southerners feared the growing political and economic power asserted by African Americans supported by Radical Republican policies.

[53] As a result of the industrial boom during the Civil War, a close relationship developed between corporations and politicians. Many politicians at all levels of government accepted special favors or illegal payments from corporations, and so it was in their interest to support industry. It was not in their interest to help freed African Americans, laborers, and other groups that lacked power.

[54] The Republican party had virtually no support in the South before the mid-1860s. In order for Reconstruction to succeed, Republicans had to gain control of southern state governments. To achieve this end, Republicans turned to African Americans, scalawags, and carpetbaggers for support.

The Expansion of American Industry (1865-1900)

Test Bank Questions

Match the terms below with the following descriptions. Write the letter of the correct answer. You will not use all the terms.

a. Thomas A. Edison
b. Alexander Graham Bell
c. anarchists
d. Andrew Carnegie
e. Henry Bessemer
f. scabs

g. Haymarket Square
h. John D. Rockefeller
i. Homestead
j. Pinkertons
k. George Pullman

1. private police force hired by employers to break up strikes

2. inventor who developed the idea of a central electric power station

3. location of a labor rally that turned into a riot after someone threw a bomb into a police formation

4. location of a strike at Carnegie steel plant that resulted in violence

5. inventor who established American Telephone and Telegraph Company

6. industrialist who preached a "gospel of wealth"

7. political radicals who oppose all government

8. strike breakers who replace striking workers

Write the letter of the correct answer.

9. Which of the following made possible the industrial growth of the late 1800s?

A) more efficient steam-powered ships

B) the development of labor unions

C) the factory system

D) technological changes

10. Which of the following became a symbol of American ingenuity?

A) the mass marketing of the typewriter

B) the building of the Brooklyn Bridge

C) the invention of the telegraph

D) the development of the Bessemer converter

Test Bank Questions

Write the letter of the correct answer.

11. How did Andrew Carnegie practice vertical consolidation?

   A) by applying the ideas of <u>laissez faire</u>

   B) by creating a cartel of steel companies

   C) by using the piecework system

   D) by controlling all phases of the steel business

12. For which of the following were the industrialists of the age of "big business" generally admired?

   A) philanthropic activities

   B) ingenuity of driving out competition

   C) conservation of natural resources

   D) ability to influence government officials

13. Which development reflected a growing discontent among workers?

   A) rejection of ideas of private property and free enterprise

   B) interest in time-and-motion studies

   C) increased interest in the labor movement

   D) widespread appeal of social Darwinism

14. Which of the following best describes the American Federation of Labor?

   A) a group of small unions, each devoted to a single craft

   B) a union of skilled and unskilled workers in a single industry

   C) a single union of farmers, factory workers, and white-collar workers

   D) a brotherhood of railway and construction workers

15. What factor forced factory workers to endure harsh conditions in the late 1800s?

   A) an ample supply of available workers

   B) ease of suing employer

   C) good benefits if sick or injured

   D) to keep employer-provided housing

16. What was the purpose of "yellow dog" contracts?

   A) to break up conglomerates

   B) to hire scabs

   C) to increase efficiency of workers

   D) to prevent workers from joining unions

Test Bank Questions

Write the letter of the correct answer.

17. How did industrial growth affect the distribution of wealth in America?

   A) widened the income gap between factory workers and farmers

   B) led to a concentration of wealth in the hands of a few industrialists

   C) led to a concentration of wealth among unionized workers

   D) improved the standard of living for most Americans

18. Which was NOT a direct effect of the invention and application of electricity?

   A) more factory jobs available for women and children

   B) wider use of trusts and cartels to limit growth of electric companies

   C) use of transformers to bring electricity into homes and offices

   D) formation of General Electric and Westinghouse companies

19. How did the building of the transcontinental railroad affect American life?

   A) lowered shipping costs for businesses

   B) had little or no effect

   C) began a communications revolution

   D) made passenger travel more dangerous

20. For what reason was Eugene Debs arrested during the Pullman strike?

   A) disrupting the delivery of the mail

   B) disobeying a federal injunction calling off the strike

   C) instructing strikers to fire on federal troops

   D) attempting to assassinate Henry Frick

21. According to Samuel Gompers, what was the primary purpose of collective bargaining?

   A) to empower the workers

   B) to improve worker productivity

   C) to promote job security

   D) to produce goods more cheaply

22. What was the lasting effect of the violent labor strikes of the late 1800s?

   A) forced government to outlaw collective bargaining

   B) forced government to be involved in business-labor relations

   C) forced government to enforce the Sherman Anti-Trust Act

   D) forced government to accept the theory of social Darwinism

Test Bank Questions

Use the information in the anarchist handbill to answer the following questions.

Attention Workingmen!

GREAT

MASS-MEETING

TO-NIGHT, at 7.30 o'clock,

AT THE

HAYMARKET, Randolph St., Bet. Desplaines and Halsted.

Good Speakers will be present to denounce the latest atrocious act of the police. the shooting of our fellow-workmen yesterday afternoon.

Workingmen Arm Yourselves and Appear in Full Force!

THE EXECUTIVE COMMITTEE

Achtung, Arbeiter!

Große

Massen-Versammlung

Heute Abend, ½8 Uhr, auf dem

Heumarkt, Randolph-Straße, zwischen Desplaines- u. Halsted-Str.

☞ Gute Redner werden den neuesten Schurkenstreich der Polizei, indem sie gestern Nachmittag unsere Brüder erschoß, geißeln.

☞ Arbeiter, bewaffnet Euch und erscheint massenhaft!

Das Executiv-Comite.

Rare Books and Manuscripts Division, The New York Public Library, Astor, Lenox and Tilden Foundations

23.   What was the purpose of the mass meeting?

24.   How would you describe the tone of the handbill? What words were used to convey this tone?

25.   Why do you think the handbill was printed in English and German?

Test Bank Questions

Answer the following questions.

26. Why do you think the federal government sided with the industrialists during the late 1800s? Explain your reasoning.

27. What were some important causes of population growth in American cities in the late 1800s? What effect did this growth have on working conditions in factories, mines, and mills?

28. How does the life of a factory worker in the late 1800s compare with the life of a factory worker today in terms of job security, working conditions, and worker support systems?

Complete each sentence below by selecting the correct word from the list. You will not use all the words.

a. collective bargaining
b. social Darwinism
c. vertical consolidation
d. horizontal consolidation
e. economy of scale
f. scabs
g. anarchists
h. socialism
i. cartel
j. trust
k. monopoly
l. piecework

29. Employers sometimes replace striking workers with other workers called _____.

30. According to the _____, as more items are produced, the cost per item goes down.

31. The philosophy that advocates collective or government ownership of property is called _____.

32. The American Federation of Labor wanted employers to participate in _____.

33. A loose arrangement of similar businesses, usually formed in secret, is called a _____.

34. The theory that supported minimal interference by government in economic matters was _____.

35. Political radicals who oppose government are called _____.

36. The merger of two or more businesses that sell the same product is an example of _____.

37. When a company has no competition for the marketing of its product, the company is said to have created a _____.

Write the letter of the correct ending.

38. The work of Thomas Edison is important because he
    A) helped make electricity more widely available.
    B) invented the talking telegraph.
    C) developed an efficient process for making steel.
    D) financed the creation of General Electric.

Test Bank Questions

Write the letter of the correct ending.

39. As a result of new methods of business communications,
   A) more women found jobs as office clerks and switchboard operators.
   B) the standard of living improved in rural areas.
   C) Alexander Graham Bell invented the telephone.
   D) the sexual division of labor between men and women decreased.

40. The rapid industrial growth of the late 1800s was made possible by all of the following factors EXCEPT
   A) financial investments.
   B) public welfare programs.
   C) a technological revolution.
   D) improved transportation systems.

41. Andrew Carnegie believed that the rich should
   A) build towns for their workers.
   B) leave their fortunes to their heirs.
   C) give away money as charity.
   D) give gifts to benefit the masses.

42. During the late 1800s, most factory workers stayed on the job despite harsh working conditions because
   A) there was a great supply of available labor.
   B) employers provided on-the-job training.
   C) government programs provided little relief for unemployed workers.
   D) workers believed in the process of "natural selection."

43. During a strike at a Carnegie steel plant, violence erupted when
   A) an anarchist threw a bomb.
   B) the governor called in the militia.
   C) Pinkertons were brought in.
   D) employers ignored a government injunction.

44. Some unions formed during the 1860s and 1870s did not last long because of
   A) enactment of social and economic reforms.
   B) economic downturns and failed strikes.
   C) growing opposition by employers.
   D) lack of members who were skilled craftspeople.

Test Bank Questions

Write the letter of the correct ending.

45. One effect of the mechanization of industry was
    A) the organization of important women's labor unions.
    B) a chance for children to help the family earn a living.
    C) a sexual division of labor, giving men better-paying jobs.
    D) new safety standards for women and children.

46. In their struggle against unions, employers used
    A) vertical consolidation.
    B) closed shop agreements.
    C) "yellow dog" contracts.
    D) the Sherman Anti-Trust Act.

47. A dramatic population shift occurred between 1860 and 1900 as thousands of
    A) Americans moved abroad to act as recruiters for potential workers.
    B) immigrants came to the industrial centers of the United States.
    C) African Americans moved into the cities of the North.
    D) native-born Americans returned to their farms, discouraged with factory work.

48. By the late 1800s, many Americans began to think that big business
    A) had consumer interests at heart.
    B) could not be trusted.
    C) was influenced by government officials.
    D) would spread the "gospel of wealth."

49. The Pullman Strike of 1894 is a turning point because it led to
    A) the breakup of the Knights of Labor.
    B) an economic depression.
    C) widespread union corruption.
    D) intervention of government in labor matters.

Test Bank Questions

Use the information in the anarchist handbill to answer the following questions.

Attention Workingmen!

GREAT

MASS-MEETING

TO-NIGHT, at 7.30 o'clock,

AT THE

HAYMARKET, Randolph St, Bet. Desplaines and Halsted.

Good Speakers will be present to denounce the latest atrocious act of the police, the shooting of our fellow-workmen yesterday afternoon.

Workingmen Arm Yourselves and Appear in Full Force!

THE EXECUTIVE COMMITTEE

Achtung, Arbeiter!

Große

Massen-Versammlung

Heute Abend, ½8 Uhr, auf dem

Heumarkt, Randolph-Straße, zwischen Desplaines- u. Halsted-Str.

Gute Redner werden den neuesten Schurkenstreich der Polizei, indem sie gestern Nachmittag unsere Brüder erschoß, geißeln.

Arbeiter, bewaffnet Euch und erscheint massenhaft!

Das Executiv-Comite.

Rare Books and Manuscripts Division, The New York Public Library, Astor, Lenox and Tilden Foundations

50. What was the purpose of the handbill?

51. Why do you think the handbill was printed in English and German?

52. Anarchists organized the rally in Haymarket Square. How can you tell that this handbill was prepared by anarchists?

53. What was the outcome of the labor rally at Haymarket?

Test Bank Questions

Answer the following questions.

54. "...I rejoice in the conviction that the bona fide trade union movement is the one great agency of the toiling masses to secure them a better and higher standard of life and work." Do you think these words, written by Samuel Gompers in his autobiography, represent Gompers's personal belief, or are they statements of fact? Explain.

55. Why do you think several of the great industrialists of the late 1800s who would not pay workers decent wages became such generous philanthropists?

56. In this chapter, you read that the role of government in the late 1800s was either to stay out of labor disputes or to side with employers. What other alternatives might government have considered in the struggle between employer and worker?

Test Bank Answer Key

[1]   j

[2]   a

[3]   g

[4]   i

[5]   b

[6]   d

[7]   c

[8]   f

[9]   D

[10] B

[11] D

[12] A

[13] C

[14] A

[15] A

[16] D

[17] B

[18] B

[19] A

[20] B

[21] A

[22] B

[23] The purpose of the meeting was to protest police action in a labor strike that had resulted in several casualties among the workers.

[24] The tone is militant calling on working men to "arm yourselves and appear in full force."

[25] Millions of immigrants, many of them from Germany, made up the industrial work force.

Test Bank Answer Key

[26] To encourage industrial growth, government sided with the industrialists who had the resources needed to exploit new inventions and technologies. Big business produced staggering wealth for the country and created job opportunities for many.

[27] Large numbers of immigrants and native-born Americans living on farms moved to the industrial cities in search of work. The growing work force made industrial growth possible and resulted in exploitation of labor and harsh working conditions.

[28] Unlike today's workers, factory workers in the late 1800s lacked government or union support systems and protection from unfair and dangerous working conditions. Because of the prevailing attitude of <u>laissez faire</u> in the 1800s, legislators resisted the

idea of creating programs such as unemployment insurance, workman's compensation, and public welfare to protect and assist workers and their families.

[29] f

[30] e

[31] h

[32] a

[33] i

[34] b

[35] g

[36] d

[37] k

[38] A

[39] A

[40] B

[41] D

[42] A

[43] C

[44] B

[45] C

[46] C

[47] B

[48] B

[49] D

[50] The purpose of the handbill was to ask workers to attend a mass meeting to protest the police shooting of fellow workers.

[51] Many of the workers in Chicago were German immigrants, so the handbill was printed in both English and German.

[52] Workers were told to arm themselves.

[53] Someone threw a bomb into a police formation, killing several policemen. In the ensuing riot, exchange of gunfire between police and workers resulted in dozens of deaths on both sides.

[54] Gompers's observation is both a personal opinion and a statement of fact. The union trade movement was an important agency for change in the United States, bringing about the enactment of important social and economic reforms that benefited the working class.

[55] Industrialists, such as Carnegie, subscribed to a "gospel of wealth." They believed that people should be free to do whatever they had to, including exploit labor, to make as much money as they could. In turn, they should use the profits they made to benefit all of humankind, not just the workers.

[56] Government could have enacted legislation to protect workers, restrict immigration, prohibit the use of child labor, tax the profits of the industrialists, or provide incentives for business to improve labor conditions.

Looking to the West

Test Bank Questions

Match the terms below with the following descriptions. Write the letter of the correct answer. You will not use all the terms.

a. Chief Joseph
b. Exodusters
c. Populists
d. squatters
e. Chief Sitting Bull

f. speculators
g. Grange
h. Frederick Jackson Turner
i. William Jennings Bryan
j. George Armstrong Custer

1. bought up large areas of land with the intention of selling it for profit at a later date

2. led the U.S. regiment wiped out by the Sioux

3. planned a mass migration to Kansas in order to escape violence and discrimination in the South

4. led the Sioux in their fight to keep their reservation

5. ran as the Democratic Party nominee in the presidential election of 1896

6. led the Nez Percé in their flight from the U.S. Army

7. moved onto land that did not belong to them

8. pushed reforms to benefit western and southern farmers

Write the letter of the correct answer.

9. What did the Morrill Land-Grant Act and Homestead Act have in common?
    A) They discriminated against African American farmers.
    B) They forced Native Americans onto reservations.
    C) They provided ways for settlers to acquire western lands.
    D) They enabled railroad companies to develop the land near their tracks.

10. Which statement best describes the lifestyle of homesteaders?
    A) Obtaining even the necessities could be a struggle.
    B) Homesteaders lived in isolation and avoided social contact.
    C) Homesteaders lived simple and secure lives.
    D) Most women worked outside the homestead.

Test Bank Questions

Write the letter of the correct answer.

11. Why did many agreements between Native Americans and the federal government fall apart?

   A) Many settlers objected to the reservation system.

   B) Native Americans and settlers had differing concepts of land ownership.

   C) Most of the treaties were never legally signed.

   D) Native Americans refused to work as tenant farmers or sharecroppers.

12. What happened at the battle at Wounded Knee?

   A) Custer and his entire regiment died.

   B) Sitting Bull surrendered to Custer.

   C) The Nez Percé fought for possession of their homeland.

   D) U.S. soldiers killed over 200 unarmed Sioux.

13. Which of the following was most responsible for the destruction of Native Americans living on the Great Plains?

   A) the Dawes Act   B) the mining boom

   C) cattle ranching   D) the extension of railroads

14. What was a bonanza farm?

   A) a government-owned experimental station for hybridization

   B) a large farm that relied on manual labor rather than mechanization

   C) a business-controlled farm specializing in a single cash crop

   D) a privately-owned farm that supported one family

15. Which statement about farming and mining is correct?

   A) Highly productive farming and mining required expensive machinery.

   B) Farming and mining led to the creation of ghost towns.

   C) Farming and mining had little effect on the western environment.

   D) Both miners and farmers took over lands in the Indian Territory.

16. What was one reason for the end of the cattle boom?

   A) invention of barbed wire   B) lack of government support

   C) falling prices for beef   D) increasing rail costs

17. What did most farmers complain about in the late 1800s?

   A) runaway inflation   B) activities of the Grange

   C) rising crop prices   D) high tariffs on manufactured goods

Test Bank Questions

Write the letter of the correct answer.

18. How did farmers think free silver would benefit them?
    A) would create inflation
    B) would stabilize interest rates
    C) would decrease the money supply
    D) would depress farm produce prices

19. Which was NOT a reform supported by the Populists?
    A) eight-hour work day
    B) increased circulation of money
    C) private ownership of transportation systems
    D) graduated income tax

20. Which democratic ideal found expression on the frontier?
    A) integrated neighborhoods
    B) equality of opportunity for all
    C) protection of civil rights
    D) popular control over government

21. What has been a lingering MYTH about the West?
    A) The settlement of the West destroyed the environment.
    B) African Americans and Asians helped settle the West.
    C) Settlers nearly destroyed Native American peoples.
    D) Settlers were adventurous, resourceful white males.

Test Bank Questions

Use the wood engraving "Go West" to answer the following questions.

"GO WEST."

22. What appears to be the white man's attitude toward the Native American?

23. How far "West" do you think the settler wants the Native American to go?

24. What important aspect of the Native American culture is shown in this engraving? What eventually happened to this part of Native American life?

Answer the following questions.

25. What are five questions you would ask a homesteader in the Dakotas to determine if you would like to migrate there?

26. Compare the ways in which Native Americans and homesteaders used land on the Great Plains.

27. In the History of the United States, published in 1894, William Nye

   writes: [The] real Indian...has the dead and unkempt hair of a busted buggy-cushion filled with feathers. He lies, he steals, he assassinates, he mutilates, he tortures. We can, in fact, only retain him as we do the buffalo, so long as he complies with our laws.

   (a) Why is Nye's account of Native Americans unreliable?
   (b) What effect do you think Nye's "history" might have had on the settlers' attitudes toward Native Americans?

Test Bank Questions

Complete each sentence below by selecting the correct word from the list. You will not use all the words.

a. Grange
b. long drive
c. squatters
d. Morrill Land-Grant Act
e. cash crops
f. Homestead Act
g. sooners
h. bonanza farms
i. deflation
j. speculators

28. Oliver H. Kelley founded the _____ to help farmers form cooperatives.

29. The _____ granted the western lands to state governments as a way to fund agricultural colleges.

30. Large businesses owned _____ which were managed by professionals.

31. During the _____, cowboys herded cattle from distant ranges to railroad centers.

32. Settlers who moved onto land not belonging to them were called _____.

33. American citizens and immigrants who planned to become citizens could acquire land directly through the 1862 _____.

34. Land _____ bought up large areas of land in the hope of selling them later for large profits.

35. Homesteaders, called _____, staked land claims in Indian Territory before noon on April 22, 1889.

Write the letter of the correct ending.

36. Settlers in the U.S. West acquired land in all of the following ways EXCEPT by
    A) purchasing land directly from the government.
    B) trading manufactured goods for Native American homelands.
    C) purchasing land from speculators.
    D) purchasing land from big business.

37. Most African American Exodusters migrated west in order to
    A) find relatives who had fled during the Civil War.
    B) prospect for gold and silver.
    C) work as sharecroppers on bonanza farms.
    D) escape discrimination in the South.

38. An example of western women's great progress toward independence was the
    A) passage of the Homestead Act.
    B) prominence of women as big business leaders.
    C) passage of woman suffrage in ten western states.
    D) establishment of agricultural colleges.

Test Bank Questions

Write the letter of the correct ending.

39. A major factor in the destruction of Native American nations was the
    A) invention of steam-powered threshers.
    B) policies of the federal government.
    C) publication of Helen Jackson Hunt's <u>A Century of Dishonor.</u>
    D) discovery of precious metals on Native American lands.

40. Chief Joseph and the Nez Percé illustrate how
    A) most Native Americans moved peacefully onto reservations.
    B) Christian missionaries converted Native Americans.
    C) the U.S. government allowed some Native Americans to keep their homelands.
    D) violent conflicts arose among settlers, the federal government, and Native Americans.

41. One way in which reformers tried to "civilize" Native Americans was by
    A) teaching them to hunt buffalo.
    B) requiring them to farm individual plots.
    C) finding them jobs on the railroads.
    D) requiring their children to attend public schools outside the reservation.

42. Farm mechanization resulted in
    A) the stabilization of crop prices.
    B) an increase in farm production.
    C) the demise of bonanza farms.
    D) a decline in the number of eastern farms.

43. The cattle boom ended in the mid-1880s largely because
    A) barbed wire caused conflict between ranchers and farmers.
    B) cow towns sprang up next to rail lines.
    C) land policies favored farmers more than cattle ranchers.
    D) too few Americans ate beef.

44. Most American farmers in the late 1800s protested
    A) the bimetallic standard.
    B) high tariffs on manufactured goods.
    C) free silver.
    D) the Interstate Commerce Act.

164   Chapter 15   © *Prentice-Hall, Inc.*

Test Bank Questions

Write the letter of the correct ending.

45. During the 1896 presidential campaign, Democratic candidate William Jennings Bryan
    A) alienated African American voters.
    B) captured the Populist nomination.
    C) gained the support of the northern states.
    D) ran on a gold-standard platform.

46. Frederick Jackson Turner's frontier thesis has been criticized for
    A) overemphasizing the role of African Americans in settling the West.
    B) equating the experiences of women and men settlers.
    C) exaggerating the importance of big business.
    D) presenting frontier life as much harder than it was.

47. The settlement of the West
    A) offered unlimited opportunity for men and women of all races.
    B) brought prosperity to the United States.
    C) helped preserve natural environments.
    D) often ignored democratic values.

48. Gold and silver strikes throughout the West eventually resulted in
    A) corporate takeover of the mining industry.
    B) wealth for most prospectors.
    C) prolonged periods of deflation.
    D) extension of railroads into the West.

Chapter 15

Test Bank Questions

Use the cartoon below to answer the following questions.

Reprinted with permission from Star Tribune, Minneapolis.

49. How would you characterize the cartoonist's attitude toward white Americans?

50. How has the cartoonist depicted the Native American?

51. What is the main idea of this cartoon?

Answer the following questions.

52. Why was farming the Great Plains so difficult? What challenges did western settlers face and how did they meet these challenges?

53. Compare the ways in which the building of the railroads affected Native Americans, farmers, and ranchers on the Great Plains.

54. During the 1896 presidential campaign, what issues united western farmers but divided them from urban industrial workers? Explain reasons for these divisions.

Test Bank Answer Key

[1] f _____

[2] j _____

[3] b _____

[4] e _____

[5] i _____

[6] a _____

[7] d _____

[8] c _____

[9] C _____

[10] A _____

[11] B _____

[12] D _____

[13] D _____

[14] C _____

[15] A _____

[16] A _____

[17] D _____

[18] A _____

[19] C _____

[20] D _____

[21] D _____

[22] The white settler appears to be disrespectful of and insensitive to Native Americans. _____

[23] The settler wants the Native American to move west of the Great Plains. _____

[24] Buffalo herds; railroad workers and settlers slaughtered the buffalo herds on which the Native Americans relied for almost all their basic needs. _____

Test Bank Answer Key

How much does land cost? What is the climate like? How difficult is it to clear away the prairie grass? What farming implements will I need? What natural challenges must I contend with? What kinds of crops grow well there?
[25]

Native Americans and homesteaders both lived off the land, but in different ways. Homesteaders grew crops and raised domestic animals; Native Americans lived off the buffalo that roamed the Plains. Furthermore, Native Americans respected and preserved the environment while homesteaders eroded and scarred the land.
[26]

(a) Nye presented an opinion, not facts. He made negative generalizations drawn from the popularly accepted stereotype of Native Americans.
(b) Nye's history may have reinforced settlers' fear, distrust, and contempt for Native Americans.
[27]

[28] a

[29] d

[30] h

[31] b

[32] c

[33] f

[34] j

[35] g

[36] B

[37] D

[38] C

[39] B

[40] D

[41] D

[42] B

[43] A

[44] B

[45] B

Test Bank Answer Key

[46]   B

[47]   D

[48]   A

[49]   The cartoonist has a negative view of white Americans and accuses them of violating Native American rights and traditions.

[50]   The cartoonist has depicted the Native American as pursuing a simple and peaceful life in the natural environment.

[51]   White Americans destroyed Native American traditions and violated the terms of treaties they signed with Native American nations.

[52]   Farming the Great Plains was difficult because the climate was dry and rainfall was unpredictable; the tough prairie sod was hard to clear; insects and plagues ruined crops and destroyed property; and water supplies were limited and often far away. Settlers met these challenges by relying on each other for many forms of support. By the 1880s, well-digging machinery made it easier for settlers to obtain water for drinking, bathing, and cooking.

[53]   The expansion of the railroads destroyed many Native American societies. As the rail lines were laid, more settlers moved west and pushed the Native Americans onto reservations. In addition, the railroad workers hunted buffalo for food and sport, thereby depleting the Native American's major source of food, shelter, and clothing. By contrast, the railroad was essential to farmers and ranchers, who relied on railroads to transport their crops and cattle to market.

[54]   Western farmers united in supporting the Democratic Party's free silver policy because they believed it would promote inflation, which in turn would increase farm prices and enable them to pay off their bank debts. Urban and industrial workers, however, feared that inflation would hurt their buying power and supported the gold-standard platform of the Republicans.

Politics, Immigration, and Urban Life (1877-1920)

Test Bank Questions

Match the terms below with the following descriptions. Write the letter of the correct answer. You will not use all the terms.

a. steerage
b. ghettos
c. political machines
d. social gospel movement
e. laissez-faire
f. Bland-Allison Act
g. blue laws
h. political boss
i. Interstate Commerce Act
j. suburbs
k. Pendleton Act

1. unofficial organizations designed to keep a particular party or group in power

2. local ordinances that prohibited behaviors such as drinking alcoholic beverages

3. areas surrounding large cities

4. open area beneath a ship's deck in which most immigrants traveled

5. sections of cities in which certain ethnic or racial groups live

6. reform movement that tried to apply the teachings of Jesus Christ directly to society

7. hands-off approach to economic matters

8. legislation that curbed railroad abuses

Write the letter of the correct answer.

9. Which was a major cause of corruption in government during the Gilded Age?
    A) the spoils system   B) the Pendleton Act
    C) a policy of soft money   D) the policy of laissez-faire

10. Which of the following led to government regulation of business during the Gilded Age?
    A) increased factory and farm productivity
    B) high tariffs
    C) unfair business practices
    D) declining business profits

Test Bank Questions

Write the letter of the correct answer.

11. What law set the precedent that private enterprise was subject to government control?

A) the Silver Purchase Act

B) the Pendleton Act

C) the Comstock Act

D) the Interstate Commerce Act

12. Why did immigration laws discriminate against the Chinese?

A) Chinese immigrants would work only for the railroads and in mining.

B) Chinese workers accepted very low wages.

C) Chinese workers did not honor their debts.

D) Chinese businesses threatened American businesses.

13. What was the major reason why some immigrants were denied entry?

A) They carried a contagious disease.

B) They were not skilled laborers.

C) They already had too many family members in the United States.

D) They refused to learn English.

14. Which of the following was a major result of both immigration and the increased productivity of factories in the post-Reconstruction era?

A) overpopulation in the South

B) mechanization of agriculture

C) high wages for factory workers

D) the rapid expansion of urban areas

15. Which statement does NOT accurately describe urban living conditions in the late 1800s and early 1900s?

A) Slum residents were threatened by fires, crime, and vice.

B) Overcrowding and poor sanitation bred disease.

C) Most ghettos reflected a specific ethnic culture.

D) Urban rich and poor lived side by side.

16. Why did many immigrants support city political machines?

A) Political machines were free of corruption.

B) Political machines provided them with jobs and other favors.

C) Political machines fought against crime in the slums.

D) Political machines opposed discrimination.

17. According to nativists, what was a major cause of urban problems?

A) immigrants   B) organized religion

C) political bosses   D) consumption of alcoholic beverages

Test Bank Questions

Write the letter of the correct answer.

18. What common goal was shared by prohibitionists and purity crusaders?
    A) to improve personal behavior of city dwellers and the immigrant class
    B) to end poverty and redistribute national wealth
    C) to make charity "scientific"
    D) to improve urban living conditions

19. What was the main goal of the social gospel and settlement movements?
    A) to bring down political bosses
    B) to improve living conditions for the poor
    C) to end immigration
    D) to create jobs for the unemployed

Use the data in the Population table to answer the following questions.

RURAL AND URBAN POPULATIONS IN THE UNITED STATES

Year	Rural (in thousands)	Urban (in thousands)
1860	25,227	6,217
1870	28,656	9,902
1880	36,026	14,130
1890	40,841	22,106
1900	45,835	30,160
1910	49,973	41,999
1920	51,553	54,158

Source: Bureau of the Census

20. (a) What years are covered in this table?
    (b) What government agency compiled the data presented in the table?

21. (a) How many people in the United States lived in rural areas in 1900?
    (b) How many people lived in urban areas in 1900?

22. (a) Describe the population trend that began to develop during the period 1910–1920.
    (b) What are two possible causes of this trend?

Test Bank Questions

Answer the following questions.

23. Many immigrants who came to the United States in the late 1800s expected to find streets paved with gold and opportunities to make their fortunes. In reality, what was life like for most immigrants?

24. Mark Twain labeled the years from 1877 to 1900 the "Gilded Age," implying that American society was "a thin layer of glitter over a cheap base." What examples can you cite to support Twain's characterization of this era in American history?

Complete each sentence below by selecting the correct word from the list. You will not use all the words.

a. Interstate Commerce Act
b. laissez-faire
c. Pendleton Act
d. Gilded Age
e. Tammany Hall
f. social gospel movement
g. blue laws
h. Hull House
i. Angel Island
j. steerage
k. ghettos
l. suburbs

25. Jane Addams and Ellen Gates Starr founded _____ to help immigrants.

26. The _____ placed restrictions on railroad rates and outlawed the practice of giving rebates and favors to powerful customers.

27. The _____ sought to apply the teachings of Jesus Christ directly to social reform.

28. William Marcy Tweed was the political boss who controlled _____.

29. President Arthur attempted to reform the spoils system by urging Congress to pass the _____.

30. During the Gilded Age, Republicans wanted to enforce _____, which prohibited specific personal behaviors.

31. Most immigrants traveled in _____ across the Atlantic to America.

32. Some urban areas turned into _____, home to certain ethnic or racial groups.

Write the letter of the correct ending.

33. During the Gilded Age, most supporters of laissez-faire policies
    A) encouraged government regulation of business.
    B) were Democrats.
    C) refused government land grants.
    D) favored high tariffs on imported goods.

34. Widespread corruption in government was largely the result of
    A) the policy of laissez-faire.   B) civil service reforms.
    C) tight money policies.   D) the spoils system.

Test Bank Questions

Write the letter of the correct ending.

35. The Interstate Commerce Commission established the precedent that
    A) businesses were subject to government control.
    B) the practice of patronage was unacceptable.
    C) government should not interfere with business.
    D) federal employees should not be forced to make campaign contributions.

36. Jacob S. Coxey called for a march on Washington to demand that government
    A) create jobs for the unemployed.
    B) protect unions.
    C) return the country to the gold standard.
    D) regulate the powerful railroads.

37. During the late 1800s and early 1900s, immigration laws discriminated most against
    A) the Chinese.   B) Mexicans.
    C) agricultural workers. D) northern Europeans.

38. In the 1890s, immigration patterns shifted dramatically with most immigrants coming from
    A) southern and eastern European countries.
    B) Mexico and Central America.
    C) Japan and China.
    D) northern European countries.

39. Each of the following contributed to rapid urbanization in the late 1800s EXCEPT
    A) the irrigation of southwestern lands.
    B) mechanization in agriculture.
    C) increased segregation and violence against African Americans in the South.
    D) the large numbers of immigrants to the United States.

40. Political machines gained power in the late 1800s largely because they
    A) controlled crime and vice in the slums.
    B) advocated political reform.
    C) provided for the welfare of immigrants and other city dwellers.
    D) protected the interest of the middle and upper classes.

Test Bank Questions

Write the letter of the correct ending.

41. The main objective of nativists was to
    A) help immigrants adjust to American culture.
    B) restrict immigration.
    C) end discriminatory laws.
    D) build tenement apartments for immigrants.

42. Prohibitionists and purity crusaders were alike in that both
    A) sought to rid society of immoral behavior.
    B) worked to end discrimination against the "new" immigrants.
    C) opposed government intervention in citizens' daily lives.
    D) promoted political machines.

43. Most settlement houses in the late 1800s offered poor city-dwellers
    A) protection from crime.
    B) aid in the form of money.
    C) asylum from corrupt city governments.
    D) social services.

Use the data in the Population table to answer the following questions.

RURAL AND URBAN POPULATIONS IN THE UNITED STATES		
Year	Rural (in thousands)	Urban (in thousands)
1860	25,227	6,217
1870	28,656	9,902
1880	36,026	14,130
1890	40,841	22,106
1900	45,835	30,160
1910	49,973	41,999
1920	51,553	54,158

Source: Bureau of the Census

44. (a) What information is presented in this table?
    (b) What is the source of the data?
    (c) Can the data be used as historical evidence?

Test Bank Questions

Use the data in the Population table to answer the following questions.

	RURAL AND URBAN POPULATIONS IN THE UNITED STATES	
Year	Rural (in thousands)	Urban (in thousands)
1860	25,227	6,217
1870	28,656	9,902
1880	36,026	14,130
1890	40,841	22,106
1900	45,835	30,160
1910	49,973	41,999
1920	51,553	54,158

Source: Bureau of the Census

45. (a) How many people in the United States lived in rural areas in 1860?
    (b) How many people lived in urban areas in 1860?

46. (a) During what ten-year period did the population of urban areas begin to exceed the population of rural areas?
    (b) What are two factors that led to the rapid growth of urban areas?

Answer the following questions.

47. Imagine that you are a young immigrant living and working in the United States in the 1890s. Your best friend back home in Russia writes to tell you that he and his family are emigrating to the United States. What kind of life would you tell you friend to expect? What advice would you give him?

48. What were some social and political effects of rapid urbanization?

Test Bank Answer Key

[1] c

[2] g

[3] j

[4] a

[5] b

[6] d

[7] e

[8] i

[9] A

[10] C

[11] D

[12] B

[13] A

[14] D

[15] D

[16] B

[17] A

[18] A

[19] B

[20] (a) 1860–1920
     (b) Bureau of the Census

[21] (a) 45,835,000
     (b) 30,160,000

[22] (a) Urban population exceeded rural population.
     (b) Causes of urbanization include increased immigration,
         the migration of African Americans to northern cities,
         farm mechanization and the migration of farm workers
         to the cities, and increased factory productivity.

Test Bank Answer Key

[23] Life was difficult for most immigrants who entered the United States in the late 1800s. They settled in urban areas where they lived in dirty, overcrowded, disease-ridden tenements. They became victims of discrimination and economic exploitation, forced to work long hours for low wages. However, they experienced personal and political freedoms unavailable in their homelands.

[24] During the Gilded Age, many businesses thrived and the economy expanded. However, there was widespread corruption in business and government. The spoils system enabled many unqualified and dishonest people to hold government jobs, and Presidents of the era did not address the social, economic, and political problems confronting the nation. Railroad companies awarded stock to legislators in exchange for favors and offered rebates to powerful customers at the expense of small businesses. The gap between rich and poor widened.

[25] h

[26] a

[27] f

[28] e

[29] c

[30] g

[31] j

[32] k

[33] D

[34] D

[35] A

[36] A

[37] A

[38] A

[39] A

[40] C

[41] B

[42] A

[43] D

Test Bank Answer Key

[44]
(a) rural and urban populations of the United States
    from 1860 to 1920
(b) Bureau of the Census
(c) Yes

[45]
(a) 25,227,000
(b) 6,217,000

[46]
(a) 1910 - 1920
(b) Factors include farm mechanization, discrimination
    and racial violence in the South, an influx of
    immigrants, and job opportunities in the cities.

[47]
The friend should not expect riches but low wages and should be
prepared for hostility, discrimination, and overcrowded living
conditions. However, he and his family would enjoy many personal and
political freedoms, and with hard work and determination could
achieve a better life than in Russia.

[48]
Rapid urbanization led to noise and air pollution, sanitation and
health problems, slums and ghettos, flight to the suburbs, political
machines, and economic and ethnic divisions.

Cultural and Social Transformations (1870-1915)

Test Bank Questions

Complete each of the following sentences by selecting the appropriate term from the choices listed in parentheses.

1. (Victorianism, The woman question) is best described as the debate about the social role of women at the turn of the century.

2. (Booker T. Washington, W.E.B. DuBois) denounced all forms of discrimination against African Americans and helped found the NAACP.

3. In the 1890s African American musicians in New Orleans developed a vibrant musical style known as (ragtime, jazz).

4. (Vaudeville, The minstrel show), in which white actors performed in blackface, consisted of exaggerated imitations of African American culture.

5. The system of legal segregation in the 1800s and early 1900s was known as (de facto discrimination, Jim Crow).

6. In the 1890s some states used a (grandfather clause, poll tax) to exempt many white men from certain voting restrictions.

7. Sensational news coverage that focused on scandals, murders, and vice came to be called (yellow journalism, lynching).

Write the letter of the correct ending.

8. As a result of compulsory school laws, by the early 1900s
    A) African American children were receiving an education equal to that of white children.
    B) many immigrant children became Americanized.
    C) most Native American children received a formal education.
    D) schools could no longer be segregated.

9. All of the following statements are true EXCEPT:
    A) Most college scholarships went to men in the late 1800s.
    B) Many colleges admitted women in the late 1800s.
    C) Low tuitions made college affordable for middle-class families.
    D) Opportunities for higher learning increased after the Civil War.

10. Both W.E.B. DuBois and Booker T. Washington urged African Americans to
    A) become well educated.   B) fight militantly for civil rights.
    C) emigrate to Africa.   D) embrace white culture.

Test Bank Questions

Write the letter of the correct ending.

11. The bicycling fad helped liberate women in the late 1800s by
    A) freeing women athletes from such restrictive clothing as tight corsets.
    B) providing an inexpensive means of transportation.
    C) dispelling the notion that physical exertion would harm a woman.
    D) proving that women had more endurance than most men.

12. In the late 1800s, an urban family was most likely to be entertained at a
    A) saloon.   B) trolley park.
    C) dance hall.   D) cabaret.

13. In the late 1800s, Victorians staunchly opposed
    A) spectator sports.
    B) yellow journalism.
    C) racist stereotypes in minstrel shows.
    D) saloons and dance halls.

14. During post-Reconstruction, many African Americans moved to the North where they experienced
    A) de facto discrimination.
    B) legalized separate public facilities.
    C) no racial violence.
    D) equality of opportunity.

15. In the early 1900s, the National Association for the Advancement of Colored People (NAACP) demonstrated how African Americans
    A) mobilized to end poverty in urban areas.
    B) used militant tactics to pursue civil rights.
    C) used the court system to fight legal discrimination.
    D) brought an end to de facto discrimination.

16. Madam C.J. Walker was an African American woman who
    A) established the first black college.
    B) led a crusade to promote Victorian morals.
    C) became a prominent business leader.
    D) founded settlement houses in black neighborhoods.

17. The "new woman" of the early 1900s promoted the idea that women should
    A) reject marriage and motherhood.
    B) be freed from all household duties.
    C) adopt more convenient hair and dress styles.
    D) have perfect manners.

Test Bank Questions

Write the letter of the correct ending.

18. In the late 1800s, middle-class women seemed most interested in
   A) joining voluntary associations.
   B) effecting political reforms.
   C) finding paid domestic work.
   D) getting a college degree.

Use the data in the bar graph of Women in the Labor Force to answer the following questions.

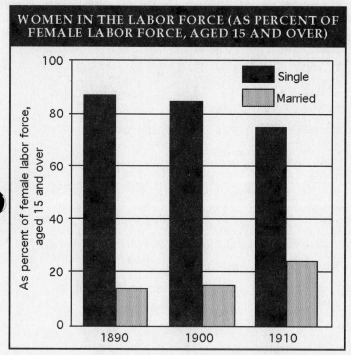

WOMEN IN THE LABOR FORCE (AS PERCENT OF FEMALE LABOR FORCE, AGED 15 AND OVER)

Source: Bureau of the Census

19. In 1890, what percentage of women in the labor force were married? Were single?

20. Describe the trend in the percentage of single and married women in the labor force between 1890 and 1910.

21. Based on the information presented in the graph, what prediction can you make about working women in the decades following 1910?

Answer the following questions.

22. How did W.E.B. DuBois's attitude toward the importance of education for African Americans compare to that of Booker T. Washington?

Test Bank Questions

Answer the following questions.

23. What were some biases that college women encountered in the late 1800s and early 1900s?

24. What effect did new educational opportunities seem to have on African Americans and women in the late 1800s and early 1900s?

Match the terms below with the following descriptions. Write the letter of the correct answer. You will not use all the terms.

a. Victorianism
b. minstrel show
c. lynching
d. literacy tests
e. jazz
f. yellow journalism
g. poll tax
h. grandfather clause
i. woman question
j. de facto discrimination
k. Jim Crow
l. ragtime
m. vaudeville

25. provision by which groups are exempted from a law if they meet specific conditions before that law was passeed

26. special fee required of African American voters in the South

27. wide-ranging debate about the social role of women

28. term used to describe the system of legal segregation in the 1800s and early 1900s

29. musical style that originated among African American musicians playing in saloons in the South and Midwest in the 1880s

30. type of variety show strictly for families

31. term used to describe "sensational" news coverage

32. theatrical performance in which white actors exaggerated African American music, dance, and humor

33. term used to describe the moral standards, attitudes, and conduct associated with the Queen of Britain from 1837 to 1901

34. illegal seizure and execution of a suspected criminal or troublemaker

Write the letter of the correct answer.

35. What was the overall effect of the public school system on immigrant children?
    A) provided immigrant children with a separate but unequal education
    B) created divisions among immigrant children of differing cultures
    C) encouraged immigrant children to retain their native cultures
    D) helped immigrant children assimilate into American culture

36. Which leisure activity was the most popular among urban women in the late 1800s?
    A) bicycling
    B) playing baseball
    C) going to a saloon
    D) watching football

Test Bank Questions

Write the letter of the correct answer.

37. Which statement best describes the educational opportunities of African American students in the late 1800s?

    A) They learned basic skills only.

    B) They were shuttled off to Native American schools.

    C) They were educated in segregated schools of lesser quality than schools for white children.

    D) They were forced to attend private religious schools.

38. What did W.E.B. Du Bois hope that education would do for African Americans?

    A) encourage pride in African and American heritages

    B) assimilate African Americans into white culture

    C) show African Americans how to win white acceptance

    D) provide leadership for African Americans in their fight for equal rights

39. Which of the following is an example of the transformation of African American culture?

    A) trolley parks   B) vaudeville

    C) baseball   D) the minstrel show

40. Why were many African Americans attracted to the North after Reconstruction?

    A) There were no lynchings in the North.

    B) There were settlement houses in black neighborhoods.

    C) There was no de facto discrimination in the North.

    D) There was no legal segregation in the North.

41. Which of the following were African Americans in the South NOT required to do before they could vote in the 1890s?

    A) own property   B) pass a literacy test

    C) pay a poll tax   D) find gainful employment

42. For what is Madam C.J. Walker remembered?

    A) becoming a self-made millionaire despite discrimination

    B) founding the first African American college

    C) becoming the first African American woman to earn a Ph.D.

    D) organizing the Niagara Movement

43. In the late 1800s, which group of women typically worked outside the home?

    A) uneducated women   B) women in the South

    C) older married women   D) young single women

Test Bank Questions

Write the letter of the correct answer.

44. Which of the following best describes the "new woman" of the early 1900s?

    A) She campaigned for radical social change.

    B) She retained Victorian morals.

    C) She rejected marriage and motherhood.

    D) She wore practical clothing.

45. By the turn of the century, what did most middle-class women consider their chief goal?

    A) voting rights   B) financial independence

    C) a college education   D) domestic fulfillment

Use the data in the bar graph of Women in the Labor Force to answer the following questions.

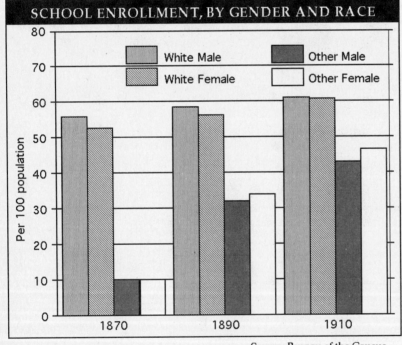

Source: Bureau of the Census

46. By 1900 many states had passed laws that reqired children eight to fourteen years old to attend school. Based on the data in the graph, do you think these laws were effective? Explain.

47. How did the school enrollment of white males compare with the enrollment of non-white males in 1910?

Test Bank Questions

Use the data in the bar graph of Women in the Labor Force to answer the following questions.

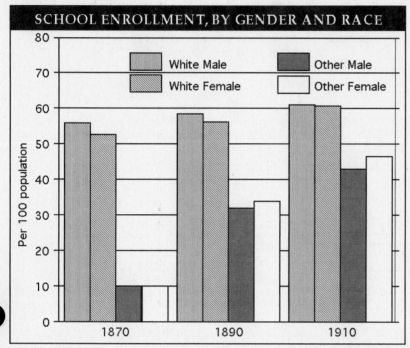

SCHOOL ENROLLMENT, BY GENDER AND RACE

Source: Bureau of the Census

48. How would you describe the trend in school enrollment of non-white females from 1870 to 1910?

Answer the following questions.

49. How do you think most Victorians felt about the increase in the number of women at coeducational universities in the late 1800s? Give reasons to support your answer.

50. What similar methods did African Americans and women use to give themselves a stronger voice in social and political affairs at the turn of the century?

51. In the late 1800s and early 1900s, African American leaders promoted different ways to handle racial violence and discrimination. What were some alternative approaches to dealing with race problems?

Test Bank Answer Key

[1]   The woman question

[2]   W.E.B. DuBois

[3]   jazz

[4]   The minstrel show

[5]   Jim Crow

[6]   grandfather clause

[7]   yellow journalism

[8]   B

[9]   C

[10] A

[11] A

[12] B

[13] D

[14] A

[15] C

[16] C

[17] C

[18] A

[19] about 14 percent, about 86 percent

[20] Between 1890 and 1910, the percentage of single women in the labor force decreased while the percentage of married women increased.

[21] The number of married women in the labor force will continue to increase steadily after 1910.

[22] Du Bois wanted the brightest African Americans to pursue an advanced liberal arts education to prepare themselves to become leaders in the pursuit of equal rights and in the fight against racial discrimination. By contrast, Washington viewed education as a way for African Americans to learn productive, profitable skills that would better the entire community and win white acceptance.

Test Bank Answer Key

[23] In the late 1800s and early 1900s, many women who wanted to attend college encountered resistance from friends and family who feared that college would make them too independent and "unmarriageable." In addition, most of American society believed that women did not have the mental capacity for higher education, and most scholarships went to men.

[24] New educational opportunities for African Americans and women seemed to increase the desire of those groups for equality of opportunity. As increased numbers of African Americans became educated, they began to question Jim Crow laws and publicly address issues such as racial violence. As a result of educational opportunities and technological changes, many women began to question their traditional role in society and insisted on economic and political power equal to that of men.

[25] h

[26] g

[27] i

[28] k

[29] l

[30] m

[31] f

[32] b

[33] a

[34] c

[35] D

[36] A

[37] C

[38] D

[39] D

[40] D

[41] D

[42] A

[43] D

Test Bank Answer Key

[44] D
_____

[45] D
_____

[46] The laws seemed to be effective. Enrollment increased for all groups between 1870 and 1910.
_____

[47] About 20 percent more white males attended school than non-white males.
_____

[48] The percentage of non-white females enrolled in school increased significantly from about 10 percent in 1870 to about 46 percent in 1910.
_____

[49] Most Victorians probably viewed the increase in the number of women at coeducational universities as a threat to women's domestic roles as well as to their femininity. They probably worried that such close association with men would promote immoral behavior and improper relations between the sexes.
_____

[50] Both African Americans and women began their fight against discrimination by establishing small organizations or clubs where members could share opinions and ideas. As club membership grew, they formed national associations to address specific concerns and educate others.
_____

[51] Some African American religious leaders promoted black pride and emigration to Africa. W.E.B. Du Bois encouraged the brightest African Americans to educate and prepare themselves to lead the civil rights movement and he helped found the NAACP to fight discrimination in the courts. Others, such as Booker T. Washington, believed African Americans should try to win white acceptance by educating themselves and succeeding in occupations whites needed to be filled.
_____

Becoming a World Power (1890-1913)

Test Bank Questions

Match the terms below with the following descriptions. Write the letter of the correct answer. You will not use all the terms.

a. Theodore Roosevelt   e. Henry Cabot Lodge
b. George Dewey   f. Albert J. Beveridge
c. Juliette Low   g. William Howard Taft
d. William Randolph Hearst

1.   Admiral in charge of the U.S. fleet in the Philippines

2.   publisher of sensational news stories

3.   founder of the American Girl Scouts

4.   President known for his "dollar diplomacy"

5.   "Rough Rider" who later became President

6.   Indiana senator who used arguments of racial superiority to justify expansionism

Complete each sentence below by selecting the correct word from the list. You will not use all the words.

a. San Juan Hill   d. Hawaii
b. the Philippine Islands e. Colombia
c. Cuba   f. Isthmus of Panama

7.   Guerrillas on the island nation of _____ destroyed U.S. property to gain support for independence.

8.   The United States annexed _____ in 1898.

9.   Congress authorized a "guilt" payment of $25 million to _____ for the rights to the Canal Zone.

10.   The "Rough Riders" made _____ the site of the most famous incident of the Spanish-American War.

11.   The Spanish-American War began in 1898 in _____, when the United States launched a surprise attack on Spanish ships in Manila Bay.

Write the letter of the correct answer.

12.   Why did many U.S. policymakers promote expansionism in the late 1800s?

     A) Americans wanted to gain the respect of foreign countries.

     B) Foreign goods were often superior to American products.

     C) Many U.S. industries were short of labor.

     D) The United States needed new markets for its goods.

Test Bank Questions

Write the letter of the correct answer.

13. Which was NOT a popular argument for expansionism in the late 1800s?
    A) "All people are entitled to self-government."
    B) "Americans have a responsibility to promote democracy."
    C) "Americans have a moral obligation to promote Protestant Christianity."
    D) "A quest for empire is needed to restore the country's pioneer spirit."

14. Which of the following demonstrated U.S. enforcement of the Monroe Doctrine in the late 1800s?
    A) The United States ordered Great Britain to withdraw from Venezuela.
    B) The United States allowed Hawaiians to import sugar duty free.
    C) The United States gained most-favored-nation status in China.
    D) The United States competed against France and Britain for Asian markets.

15. Which event led to the Spanish-American War?
    A) The United States annexed Cuba.
    B) Cuban rebels blew up the U.S.S. Maine
    C) Spain destroyed U.S. sugar plantations in Cuba.
    D) Cubans rebelled against Spanish rule.

16. Why was the Open Door policy important to the United States?
    A) It gave the United States territory in China.
    B) It gave the United States access to millions of Chinese consumers.
    C) It increased Chinese investments in the United States.
    D) It stemmed the flow of Chinese immigrants to the United States.

17. Why did many of Roosevelt's opponents disapprove of his building the Panama Canal?
    A) They thought Roosevelt paid Colombia too much money to lease the land.
    B) They thought the canal was unnecessary.
    C) They thought Roosevelt gave Panama too much control over the Canal.
    D) They opposed Roosevelt's involvement in the Panamanian "revolution."

Test Bank Questions

Write the letter of the correct answer.

18. What was the central message of the Roosevelt Corollary?

   A) The United States would use military force to prevent other powers from intervening in the affairs of neighboring countries.

   B) The United States would support only those revolutionary movements promoting democratic principles.

   C) U.S. territories could not enter any foreign agreements.

   D) U.S. territories would remain "unincorporated."

19. Which of these arguments against imperialism was favored most by southern Democrats in the late 1800s and early 1900s?

   A) "All people, regardless of race or color, are entitled to liberty."

   B) "More people of different races will move to the United States and create more problems."

   C) "Maintaining peace in the territories will cost too many American lives."

   D) "The U.S. economy cannot support expansion."

20. Which of the following statements accurately describes the paradox of power experienced by the United States in the early 1900s?

   A) Many U.S. territories wanted self-government but lacked the skills to govern themselves effectively.

   B) The United States had the world's most powerful navy but rarely used it.

   C) Many countries asked the United States government for help, then resented American aid.

   D) The United States had become a major power but followed an isolationist policy.

Test Bank Questions

Use the map of Central America to answer the following questions.

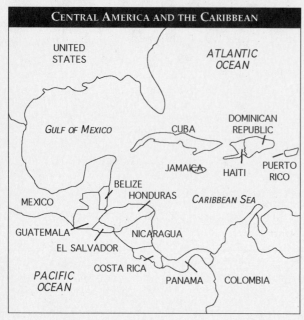

CENTRAL AMERICA AND THE CARIBBEAN

UNITED STATES

ATLANTIC OCEAN

GULF OF MEXICO

CUBA

DOMINICAN REPUBLIC

JAMAICA

HAITI

PUERTO RICO

BELIZE

HONDURAS

CARIBBEAN SEA

MEXICO

GUATEMALA

NICARAGUA

EL SALVADOR

COSTA RICA

PANAMA

COLOMBIA

PACIFIC OCEAN

21. Why should the United States be concerned with revolutionary activities in Cuba?

22. Why was Panama the logical choice for a Canal Zone?

23. In the late 1800s, why do you think the United States was wary of a European presence in Central America and the Caribbean?

Answer the following questions.

24. How was imperialism inconsistent with basic American principles?

25. What were some problems with "dollar diplomacy" in the early 1900s?

26. Based on his performance as President, how do you think Teddy Roosevelt defined the concept of "leadership"? Give examples to support your answer.

Match the terms below with the following descriptions. Write the letter of the correct answer. You will not use all the terms.

a. Roosevelt Corollary   f. Open Door policy
b. imperialism   g. most-favored nation
c. dollar diplomacy   h. paradox of power
d. jingoism   i. annexation
e. sphere of influence   j. yellow journalism

27. U.S. policy of maintaining stability in other countries by increasing investments in the economies of these countries

Test Bank Questions

Match the terms below with the following descriptions. Write the letter of the correct answer. You will not use all the terms.

a. Roosevelt Corollary
b. imperialism
c. dollar diplomacy
d. jingoism
e. sphere of influence

f. Open Door policy
g. most-favored nation
h. paradox of power
i. annexation
j. yellow journalism

28. practice by which stronger nations attempt to create empires by dominating weaker nations

29. area or country in which another nation has strong economic control

30. addition of a new territory to an existing country

31. status of having the same trading rights in a country as other nations

32. extreme nationalism marked by an aggressive foreign policy

33. policy that gave equal access for commercial relations with China to all nations

34. policy establishing the United States as "an international police power"

Write the letter of the correct ending.

35. The United States followed a policy of expansionism in the late 1800s largely because
    A) U.S. factories needed foreign laborers.
    B) many Americans were demanding high-quality foreign goods.
    C) European nations were eager to sell rights to their colonies.
    D) the nation needed more markets for its goods.

36. Americans such as Henry Cabot Lodge and Albert J. Beveridge promoted expansionism for all of the following reasons EXCEPT to
    A) promote Protestant Christianity.
    B) preserve the cultures of "primitive" societies.
    C) restore the country's pioneer spirit.
    D) solve the nation's economic problems.

37. The United States reaffirmed the Monroe Doctrine in the late 1800s by
    A) refusing to support Cuban guerrillas.
    B) warning Great Britain to back out of a territorial dispute with Venezuela.
    C) allowing Hawaiians to import sugar duty free.
    D) passing the Platt Amendment.

Write the letter of the correct ending.

38. In the late 1800s, yellow journalists William Randolph Hearst and Joseph Pulitzer were largely responsible for
    A) starting the Boxer rebellion.
    B) increasing public sympathy for Cuban rebels.
    C) the election of President Theodore Roosevelt.
    D) repeal of the Monroe Doctrine.

39. The main goal of the United States during the Spanish-American War was to
    A) convert the Atlantic Ocean into an "American lake."
    B) protect business investments in Spain.
    C) free Cuba from Spanish rule.
    D) gain spheres of influence in South America.

40. As a result of the Spanish-American War,
    A) Puerto Rico became a protectorate of the United States.
    B) the Philippines became a Spanish colony.
    C) Cuba was divided into spheres of influence.
    D) the United States gained rights to the Panama Canal.

41. President Theodore Roosevelt is often remembered for
    A) promoting "dollar diplomacy."
    B) promoting self-government in former colonies.
    C) expanding presidential power.
    D) opposing the annexation of new territories.

42. The building of the Panama Canal was important because it
    A) promoted European investment in the United States.
    B) facilitated trade between Atlantic and Pacific ports.
    C) helped stabilize the economies of Latin American countries.
    D) improved relations between Colombia and the United States.

43. The success of the Boy Scouts and American Girl Scouts in the early 1900s showed that many Americans
    A) were anti-imperialists.
    B) were concerned about their natural environment.
    C) wanted to improve relations with neighboring countries.
    D) still shared a "frontier mentality."

Test Bank Questions

Write the letter of the correct ending.

44. In the early 1900s, anti-imperialists used all of the following arguments EXCEPT:

   A) "The United States should establish protectorates over nations until the people are ready for self-government."

   B) "Imperialism will increase immigration and cause more social problems."

   C) "Territories controlled by the United States should be subject to the same guarantees as American citizens."

   D) "Expansion costs too much."

Use the map of Central America to answer the following questions.

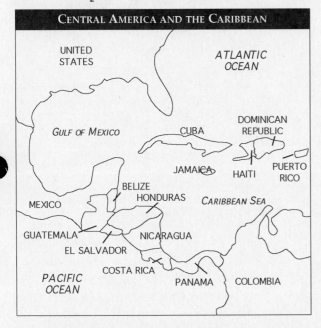

45. What two Caribbean islands became U.S. territories after the Spanish-American War?

46. Geographically, why was Panama a better site for a canal than Nicaragua?

47. In the late 1800s, why do you think the United States was wary of a European presence in Central America and the Caribbean?

Answer the following questions.

48. Compare President Theodore Roosevelt's approach to foreign policy with that of President William Howard Taft. How were they alike and different?

49. Explain how "dollar diplomacy" contributed to the paradox of power that the United States faced in Central and Latin America.

Test Bank Questions

Answer the following questions.

50. Explain how bias was displayed in both imperialist and
     anti-imperialist viewpoints.

Test Bank Answer Key

[1]   b

[2]   d

[3]   c

[4]   g

[5]   a

[6]   f

[7]   c

[8]   d

[9]   e

[10] a

[11] b

[12] D

[13] A

[14] A

[15] D

[16] B

[17] D

[18] A

[19] B

[20] C

[21] Cuba is located directly off the Florida Coast.

[22] Panama is the most narrow country in Central America and is easily accessible by sea.

[23] The United States probably feared that Europeans would establish naval bases in Central America or the Caribbean and might interfere with U.S. trade and shipping.

Test Bank Answer Key

Imperialism violated the principles of "liberty for all," natural rights, and popular sovereignty on which the nation was founded and endangered the nation's democratic institutions. In addition, most people in the territories were not granted U.S. citizenship and were
[24] not protected by the Constitution.

"Dollar diplomacy" was not always profitable for investors in the United States because of revolutionary activities or interference from other nations. Dollar diplomacy damaged U.S. relations with many countries, especially in the Caribbean and Central America, where local residents organized revolutionary movements to oppose U.S.
[25] influence.

To President Roosevelt, leadership meant taking charge of situations, acting decisively and, when necessary, independently and in a high-handed manner. His resignation from the navy to organize the "Rough Riders" as well as the way in which he bypassed Congress to
[26] secure rights to the Canal Zone reflect his philosophy of leadership.

[27] c

[28] b

[29] e

[30] i

[31] g

[32] d

[33] f

[34] a

[35] D

[36] B

[37] B

[38] B

[39] C

[40] A

[41] C

[42] B

[43] D

Test Bank Answer Key

[44] A

[45] Cuba and Puerto Rico

[46] Panama was the most narrow country in Central America and had easy access to both the Atlantic and Pacific Oceans.

[47] The United States probably feared that Europeans would establish naval bases in Central America or the Caribbean and might interfere with U.S. trade and shipping.

[48] Roosevelt and Taft both promoted expansionism and intervened in the affairs of weaker countries to safeguard American interests. However, Roosevelt relied on military force to preserve stability and order in neighboring countries, while Taft promoted U.S. investment in foreign economies.

[49] "Dollar diplomacy" increased U.S. investment in many Central and Latin American countries. As a result, the United States often had to defend governments that supported its economic and political interests, even though such actions were unpopular with local inhabitants. Many Central and Latin American countries developed a love-hate relationship with the United States--welcoming U.S. investments, but resenting U.S. influence.

[50] Many imperialists favored expansionism in order to introduce "primitive" societies to the superior and advanced culture of the Anglo-Saxon and Teutonic "races." By contrast, some anti-imperialists opposed expansionism for fear that immigrants of inferior race would overtake the United States.

The Era of Progressive Reform (1890-1920)

Test Bank Questions

Complete each sentence below by selecting the correct word from the list. You will not use all the words.

a. direct primary
b. holding company
c. New Freedom
d. muckrakers
e. arbitration
f. home rule
g. New Nationalism
h. Bull Moose party
i. progressivism
j. social welfare programs

1. A _____ owns a controlling interest of the stocks and bonds of numerous companies.

2. Under _____, cities exercise a limited degree of self-government.

3. Calling his policy the _____, Woodrow Wilson promised to enforce antitrust laws while still preserving free economic competition.

4. Progressives wanted government to create various _____ to ensure a basic standard of living for all Americans.

5. Collective social and political reform ideas in the late 1800s and early 1900s became known as _____.

6. In a procedure called _____, an impartial third party decides on a legally binding solution to a labor dispute.

7. In a _____, voters cast ballots to select nominees for upcoming elections.

8. In the 1910 midterm elections, Theodore Roosevelt campaigned for insurgent Republican candidates, calling his program the _____.

Write the letter of the correct ending.

9. In the late 1800s, journalists Henry George and Edward Bellamy promoted their ideas of ways to

    A) reform society.

    B) slow the pace of industrialization.

    C) increase the profits of free enterprise.

    D) discourage single-tax speculation.

10. Most progressives agreed that the government should

    A) outlaw unions.

    B) protect workers.

    C) nationalize industries.

    D) abolish home rule in cities and states.

Write the letter of the correct ending.

11. The efforts of Florence Kelley convinced many states to abolish
    A) direct primaries.   B) single-tax colonies.
    C) minimum wage legislation.   D) child labor.

12. President Roosevelt's progressive record included all of the following EXCEPT
    A) establishment of the Federal Reserve System.
    B) regulation of food and drugs.
    C) conservation of forest land.
    D) breakup of several trusts deemed harmful to the public.

13. In the early 1900s, most municipal reformers wanted city utilities to be controlled by
    A) the federal government.   B) the city.
    C) the state.   D) holding companies.

14. President Taft continued Roosevelt's progressive program by
    A) abolishing Jim Crow practices in federal offices.
    B) pursuing antitrust cases.
    C) creating the Fair Trade Commission to regulate tariffs on trade.
    D) selling several million acres of Alaskan public lands.

15. An insurgent movement arose during Taft's presidency when he
    A) failed to reduce the tariff.
    B) supported the Sixteenth Amendment.
    C) opposed direct election of senators.
    D) removed big businesses' control of telephone and telegraph rates.

16. During the presidential campaign of 1912, many woman suffragists campaigned for candidates of the
    A) Democratic party.   B) Bull Moose party.
    C) Republican party.   D) Socialist party.

17. In the early 1900s, some of the greatest opposition to the woman suffrage movement came from
    A) women who took on men's jobs during World War I.
    B) those who feared voting rights would make women more masculine.
    C) politicians from western states.
    D) those women who worked in voluntary organizations.

Test Bank Questions

Write the letter of the correct ending.

18. All of the following helped increase support for woman suffrage EXCEPT
    A) World War I.
    B) Carrie Chapman Catt's "Winning Plan."
    C) adoption of the prohibition amendment.
    D) efforts of the NAACP.

Use the map of Woman Suffrage to answer the following questions.

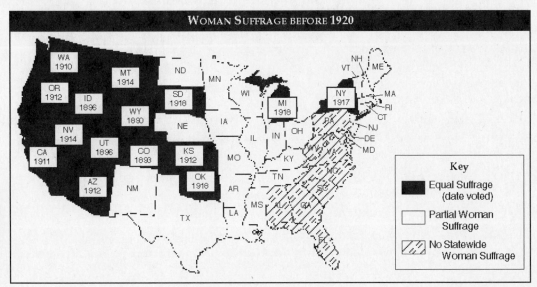

WOMAN SUFFRAGE BEFORE 1920

19. By 1900, what states had granted women the vote?

20. In which region of the nation was the woman suffrage movement least successful? Why?

21. In which region of the United States was the woman suffrage movement most successful? Why?

Answer the following questions.

22. How did progressivism affect the role of the federal government in the early 1900s?

23. How was President Wilson's approach to economic reform similar to that of Theodore Roosevelt? How did Wilson's approach differ?

Test Bank Questions

Match the terms below with the following descriptions. Write the letter of the correct answer. You will not use all the terms.

a. New Freedom
b. direct primary
c. muckrakers
d. Bull Moose party
e. home rule

f. New Nationalism
g. progressivism
h. arbitration
i. holding company
j. social welfare programs

24. political group represented by Theodore Roosevelt and his supporters in the presidential election of 1912

25. self-government in a political territory such as a city

26. movement that promoted social reform and moderate political change by governmental action

27. name of Woodrow Wilson's reform policy during the presidential campaign of 1912

28. election in which voters cast ballots to select nominees for elections

29. process in which labor disputes are resolved by a third party whose decision is binding

30. efforts made by the federal government to ensure a basic standard of living for all Americans

31. Theodore Roosevelt's name for his progressive reform program

Write the letter of the correct answer.

32. According to journalist Henry George, how could Americans eliminate poverty?
    A) by allowing home rule in cities and states
    B) by nationalizing industries
    C) by ending capitalism
    D) by ending land speculation

33. Which belief was held by most progressives?
    A) The government should protect agricultural interests.
    B) The government should own American industries.
    C) The government should intervene in unfair business practices.
    D) Housing and health care should remain private.

34. Which method was LEAST popular among progressives?
    A) organizing nationwide strikes
    B) using mass-circulation publications
    C) conducting thorough investigations
    D) organizing grassroots movements

Test Bank Questions

Write the letter of the correct answer.

35. Which did many municipal reformers favor in the early 1900s?

    A) city control of utilities

    B) strong, independent political machines

    C) federal regulation of city services

    D) abolishment of home rule

36. Which of the following illustrates how protective legislation for women created a "paradox"?

    A) Many employers hired men instead of women.

    B) Women were denied on-the-job training.

    C) Women were paid less than men.

    D) Protective legislation was applied only to child laborers.

37. How did President Roosevelt react to the United Mine Workers' strike in 1902?

    A) He sent the army to seize and operate the mines.

    B) He appointed arbitrators to resolve the dispute.

    C) He dissolved the union.

    D) He refused to interfere with labor and industrial relations.

38. Which action hurt President Taft's popularity and angered Republican insurgents?

    A) Taft's support of woman suffrage

    B) Taft's failure to pursue antitrust cases

    C) Taft's support of the Seventeenth Amendment

    D) Taft's handling of the Ballinger-Pinchot affair

39. How did Woodrow Wilson's reform platform during the 1912 campaign differ from that of Theodore Roosevelt?

    A) Wilson supported federal regulation of business.

    B) Wilson supported tariff reduction.

    C) Wilson wanted to preserve free economic competition.

    D) Wilson promised to enforce antitrust laws.

40. Which was NOT a typical argument used by opponents of woman suffrage?

    A) "Women will vote to establish prohibition."

    B) "Women are powerful enough."

    C) "Women will lose political representation."

    D) "Women will become too masculine."

Test Bank Questions

Write the letter of the correct answer.

41. Which of the following caused internal division in the woman suffrage campaign?

    A) World War I

    B) Alice Paul's militant-style protests

    C) the decision to press for a constitutional amendment

    D) Carrie Chapman Catt's "Winning Plan"

Use the map of Woman Suffrage to answer the following questions.

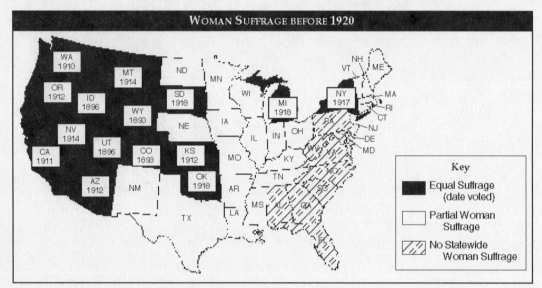

42. In what year did the first state grant women the vote? By 1900, in what other states could women vote?

43. In which region(s) of the United States did the woman suffrage movement have the most difficulty?

44. What conclusions can you draw about social attitudes toward women in various regions of the United States during the progressive era?

Answer the following questions.

45. What are three questions that progressives would likely ask candidates in the 1912 presidential campaign? How would a candidate answer those questions in order to gain the votes of progressives?

46. What alternative strategies did woman suffrage activists follow in the late 1800s and early 1900s? How did each strategy contribute to the passage and ratification of the Nineteenth Amendment?

Test Bank Answer Key

[1] b

[2] f

[3] c

[4] j

[5] i

[6] e

[7] a

[8] g

[9] A

[10] B

[11] D

[12] A

[13] C

[14] B

[15] A

[16] B

[17] B

[18] D

[19] Wyoming, Colorado, Utah, Idaho

[20] The movement appears least successful in the East, particularly in several Mid-Atlantic and southern states. The South was not heavily industrialized and women had fewer opportunities to work outside the home. These eastern states may have had powerful conservative senators and representatives in both local and national legislatures who feared change in the social order.

[21] The movement was most successful in the West. Possible reasons: The difficult frontier life encouraged more blending of gender roles, and consequently, more equality.

Test Bank Answer Key

[22] Progressivism encouraged the federal government to enforce antitrust legislation and to regulate the railroads and food and drug production. In addition, progressivism encouraged government involvement in preserving the environment and in enacting social legislation that protected women and children.

[23] Both supported many of the same reforms, such as lower tariffs, antitrust laws, and other forms of federal regulation of big business. However, Wilson claimed to be more concerned with preserving free economic competition than Roosevelt.

[24] d

[25] e

[26] g

[27] a

[28] b

[29] h

[30] j

[31] f

[32] D

[33] C

[34] A

[35] A

[36] A

[37] B

[38] D

[39] C

[40] C

[41] B

[42] 1890; Idaho, Colorado, Utah

[43] in the East

Test Bank Answer Key

[44] In the West, survival depended on the combined efforts of men and women. Consequently, there was a greater sense of equality. People in the central and eastern regions may have been more conservative, perhaps wary of the effects that woman suffrage might have on society.

[45] Progressives might ask for candidates' opinions about antitrust cases, tariff reduction, and conditions in the workplace. A candidate who sought progressive votes would promise to file antitrust suits whenever trusts became too powerful, to lower tariffs, and to support legislation that limited working hours and set standards for the safety of working conditions.

[46] One suffragist strategy was to convince individual states to grant voting rights to women. While suffragists were successful in the western states, they encountered strong resistance from most central and eastern states. Another alternative was to push for a federal amendment to the Constitution. For about fifty years, a proposed amendment was either stalled or defeated in Congress. In the end, it took both strategies to get the proposed amendment passed in Congress and finally ratified by the states.

The World War I Era (1914-1920)

Test Bank Questions

Match the terms below with the following descriptions. Write the letter of the correct answer. You will not use all the terms.

a. Zimmerman note
b. Versailles Treaty
c. Allies
d. Fourteen Points
e. reparations
f. League of Nations
g. autocratic
h. self-determination
i. American Expeditionary Force
j. armistice
k. Industrial Workers of the World
l. Central Powers

1. radical labor organization founded in 1905 that sought the overthrow of capitalism

2. name of the United States armed forces during World War I

3. President Wilson's peace program

4. telegram to Mexico that revealed Germany's intention to ally itself with Mexico if the United States entered the war

5. temporary cease-fire between opponents

6. alliance that would help ensure security and peace for all members

7. principle that a territorial unit should select its own future political status

8. repayment by the enemy nation for economic injury suffered during a war

9. countries that fought against Germany and Austria-Hungary during World War I

Write the letter of the correct answer.

10. What was the immediate cause of World War I?

    A) the assassination of the heir to the Austrian-Hungarian throne

    B) the German-French dispute over Alsace-Lorraine

    C) the sinking of the Lusitania

    D) Russia's quest for a warm-water port

11. Which of the following best describes the first few years of World War I?

    A) Both sides were locked in a stalemate.

    B) The Central Powers had conquered most of Europe.

    C) Victory for the Allies seemed imminent.

    D) There was little actual fighting.

Test Bank Questions

Write the letter of the correct answer.

12. How did most Americans view Germany during the early years of the war?

A) The were indifferent toward Germany.

B) They sympathized with Germany.

C) They viewed Germany as very heroic.

D) They viewed Germany as coldblooded and cruel.

13. Which of the following was a major factor in the United States' decision to enter World War I?

A) Vladimir Lenin's rise to power in Russia

B) Germany's unrestricted submarine warfare

C) Britain's naval blockade of Germany

D) the fall of France to the Central Powers

14. Which was true of African Americans during World War I?

A) African American troops were segregated and rarely allowed to engage in combat.

B) African American troops were usually reserved for offensive action.

C) African Americans were not allowed to serve in the war.

D) Almost as many African Americans served during the war as did white Americans.

15. How did most women contribute to the war effort?

A) They joined military convoys.

B) They often volunteered as nurses.

C) all of these answers

D) They served as translators.

16. What role did the federal government play in the economy during the war?

A) The government stripped the corporate world of most of its power.

B) The government regulated industrial production of war goods.

C) The government lowered taxes to promote economic growth.

D) The government gave industries more economic freedom.

17. Which of the following was NOT an effect of World War I on life in the United States?

A) Prohibition was passed.

B) Women gained greater job opportunities.

C) Immigration increased greatly.

D) The government curbed civil liberties.

Test Bank Questions

Write the letter of the correct answer.

18. Why did many senators oppose the Versailles Treaty?
    A) They felt the treaty violated the Fourteen Points.
    B) They opposed reparations for the Allies.
    C) The did not want the United States to join the League of Nations.
    D) They wanted harsher terms for Germany.

19. Which of the following made postwar adjustment difficult for the United States?
    A) There were more jobs available than there were workers.
    B) The government continued to control the economy.
    C) There was no plan for reintegrating returning troops into society.
    D) The United States became the world's largest debtor nation.

Use the table of US Foreign Trade to answer the following questions.

UNITED STATES FOREIGN TRADE DURING WORLD WAR I			
	1914	**1915**	**1916**
To Allied Countries	$824,860,237	$1,991,747,493	$3,214,480,547
To Central Powers	$169,289,775	$11,878,153	$1,159,653
To Northern Neutrals	$187,667,040	$330,110,646	$279,786,219

20. With which countries did the United States have the strongest commercial ties in 1914?

21. Based on the table, what conclusions can you draw about the relations between Germany and the United States during the early years of World War I? Explain.

22. Use the table to support or refute the following statement: <u>The United States remained neutral during the early years of World War I</u>.

Answer the following questions.

23. Your text states that the United States fought World War I at home, too. What evidence can you cite to support this conclusion?

24. What role did public opinion play in the decisions of the United States to enter and participate in World War I?

Test Bank Questions

Answer the following questions.

25. Congresswoman Jeannette Rankin said that she voted against U.S. involvement in World War I because it was "a commercial war." Do you think Rankin's statement represented her personal belief, or was it a fact? Explain.

Complete each sentence below by selecting the correct word from the list. You will not use all the words.

a. Fourteen Points
b. self-determination
c. Liberty Bonds
d. Zimmerman note
e. U-boat
f. Versailles Treaty
g. reparations
h. Industrial Workers of the World
i. League of Nations
j. American Expeditionary Force
k. doughboys

26. The radical views of the _____ distressed moderate labor leaders such as Samuel Gompers.

27. In the _____, Germany proposed an alliance with Mexico should the United States enter World War I.

28. The principle that people in a territorial unit should choose their own future political status is known as _____.

29. The German _____ altered the rules of naval warfare.

30. The _____ outlined the terms for peace after World War I.

31. In 1918 President Wilson delivered a peace program called the _____ to Congress.

32. The United States government sold _____ to finance the war.

33. President Wilson hoped that the _____ would ensure security and peace for all member nations.

34. Britain wanted _____, payment for economic injuries suffered during the war.

Write the letter of the correct ending.

35. The most immediate cause of World War I was the
    A) assassination of the heir to the Austrian-Hungarian throne.
    B) Serbian invasion of Hungary.
    C) Zimmerman note.
    D) German seizure of Alsace-Lorraine.

36. In the early 1900s, Germany was a(n)
    A) democratic state.   B) socialist state.
    C) autocratic state.   D) communist state.

Test Bank Questions

Write the letter of the correct ending.

37. During the early years of World War I, the United States
    A) sided with the Central Powers.
    B) broke off commercial ties with Great Britain.
    C) was decidedly neutral and treated both sides equally.
    D) loaned money to the Allies.

38. All of the following convinced the United States to enter World War I EXCEPT
    A) the revolution in Russia.
    B) commercial ties with Great Britain.
    C) the British naval blockade on the United States.
    D) the German use of submarine warfare.

39. Most African Americans who served during World War I
    A) never saw combat.
    B) were reserved for defensive action.
    C) fought along the front.
    D) joined the marines.

40. After Vladimir Lenin seized control of Russia in 1917,
    A) the Allies accepted Germany's peace terms.
    B) Germany surrendered.
    C) the Allies declared war on Russia.
    D) Russia withdrew from the war.

41. The government tried to control the economy during World War I by
    A) founding the Industrial Workers of the World.
    B) regulating industries.
    C) filing a record number of antitrust suits.
    D) enacting price controls and rationing.

42. Fear of spies and sabotage in the United States during the war resulted in
    A) restrictions on immigration.
    B) repression of free speech.
    C) discrimination and violence toward Germans.
    D) all of these answers.

Test Bank Questions

Write the letter of the correct ending.

43. At the end of the war, President Wilson and Congress disagreed most over
    A) the Fourteen Points.
    B) the League of Nations.
    C) self-determination of ethnic groups in Austria-Hungary.
    D) the issue of reparations for the Allies.

44. The immediate postwar years in the United States were best described as a period of
    A) disillusionment.   B) optimism.
    C) affluence.   D) indifference.

Use the table of US Foreign Trade to answer the following questions.

UNITED STATES FOREIGN TRADE DURING WORLD WAR I			
	1914	**1915**	**1916**
To Allied Countries	$824,860,237	$1,991,747,493	$3,214,480,547
To Central Powers	$169,289,775	$11,878,153	$1,159,653
To Northern Neutrals	$187,667,040	$330,110,646	$279,786,219

45. If the United States had entered World War I in 1914 to protect its commercial interests, with which side would it likely have allied itself? Explain.

46. Use the table to support or refute the following conclusion:
    <u>Commercial relations between the United States and Germany</u>
    <u>deteriorated rapidly during the early years of World War I.</u>

47. Do you think the United States was really "neutral" during the early years of World War I? Explain.

Answer the following questions.

48. Why did many Americans regard the Germans as coldhearted and almost sinister during World War I?

49. Do you think the participation of American women in World War I was a help to the woman suffrage movement? Explain.

50. What role did bias play in World War I? Do you think the war would have occurred at all had it not been for one ethnic group's bias against another? Explain.

Test Bank Answer Key

[1] k

[2] i

[3] d

[4] a

[5] j

[6] f

[7] h

[8] e

[9] c

[10] A

[11] A

[12] D

[13] B

[14] A

[15] B

[16] B

[17] C

[18] C

[19] C

[20] with the Allied countries (Britain, France, Italy, Russia)

[21] U.S.-German relations deteriorated rapidly during the early years of the war, as trade with the Central Powers dropped to a little over a million dollars by 1916.

[22] Refute--The United States clearly favored the Allies through trade; trade increased rapidly with the Allies while trade with the Central Powers dropped sharply during the first few years of the war.

Test Bank Answer Key

In order to prepare the nation for war, the government took control of much of the economy and launched a propaganda campaign both to raise money for the war effort and to sway public opinion in favor of joining the Allies. It might also be said that the United States fought a war at home as evidenced by the acts of violence and discrimination toward German culture and German Americans, and by the
[23] repression of civil liberties in the Sedition and Espionage Acts.

The United States did not enter World War I until American public opinion was decidedly against the Germans and in favor of the Allies. Although many Americans still protested war, sympathy toward Britain and outrage at Germany, in addition to fear of losing commercial ties, were enough to convince Congress to finally pass a war resolution. However, American participation was cautious and limited until enthusiastic patriots and investors prevailed over antiwar
[24] sentiment.

Rankin's statement was both a personal opinion and a fact. Commercial interests played a major role in American support for the Allies and in the final decision to join the war to protect those interests. However, other factors, such as American idealism and patriotism, as well as Germany's refusal to respect American claims to neutrality by practicing unrestricted submarine warfare, led many Americans to
[25] believe they were fighting to safeguard liberty and democracy.

[26] h

[27] d

[28] b

[29] e

[30] f

[31] a

[32] c

[33] i

[34] g

[35] A

[36] C

[37] D

[38] C

[39] A

Test Bank Answer Key

[40] D

[41] B

[42] D

[43] B

[44] A

[45] It would have allied with the Allies. The United States traded hundreds of millions more with the Allies, which included Great Britain, than with other nations from 1914 to 1916.

[46] Support--Trade with the Central Powers (which included Germany) decreased by about $168 million from 1914 to 1916.

[47] No; the United States increased trade with the Allies while greatly decreasing trade with the Central Powers.

[48] Germany was an autocratic, militaristic state which ran counter to United States democracy. The British controlled news reports and used propaganda to sway American public opinion. Finally, the German use of U-boats to attack ships, many of which were carrying passengers, turned Americans against Germany. Some of the actions of the German government justified the image, which in turn was exaggerated by the U.S. press and commercial interests.

[49] World War I was probably a great help to the suffrage movement. The war opened up many work opportunities for women and enabled them to serve in the military and in traditionally male-dominated jobs. Such working women may have helped change public opinion about a woman's "proper" place in society.

[50] Bias played a major role in the war. Bias led Austria-Hungary to blame and declare war on Serbia for the assassination of the heir to the Austrian-Hungarian throne. Ethnic bias among Serbs and Bosnian minorities helped fan the flames of the conflict. Finally, U.S. commercial interests and cultural ties created a U.S. bias in favor of the Allies and against the Central Powers.

A Stormy Era (1919-1929)

Test Bank Questions

Match the terms below with the following descriptions. Write the letter of the correct answer. You will not use all the terms.

a. general strike   e. red scare
b. bootlegging   f. communist
c. flapper   g. Harlem Renaissance
d. fundamentalism

1.   fear of communism and other revolutionary ideas

2.   African American literary movement of the 1920s

3.   action in which many unions participated in a show of worker unity

4.   smuggling, distilling, and illegal selling of alcoholic beverages

5.   religious movement that insisted upon literal interpretation of the Bible

Complete each sentence below by selecting the correct word from the list. You will not use all the words.

a. Calvin Coolidge   e. Warren G. Harding
b. Charles A. Lindbergh   f. Vladimir I. Lenin
c. T.S. Eliot   g. Herbert Hoover
d. F. Scott Fitzgerald

6.   "The business of America is business," observed _____, elected President in 1924.

7.   Aviator _____ became a national hero after flying nonstop from New York to Paris.

8.   _____ and the Bolsheviks set up a communist form of government in the Soviet Union.

9.   Elected in 1920, Republican President _____ promised a "return to normalcy."

10.   _____ criticized the culture of the 1920s in The Great Gatsby.

Write the letter of the correct ending.

11.   The postwar economy entered a period of adjustment because

     A) the number of immigrant laborers decreased.

     B) assembly-line work created fewer jobs.

     C) wartime demand for goods dropped.

     D) the cost of living declined dramatically.

Test Bank Questions

Write the letter of the correct ending.

12. As a result of labor strikes and terrorist acts, many Americans supported
   A) prohibition.
   B) progressive government reforms.
   C) technological change.
   D) nativism.

13. Both the Palmer raids and the Sacco and Vanzetti case demonstrated how
   A) fundamentalism had permeated society.
   B) traditional social conventions were breaking down.
   C) the red scare provoked injustice.
   D) Americans were beginning to reject isolationism.

14. In the 1920s, women's suffrage seemed to have its greatest impact in
   A) promoting the nomination of women for national office.
   B) changing local politics.
   C) supporting legislation favorable to women.
   D) ending militant groups such as the National Woman's party.

15. Marcus Garvey led a movement to
   A) integrate African Americans into the larger white culture.
   B) end racial violence in northern cities.
   C) unionize African American factory workers.
   D) encourage racial pride and self-pride among African Americans.

16. Herbert Hoover was elected President in 1928 largely because
   A) women voters supported Hoover.
   B) the Teapot Dome scandal had shaken voter confidence in the Democratic party.
   C) the economy had soared under Republican leadership during the 1920s.
   D) the Republican platform favored workers' rights.

17. The ultimate symbol of Jazz Age culture was a young woman who
   A) enjoyed a greater freedom in morals and manners than previous generations.
   B) preferred long hair and rejected makeup.
   C) rejected college in favor of marriage.
   D) worked as a physician or lawyer.

18. The growth of mass media and advances in transportation
   A) promoted the creation of a national culture.
   B) simplified life for most Americans.
   C) encouraged Americans to work longer hours.
   D) promoted a mass migration to rural areas.

Test Bank Questions

Write the letter of the correct ending.

19. One result of prohibition during the 1920s was
    A) the creation of urban artistic colonies.
    B) a decline in dancing and socializing.
    C) an increase in alcoholism.
    D) the rise of organized crime.

20. During the 1920s, the main goal of the Ku Klux Klan was to
    A) repeal prohibition.   B) prevent women from voting.
    C) teach evolution.   D) promote white supremacy.

21. Henry Ford made automobiles more affordable by
    A) setting up assembly lines.
    B) offering low-interest car loans.
    C) allowing buyers to select options.
    D) reducing workers' hourly wages.

Use the bar graph of Immigration to answer the following questions.

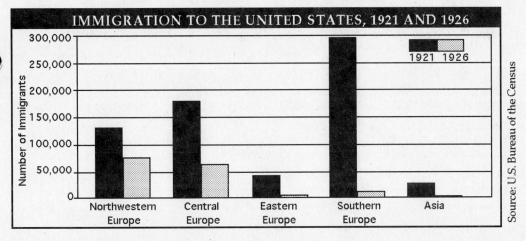

IMMIGRATION TO THE UNITED STATES, 1921 AND 1926

Source: U.S. Bureau of the Census

22. (a) From which part of the world did the largest number of
       immigrants come in 1921?
    (b) About how many people emigrated from this region in 1921?

23. A 1924 law limited the number of some immigrants. Based on the data
    in the graphs, which two European groups were most affected?

24. Describe the overall trend of immigration from 1921 to 1926.

Answer the following questions.

25. Why did so many Americans fear the spread of communist ideology? What
    changes would a communist takeover bring to the United States?

Test Bank Questions

Answer the following questions.

26. Imagine that a flapper and a fundamentalist have been asked to describe American culture during the 1920s. How would their descriptions differ?

27. Explain how the mass production of automobiles in the 1920s affected the economy and culture of the United States.

Complete each sentence below by selecting the correct word from the list. You will not use all the words.

a. Harlem Renaissance   e. Jazz Age
b. general strike   f. red scare
c. Scopes trial   g. flapper
d. Teapot Dome

28. The _____ scandal tarnished the reputation of the Harding administration.

29. So strong was the impact of this musical art form on the 1920s that the era became known as the _____.

30. Literary life flourished among African Americans as part of a movement called the _____.

31. A high school biology teacher was convicted of teaching Darwin's theory of evolution in the _____.

32. Unions participated in a show of worker unity in the _____ of 1919.

Match the terms below with the following descriptions. Write the letter of the correct answer. You will not use all the terms.

a. Calvin Coolidge   e. Henry Ford
b. Nicola Sacco   f. T.S. Eliot
c. Vladimir I. Lenin   g. Warren G. Harding
d. Marcus Garvey

33. Jamaican who inspired a "black pride" movement among African Americans

34. disillusioned poet who wrote "The Waste Land"

35. engineer who pioneered the assembly line

36. admitted anarchist whose conviction as a murderer divided the country

37. shy, silent Republican President who worked to protect American business

Write the letter of the correct answer.

38. Which was a major cause of economic hardship in the postwar United States?

A) Returning veterans refused to work in low-paying factory jobs.

B) International trade collapsed.

C) Consumer demand outstripped factory production.

D) The cost of living more than doubled.

Test Bank Questions

Write the letter of the correct answer.

39. Why did many Americans fear Vladimir I. Lenin and his followers, the Bolsheviks?
    A) They had abolished the Russian monarchy.
    B) They encouraged other nations to reject socialism.
    C) They refused to pay back Russia's war debts.
    D) They promoted a worldwide communist revolution.

40. Which of the following was a leading cause of nativism after World War I?
    A) the rise of organized crime
    B) decreased immigration
    C) the red scare and labor unrest
    D) the rise of economic prosperity in Europe

41. What impact did women's suffrage have on public life during the 1920s?
    A) Women were elected to state offices for the first time.
    B) Women began to serve on juries in many states.
    C) Mass numbers of women began to vote in national elections.
    D) Many women assumed national leadership positions in the Democratic party.

42. Which was NOT a reason for the mass migration of African Americans to the North?
    A) Prejudice and discrimination remained deeply rooted in the South.
    B) There was little or no racial violence in northern cities.
    C) Opportunities for education were poor in the South.
    D) Jobs in the North offered higher wages than most jobs in the South.

43. What helped Herbert Hoover to win a landslide victory in the 1928 presidential election?
    A) His support of the ERA campaign.
    B) His Teapot Dome scandal.
    C) His promise to end prohibition.
    D) The nation's general prosperity.

44. What effect did the 1920s have on women?
    A) Women began to dominate the work force, often taking jobs from men.
    B) Married women found it much easier to balance careers and family life.
    C) Women felt freer to experiment with bolder styles and manners.
    D) Most women grew long hair and stopped using makeup.

Test Bank Questions

Write the letter of the correct answer.

45. To those who idolized him, what did Charles A. Lindbergh symbolize?
A) The country's national spirit.
B) The superficiality of American culture.
C) The genius of American history.
D) The rebellious urban youth culture.

46. Which was a result of the boom in the automobile industry?
A) The tourist industry declined.
B) Gasoline had to be rationed.
C) The government built new road systems.
D) Workers in Ford plants earned low wages.

47. Why did prohibition seem to fail during the 1920s?
A) Prohibition weakened the American economy.
B) Prohibition proved difficult to enforce.
C) Prohibition increased alcoholism in the United States.
D) Prohibition led to increased racial violence by the Ku Klux Klan.

48. With which of the following issues were fundamentalists most concerned during the 1920s?
A) The theory of evolution.   B) Movie censorship.
C) Organized crime.   D) Technological change.

Use the bar graph of Immigration to answer the following questions.

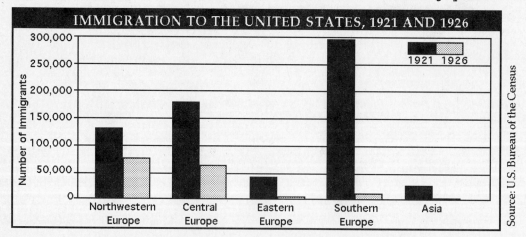

49. Which group experienced the sharpest decline in immigration from 1921 to 1926?

50. What can you assume was the effect of the 1924 immigration laws on immigration from central Europe?

Test Bank Questions

Use the bar graph of Immigration to answer the following questions.

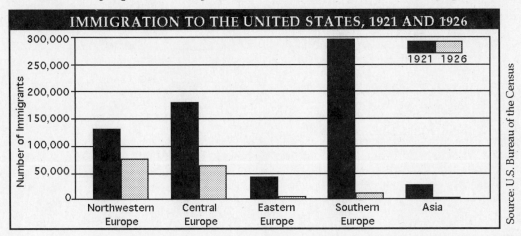

IMMIGRATION TO THE UNITED STATES, 1921 AND 1926

Number of Immigrants — Northwestern Europe, Central Europe, Eastern Europe, Southern Europe, Asia

1921 1926

Source: U.S. Bureau of the Census

51. Compare the graphs. What assumption might you make about American attitudes toward foreigners during the mid–1920s?

Answer the following questions.

52. Discuss three social or political incidents or situations from the 1920s that resulted from bias in American society.

53. What did many prohibitionists assume would be the results of prohibition? Discuss one CORRECT and one INCORRECT assumption.

54. Compare the governments of the United States and the Soviet Union during the 1920s. How did each country try to protect its political and economic systems from the threat of foreign ideas?

Test Bank Answer Key

[1]   e

[2]   g

[3]   a

[4]   b

[5]   d

[6]   a

[7]   b

[8]   f

[9]   e

[10] d

[11] C

[12] D

[13] C

[14] C

[15] D

[16] C

[17] A

[18] A

[19] D

[20] D

[21] A

[22] (a) southern Europe
      (b) almost 300,000

[23] southern and eastern Europeans

[24] decreased

[25] Americans realized that Marx's communist ideology would destroy both
      democracy and capitalism in the United States. Personal, political,
      and economic freedoms would be threatened.

Test Bank Answer Key

The flapper might describe the 1920s as a positive and liberating era in which women were free to experiment with new manners. The fundamentalist would characterize the 1920s as a period of moral decay in which traditional social and religious values were

[26] threatened.

The boom of the automobile industry stimulated the American economy by increasing the demand for gasoline, petroleum, rubber, new road systems, and even advertising. Increased travel led to a greater sharing of values and experiences, which led to the creation of a

[27] national culture.

[28] d

[29] e

[30] a

[31] c

[32] b

[33] d

[34] f

[35] e

[36] b

[37] a

[38] D

[39] D

[40] C

[41] B

[42] B

[43] D

[44] C

[45] A

[46] C

[47] B

[48] A

Chapter 21

Test Bank Answer Key

[49] Southern Europeans

[50] Reduced it from about 180,000 in 1921 to about 60,000 in 1926.

[51] Americans thought too many foreigners and revolutionary ideas were taking hold in the country.

[52] Bias against those suspected of adhering to communist or socialist ideologies resulted in violence and injustice. Bias against foreigners led to a policy of isolationism and the passage of restrictive immigration laws. Racial prejudice sparked the mass migration of African Americans from the South and subsequent racial violence in northern cities.

[53] Many prohibitionists assumed correctly that prohibition would decrease the consumption of alcoholic beverages. They assumed incorrectly that prohibition would solve urban social problems.

[54] The Soviet Union was a communist dictatorship while the United States was a democracy. The Soviet leadership believed that if communism were to survive, they would need to incite communist revolutions in other parts of the world. The United States sought to protect the democratic process from revolutionary ideas by adopting a policy of nativism and isolationism.

Crash and Depression (1929-1933)

Test Bank Questions

Match the terms below with the following descriptions. Write the letter of the correct answer. You will not use all the terms.

a. installment buying e. Dow Jones industrial average
b. real wages f. buying on margin
c. speculation g. Gross National Product
d. welfare capitalism h. collateral

1.   employers' practice of providing workers with raises and benefits

2.   paying for expensive purchases in monthly payments at fairly high interest rates

3.   actual purchasing power

4.   taking business risks, such as investing in stocks

5.   something pledged as security for a loan

6.   method of buying stocks in which stockbrokers loaned investors part of the purchase price

Complete each sentence below by selecting the correct word from the list. You will not use all the words.

a. Eleanor Roosevelt e. John Maynard Keynes
b. Herbert Hoover f. Franklin Delano Roosevelt
c. Norman Thomas g. the Scottsboro Boys
d. Father Divine

7.   In New York in the 1920s, _____ worked for legislation to improve conditions for working women.

8.   _____ was the Socialist party's candidate in the 1932 presidential election.

9.   During the Depression, the followers of _____ opened soup kitchens in Harlem.

10. President _____ argued against direct federal relief.

11. The economist _____ advocated massive government spending to help a collapsing economy.

Write the letter of the correct ending.

12. During the 1920s, most Americans attributed the strong economy to

    A) business leaders.   B) the government.
    C) union leaders.   D) consumers.

Test Bank Questions

Write the letter of the correct ending.

13. One sign that the economy might be weakening in the 1920s was
    A) rural bank failures.   B) rising wages.
    C) an increase in personal savings.   D) high unemployment.

14. When the Dow Jones industrial average began to drop sharply in late October 1929,
    A) most bankers pardoned personal loans and mortgages.
    B) stockbrokers sold record shares.
    C) President Hoover warned Americans to stop investing.
    D) investors raced to sell their shares.

15. One cause of the Great Depression was
    A) too much government intervention in the economy.
    B) an uneven distribution of wealth.
    C) the decline of credit buying.
    D) low interest rates.

16. The collapse of the U.S. economy hurt European economies when the United States
    A) lowered tariffs.
    B) pardoned war debts.
    C) stopped investing in Germany.
    D) increased American exports.

17. Wage cuts and unemployment in the early 1930s resulted in
    A) mass migration to rural communities.
    B) bank failures.
    C) the construction of Hoovervilles.
    D) an increase in food prices.

18. During the Depression, women and African Americans
    A) often lost their jobs to white men.
    B) were encouraged to start their own businesses.
    C) became tenant farmers planting "relief gardens."
    D) made great strides in equal rights legislation.

19. The Scottsboro case showed how
    A) the Depression affected people psychologically.
    B) relief and job programs discriminated against African Americans.
    C) African Americans coped with poverty and starvation during the Depression.
    D) the justice system ignored the civil rights of African Americans.

Test Bank Questions

Write the letter of the correct ending.

20. Most Americans who lived through the Depression
    A) insisted on radical social change.
    B) still had faith in the democratic process.
    C) became ardent supporters of communism.
    D) supported repeal of the Twenty-first Amendment.

21. President Hoover tried to end the Depression by
    A) forcing industrialists to maintain dividends paid to stockholders.
    B) encouraging voluntary controls and actions.
    C) lowering import duties.
    D) encouraging massive government spending.

22. Franklin D. Roosevelt won the 1932 presidential election partly because he
    A) blamed the Depression on worldwide economic conditions.
    B) promised to take strong action against the Bonus Army.
    C) had a political history of establishing relief programs.
    D) supported the Reconstruction Finance Corporation.

23. Since the 1930s, the federal government has
    A) nationalized the banks.
    B) adopted <u>laissez-faire</u> policies.
    C) acted to protect citizens' welfare.
    D) restricted installment buying.

Test Bank Questions

Use the line graph of the US Economy to answer the following questions.

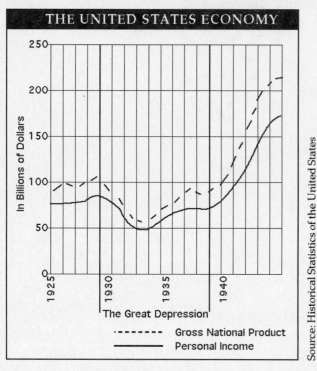

24. How much did the Gross National Product (GNP) decrease from 1929 to 1932?

25. What appears to be the relationship between personal income and a country's GNP?

26. Why is 1939 considered the last year of the Great Depression?

Answer the following questions.

27. Did President Hoover present a false or an accurate image of the Depression to the American public? Cite examples to support your answer.

28. How relevant were Franklin D. Roosevelt's political experience and ideology to the challenges facing his presidency? Explain.

29. What kind of advice do you think a survivor of the Great Depression might give young couples today?

Test Bank Questions

Complete each sentence below by selecting the correct word from the list. You will not use all the words.

a. Reconstruction Finance Corporation
b. Twenty-first Amendment
c. welfare capitalism
d. Gross National Product
e. Bonus Army
f. Dow Jones industrial average
g. Hawley-Smoot tariff
h. real wages

30. The _____ is the total value of goods and services produced by a country.

31. Investors keep track of the prices of leading stocks by reading the _____.

32. In 1930 Congress passed the _____ to raise import duties.

33. The _____, ratified in 1933, repealed the ban on alcoholic beverages.

34. President Hoover established the _____ to aid financial institutions.

35. To counter moves to unionize workers, many companies turned to _____.

Match the terms below with the following descriptions. Write the letter of the correct answer. You will not use all the terms.

a. Herbert Hoover
b. Norman Thomas
c. Eleanor Roosevelt
d. Father Divine
e. John Maynard Keynes
f. Franklin Delano Roosevelt

36. economist who believed that massive government spending programs could revive a failing economy

37. activist who worked for public housing and for government reform in New York

38. Socialist party presidential candidate

39. evangelist whose followers opened soup kitchens in Harlem

40. President who promised the nation a "new deal"

Write the letter of the correct answer.

41. Which group faced particularly hard times during most of the 1920s?

A) manufacturers
B) small investors
C) urban bankers
D) farmers

42. Which statement best describes the American economy during the 1920s?

A) The economy weakened and wages decreased.
B) The economy grew steadily as investments increased.
C) Small business dominated American industry.
D) Unemployment was at an all-time high.

Write the letter of the correct answer.

43. Which of the following was a sign of a troubled economy during the 1920s?

A) Personal debt was decreasing.

B) The Dow Jones industrial average was rising.

C) Wealth was unevenly distributed.

D) Wages were keeping pace with production.

44. How did most investors react to a sudden fall in stock prices in late October 1929?

A) raced to sell their stocks

B) called in their loans

C) pledged their stocks as collateral

D) pooled money to buy stocks

45. Why was rapid economic recovery impossible after the crash of 1929?

A) Farm prices rose as farmers destroyed their crops in protest.

B) The American economic structure was unstable.

C) Germany suspended reparation payments.

D) Low tariffs hurt international trade.

46. Which was one effect of wage cuts and unemployment in the early 1930s?

A) Banks pardoned thousands of farm mortgages.

B) Most industries gave top jobs to married women.

C) Hoovervilles sprang up throughout the nation's cities.

D) The divorce rate almost tripled.

47. Against which of the following groups did relief and job programs discriminate most during the Depression?

A) farmers   B) white-collar workers

C) African Americans   D) single white women

48. Which would most likely be a "good" memory for members of the Depression-era generation?

A) the Depression-era policies of Henry Ford

B) "relief gardens"

C) the building of the Empire State Building

D) the Scottsboro Boys case

49. How did President Hoover attempt to solve the nation's economic problems?

A) by enacting massive government spending programs

B) by controlling financial institutions

C) by encouraging private and local relief efforts

D) by taking action to curb unwise speculation and credit buying

Test Bank Questions

Write the letter of the correct answer.

50. What was a major reason for Roosevelt's overwhelming victory in 1932?

    A) He promoted the theory of "trickle down" economics.

    B) He pledged immediate payment of pension bonuses to veterans.

    C) He supported the Twenty-first Amendment.

    D) He promised federal relief programs and controls on business.

51. After the 1929 crash how did many Americans view the role of the federal government?

    A) protector of business and industry

    B) responsible for its citizens' welfare

    C) leader in global economics

    D) supporter of radical social change

Use the line graph of the US Economy to answer the following questions.

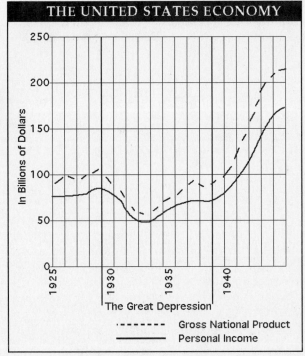

52. Which year of the Great Depression do you think was most difficult for Americans? Support your answer.

53. Explain how Roosevelt would probably have used the data in the graphs during the 1932 presidential campaign.

Test Bank Questions

Use the line graph of the US Economy to answer the following questions.

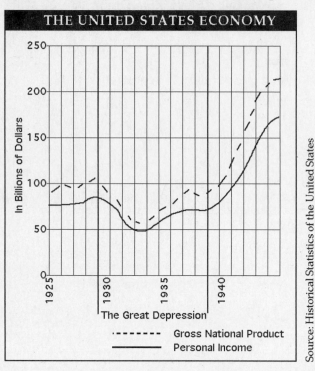

THE UNITED STATES ECONOMY

In Billions of Dollars

The Great Depression

·------- Gross National Product
——— Personal Income

Source: Historical Statistics of the United States

54. If the total Gross National Product increased, what would most likely happen to personal income?

Answer the following questions.

55. During the Depression, many Americans believed that President Hoover was cold and insensitive. Do you think this was an accurate impression of the President? Support your answer.

56. In your opinion, what was the greatest single effect of the Depression on the country? On members of the Depression-era generation? Support your answer.

57. Explain whether the maxim, "Work hard, be thrifty, don't borrow," from Benjamin Franklin's <u>Poor Richard's Almanac</u>, is consistent or inconsistent with American attitudes in the late 1920s.

Test Bank Answer Key

[1] d

[2] a

[3] b

[4] c

[5] h

[6] f

[7] a

[8] c

[9] d

[10] b

[11] e

[12] A

[13] A

[14] D

[15] B

[16] C

[17] C

[18] A

[19] D

[20] B

[21] B

[22] C

[23] C

[24] about $40 billion

[25] They parallel each other. When a country has a high GNP, its economy is strong, most people are employed, and personal incomes are high.

[26] By 1939, the Gross National Product and personal income were climbing steadily and had almost reached 1929 levels.

Test Bank Answer Key

[27] Hoover presented a false image of the Depression. He insisted that the Depression was only temporary when in fact it lasted an entire decade. He also blamed the Depression on global economic conditions while most causes were domestic.

[28] Roosevelt's experience was very relevant to the challenges of the Depression era. As governor of New York, he had worked for Depression relief in that state by establishing an unemployment commission and a relief administration, the first state agencies to help the poor. Equally important, Roosevelt was an experimenter and unconcerned with maintaining the government's status quo. He was willing to implement bold new programs to revive the ailing economy.

[29] A survivor of the Depression would probably encourage young couples to save regularly, to limit credit spending, to work diligently to pay off home mortgages, and NOT to speculate in the stock market, but to make safer, more solid investments.

[30] d

[31] f

[32] g

[33] b

[34] a

[35] c

[36] e

[37] c

[38] b

[39] d

[40] f

[41] D

[42] B

[43] C

[44] A

[45] B

[46] C

[47] C

Test Bank Answer Key

[48] C

[49] C

[50] D

[51] B

[52] 1933; Gross National Product and personal income were at their lowest level.

[53] Roosevelt would probably have used the data to argue that both the Gross National Product and personal income had dropped by about $40 billion during Hoover's presidency.

[54] Personal income would rise.

[55] Hoover pursued some ineffective policies during his presidency, but he meant well. Many of his mistakes stemmed from his belief that voluntary cooperation was the key to economic recovery. Although he made attempts to revive the economy, his efforts were too little and too late. His reluctance to meet public demands for direct federal relief, as well as insensitive remarks, contributed to his negative image.

[56] The greatest effect of the Depression was the way in which it permanently altered Americans' perception of the federal government. Prior to the Depression, many Americans had prided themselves on making it on their own. During the Depression, many Americans came to believe that the government should assume responsibility for meeting citizens' needs. The greatest effect on members of the Depression-era generation was a change in their economic behavior and their attitude toward spending and saving.

[57] The maxim is inconsistent with American attitudes in the late 1920s when many Americans embraced a "get-rich-quick" attitude and eagerly invested their life savings in the stock market. Liberal spending and borrowing, whether to buy stocks, automobiles, or appliances, were common and socially acceptable practices then.

The New Deal (1933-1938)

Test Bank Questions

Match the terms below with the following descriptions. Write the letter of the correct answer. You will not use all the terms.

a. political right
b. sit-down strike
c. public works program
d. New Deal
e. national debt
f. hundred days

g. Wagner Act
h. demagogues
i. Social Security Act
j. political left
k. Congress of Industrial Organizations
l. Federal Securities Act

1. period in 1933 during which FDR pushed many programs through Congress

2. legislation designed to protect union workers' rights

3. government-funded projects to build public facilities

4. political group that often seeks radical governmental change

5. name of FDR's program to spur economic recovery and provide relief in the 1930s

6. labor organization that welcomed all workers regardless of sex, color, or skill

7. legislation that provided for old-age pensions for workers, unemployment insurance, and other welfare programs

8. the total amount of borrowed money the federal government has yet to pay back

9. group of people who want to preserve a current system or power structure

10. work stoppage in which workers refuse to leave the premises

Write the letter of the correct answer.

11. How did the FDR administration react to a second Bonus March on Washington in 1933?

   A) provided campsites for the war veterans

   B) sent in the National Guard to break up the riot

   C) ignored the situation

   D) handed out money to the veterans

Test Bank Questions

Write the letter of the correct answer.

12. Which New Deal agency was created to help business?

    A) National Recovery Administration

    B) Civilian Conservation Corps

    C) Tennessee Valley Authority

    D) Federal Reserve Board

13. Why did the Supreme Court declare the National Recovery Administration unconstitutional?

    A) It weakened the power of the judicial branch.

    B) It called for unfair taxation.

    C) It gave the President law-making powers.

    D) It enabled the federal government to manipulate the economy.

14. Who was Mary McLeod Bethune?

    A) director of the Division of Negro Affairs who vied for New Deal funds to help African Americans

    B) member of Roosevelt's brain trust

    C) founder of the National Urban League during FDR's administration

    D) first woman appointed Secretary of Labor of FDR

15. What issue did the New Deal programs fail to address?

    A) Native Americans' need for schools, hospitals, and irrigation systems

    B) lynchings and discriminatory practices

    C) crop production and farm prices

    D) the unhealthy banking system

16. Which group was most likely to vote against FDR in the election of 1936?

    A) skilled and unskilled workers   B) recent immigrants

    C) northern African Americans   D) business leaders

17. Why did the political left criticize the New Deal?

    A) It promoted a regimented, militaristic society.

    B) It did not do enough to redistribute the nation's wealth.

    C) Many programs smacked of "Bolshevism."

    D) It unfairly taxed successful, hardworking people.

Test Bank Questions

Write the letter of the correct answer.

18. Why are Huey Long and Father Charles E. Coughlin referred to as demagogues?

    A) They resorted to bribery in order to pass FDR's programs.

    B) They planned, but did not receive credit for, most New Deal programs.

    C) They manipulated people with half-truths and scare tactics.

    D) They called for state ownership of factories and farms.

19. Which of the following greatly harmed FDR's popularity?

    A) government funding of the arts   B) his court-packing reform

    C) the social security system   D) the Wagner Act

20. What was perhaps the most important legacy of the New Deal?

    A) the end of the Great Depression

    B) the expansion of the President's power

    C) guaranteed health insurance for all citizens

    D) improved relations between business and labor

Use the cartoon of President Roosevelt to answer the following questions.

21. What was the significance of the Supreme Court building outside FDR's door?

Test Bank Questions

Use the cartoon of President Roosevelt to answer the following questions.

22. How did the Supreme Court justices view FDR's leadership?

23. How can you tell that many Supreme Court justices were resentful and angry over FDR's court-packing reform?

Answer the following questions.

24. What incorrect assumptions did President Franklin D. Roosevelt make about the Great Depression, the NRA, and the Wagner Act?

25. Why do you think some New Deal critics feared the programs might lead to socialism?

Complete each sentence below by selecting the correct word from the list. You will not use all the words.

a. Wagner Act
b. hundred days
c. New Deal
d. political left
e. sit-down strikes

f. national debt

g. political right
h. public works programs
i. Social Security Act
j. demagogues
k. Congress of Industrial Organizations
l. Fair Labor Standards Act

26. In the 1930s, many workers participated in _____ and refused to leave the premises.

Test Bank Questions

Complete each sentence below by selecting the correct word from the list. You will not use all the words.

a. Wagner Act
b. hundred days
c. New Deal
d. political left
e. sit-down strikes
f. national debt
g. political right
h. public works programs
i. Social Security Act
j. demagogues
k. Congress of Industrial Organizations
l. Fair Labor Standards Act

27. The _____ generally seeks governmental change to better the lives of common people.

28. The _____ welcomed all workers regardless of sex, color, or skill.

29. FDR's broad program to spur economic recovery and provide relief for Americans was called the _____.

30. Those who belong to the _____ usually want to preserve the current system or power structure.

31. Funded through contributions from employers and workers, the _____ established many social welfare programs.

32. FDR pushed many programs through Congress during a period known as the _____.

33. In the 1930s, the government sponsored _____ to build public facilities.

34. The _____ was designed to protect union workers' rights by legalizing such practices as collective bargaining and closed shops.

35. The _____ is the total amount of borrowed money that the federal government has yet to repay.

Write the letter of the correct ending.

36. First Lady Eleanor Roosevelt defied tradition by
    A) refusing most public appearances.
    B) actively and aggressively promoting the New Deal.
    C) rallying opposition to many of her husband's programs.
    D) serving as one of her husband's cabinet members.

37. Of the following federal relief programs of the 1930s, the one declared unconstitutional by the Supreme Court was the
    A) Civilian Conservation Corps.
    B) Tennessee Valley Authority.
    C) National Recovery Administration.
    D) Civil Works Administration.

Test Bank Questions

Write the letter of the correct ending.

38. Those who opposed the Securities and Exchange Commission and many other New Deal programs were most likely to be
    A) business leaders.   B) recent immigrants.
    C) farmers.   D) union members.

39. Frances Perkins is most noted for
    A) becoming the first woman appointed to a President's cabinet.
    B) founding the National Council of Negro Women.
    C) pushing through a New Deal provision to protect domestic workers.
    D) fighting employment discrimination against women.

40. In the 1930s, federal relief programs in the South
    A) greatly improved the standard of living for African Americans.
    B) helped to wipe out unemployment among African Americans.
    C) helped end discriminatory practices.
    D) reinforced racial segregation.

41. Socialists and progressives attacked FDR's New Deal the most for
    A) penalizing successful, hardworking people.
    B) creating a regimented society.
    C) limiting individual freedom.
    D) not doing enough to redistribute the nation's wealth.

42. The most immediate effect of the Wagner Act was
    A) increased prosperity for most Americans.
    B) a decline in working conditions for most Americans.
    C) a barrage of union strikes, often resulting in violence.
    D) industrial peace between employees and employers.

43. FDR's popularity experienced the greatest decline when he
    A) failed to balance the budget.
    B) earmarked Works Progress Administration funds for the arts.
    C) proposed his court-packing reform.
    D) refused to use the militia against the General Motors strike.

44. All of the following were legacies of the New Deal EXCEPT
    A) a rising national debt.
    B) government support for the arts.
    C) state-controlled farms.
    D) the increased power of labor unions.

Test Bank Questions

Write the letter of the correct ending.

45. Over the years, social security has been reformed to
    A) end discrimination against women.
    B) end discrimination against wealthy citizens.
    C) provide benefits for working children.
    D) include Native Americans.

Use the cartoon of President Roosevelt to answer the following questions.

46. How can you tell that the valentines in the cartoon were sent to FDR by the Supreme Court?

47. How did the Supreme Court justices appear to feel about Roosevelt?

48. Select two valentines and explain how they relate to FDR's court-packing reform.

Answer the following questions.

49. Many New Deal programs were biased against African Americans, yet FDR had the support of a large portion of African American voters. How can you explain this apparent inconsistency?

50. Based on what you have learned about the New Deal, why do you think the program was unable to end the Great Depression?

Test Bank Answer Key

[1]   f

[2]   g

[3]   c

[4]   j

[5]   d

[6]   k

[7]   i

[8]   e

[9]   a

[10]   b

[11]   A

[12]   A

[13]   C

[14]   A

[15]   B

[16]   D

[17]   B

[18]   C

[19]   B

[20]   B

[21]   The cartoonist is hinting that the Supreme Court was behind the nine valentines.

[22]   They thought he was acting unjustly and had assumed too much power.

[23]   Many valentines such as "Faithful Unto Death!" and "Youth Must Be Served" show resentment and anger toward FDR's claim that he wanted to appoint younger justices to ease the burden on those over 70 years of age.

Test Bank Answer Key

[24] The President assumed incorrectly that a massive increase in government spending would end the Great Depression. FDR also assumed incorrectly that the NRA would ultimately stop the decline in industrial prices and that the Wagner Act would bring peace to industrial relations between employers and workers.

[25] The government was assuming more control over the economy and becoming more responsible for citizens' welfare. These critics viewed such programs such as the TVA and unemployment insurance as very socialistic. Other programs, such as the Social Security Act and tax increases on wealthy citizens, seemed to penalize hardworking people and undermine capitalism.

[26] e

[27] d

[28] k

[29] c

[30] g

[31] i

[32] b

[33] h

[34] a

[35] f

[36] B

[37] C

[38] A

[39] A

[40] D

[41] D

[42] C

[43] C

[44] C

[45] A

Test Bank Answer Key

[46] There are nine valentines, one for every justice, and the Supreme Court building appears in the background.

[47] resentful, angry

[48] "Faithful Unto Death!" "Youth Must Be Served" and "Your Idea of a Chief Justice" relate to FDR's claim that he wanted to appoint younger justices to lighten the burden of those over 70; several others hint that FDR wanted to control the Court so that he could have unchecked powers.

[49] Many New Deal programs discriminated against African Americans when they were carried out, not when FDR planned them (although the government might still be criticized for failing to act against discrimination). Furthermore, most African Americans who supported FDR lived in the North, where they reaped more New Deal benefits than did those in the South. In addition, FDR was admired by African American voters for appointing more than a hundred African Americans to policy-making posts.

[50] Some programs (such as the NRA) failed to help business, and instead resulted in overproduction and underconsumption. Other programs could not do enough; for example, the Fair Labor and Standards Act covered fewer than one quarter of all gainfully employed workers. Still other programs were not carried out correctly or did nothing to end discriminatory practices (e.g., southern landlords pocketed AAA subsidies and took land out of production). Another factor might have been the Social Security Act, which actually reduced consumer income. Finally, some Americans who earned more money might have felt too insecure to spend it.

World War II (1939-1945)

Test Bank Questions

Match the terms below with the following descriptions. Write the letter of the correct answer. You will not use all the terms.

a. Douglas MacArthur   f. Harry Truman
b. Adolf Hitler   g. Winston Churchill
c. Josef Stalin   h. Benito Mussolini
d. Chester Nimitz   i. Dwight D. Eisenhower
e. Albert Einstein   j. J. Robert Oppenheimer

1. leader of the Fascist party who became dictator of Italy

2. U.S. General who returned to liberate the Philippines

3. leader of the Soviet Union during World War II

4. physicist who developed the theory of relativity and convinced Roosevelt to look into developing an atomic bomb

5. British Prime Minister during World War II

6. President who authorized the deployment of the atomic bomb during World War II

7. leader of the Nazi party in Germany

8. U.S. General who commanded Allied forces in North Africa and later in northern France

Write the letter of the correct answer.

9. What did Italy, Germany, and Japan have in common in the 1930s?

    A) They angered other nations for their persecution of Jews.

    B) They overturned traditional governments and established democracies.

    C) They were economic giants and together controlled world trade.

    D) They were fascist nations seeking world power.

10. What was the United States' position during the early years of World War II?

    A) remained neutral but loaned war supplies to Great Britain

    B) followed a foreign policy of appeasement

    C) terminated all trade agreements with warring nations

    D) denounced Britain and France for declaring war against Germany

Test Bank Questions

Write the letter of the correct answer.

11. What finally prompted the United States to enter the war in 1941?

A) Germany's invasion of the Rhineland

B) the Japanese attack on Pearl Harbor

C) the non-aggression pact between the Soviet Union and Germany

D) the imprisonment of Jews in German concentration camps

12. Which of the following was NOT a war goal described in the Atlantic Charter?

A) self-determination for all nations

B) equal trading rights for all

C) a system of general security to keep the peace

D) restrictions on the deployment of atomic weapons

13. After the United States entered the war, which nation did the Allies concentrate on defeating first?

A) Germany   B) Manchuria

C) Japan   D) the Soviet Union

14. Which Allied military strategy led to the liberation of France?

A) "island-hopping" through the Pacific

B) Operation Torch

C) the Battle of the Bulge

D) the invasion of Normandy

15. What term is used to describe the extermination of 6 million Jews in Nazi Germany?

A) Mein Kampf   B) the Manhattan Project

C) the holocaust   D) the German blitzkrieg

16. During World War II, which group in the United States was barred from engaging in combat?

A) Native Americans   B) women

C) Mexican Americans   D) African Americans

17. In what way did the U.S. military discriminate against African American soldiers?

A) African Americans were not allowed to fight overseas.

B) The army was segregated.

C) Only well-educated African Americans could join the air force.

D) The Red Cross did not accept blood donations from African Americans.

Test Bank Questions

Write the letter of the correct answer.

18. How did the typical soldier view life on the front line?
    A) as a great adventure
    B) as a romantic struggle
    C) as an ongoing struggle just to stay alive
    D) as an escape from the boredom of everyday life

19. Why was the Interim Committee created?
    A) to create a secret code for transmitting Allied messages by radio
    B) to discuss peace terms
    C) to debate alternatives to dropping the bomb
    D) to draw up plans for destroying German submarines

20. What finally brought an end to World War II?
    A) a massive Soviet invasion of the Japanese islands
    B) the unconditional surrender of Germany
    C) the dropping of atomic bombs on Hiroshima and Nagasaki
    D) U.S. naval blockade of Japan

21. How did the development of nuclear technology affect international relations?
    A) Nations stopped fighting "limited wars."
    B) Nuclear technology had little impact on international relations.
    C) The United States and the Soviet Union began competing in the arms race.
    D) Fear of nuclear weapons forced improved relations.

Test Bank Questions

Use the map of Europe During WWII to answer the following questions.

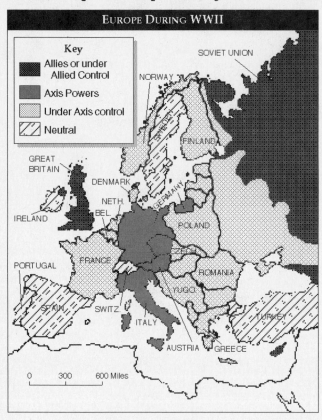

22. Which countries remained neutral during World War II?

23. How did Britain's geographic location help that nation to avoid a German invasion?

24. Why might it have been a mistake for Germany to have broken its non-aggression pact with the Soviet Union?

Answer the following questions.

25. What factors motivated Italian, German, and Japanese leaders to pursue aggressive foreign policies during the 1930s?

26. Compare the responses of the United States, France, and Great Britain to early acts of Axis aggression. What role might geography have played in the response of each nation?

27. Do you think the Allies could have won World War II without the aid of the United States? Explain.

Test Bank Questions

Complete each sentence below by selecting the correct word from the list. You will not use all the words.

a. anti-Semitism
b. GI
c. appeasement
d. holocaust
e. Interim Committee
f. fascism
g. Lend-Lease Act
h. blitzkrieg
i. WAC
j. Nazi party
k. Battle of the Bulge
l. Manhattan Project

28. The term _____ refers to a political philosophy that values the nation or race more than the individual.

29. The term _____ refers to a series of sudden and massive attacks by land and air forces.

30. Hatred of or discrimination against Jews is known as _____.

31. During World War II, an American soldier was called a _____.

32. The Nazis murdered 6 million Jews during the _____.

33. In the 1930s, England and France tried to prevent war by following a policy of _____.

34. During World War II, the _____ was organized to debate the deployment of the atomic bomb.

35. The _____ enabled the United States to provide war supplies to Great Britain.

Write the letter of the correct ending.

36. During the 1930s, Hitler, Mussolini, and the military leaders of Japan

   A) bolstered national pride by calling for free elections.

   B) had a monopoly on world trade.

   C) organized the League of Nations.

   D) began invading neighboring lands.

37. During the early years of World War II, the United States

   A) sent military and economic aid to all nations at war.

   B) organized several peace talks between the Allies and the Axis Powers.

   C) tried to remain neutral while becoming the "arsenal of democracy."

   D) stopped trading with all nations at war.

38. As part of their strategy to win the war, Roosevelt and Churchill decided to concentrate first on defeating

   A) Adolf Hitler.

   B) Erwin Rommel, the "desert fox."

   C) Emperor Hirohito.

   D) Josef Stalin.

Test Bank Questions

Write the letter of the correct ending.

39. The Japanese attack on Pearl Harbor was significant because it
    A) marked the final Japanese victory of the war.
    B) prompted the United States to enter the war.
    C) led to the liberation of the Philippines.
    D) displayed the strength of the United States naval fleet.

40. Allied troops were able to drive the Germans out of France as a result of the
    A) Battle of the Bulge.
    B) destruction of German submarines in the Atlantic.
    C) signing of the Atlantic charter.
    D) amphibious invasion of Normandy.

41. The Allied strategy against the Japanese was best described as
    A) the Manhattan Project.   B) blitzkrieg.
    C) Operation Overlord.   D) island-hopping.

42. A significant consequence of the battles of Midway and Guadalcanal was the
    A) shifting of the balance of power in the Pacific to the Allies.
    B) destruction of the American fleet in the Atlantic.
    C) surrender of Germany and Italy.
    D) breaking of the Japanese military code.

43. During World War II, women were prohibited from
    A) joining the air force.   B) volunteering in the navy.
    C) engaging in combat.   D) serving in the military.

44. Most African Americans, Native Americans, and Mexican Americans served in the
    A) navy.   B) air force.
    C) army.   D) marines.

45. For most soldiers, life on the battle front was a
    A) struggle between good and evil.
    B) welcome change from the boredom of everyday life.
    C) desperate struggle for survival.
    D) great adventure.

Test Bank Questions

Write the letter of the correct ending.

46. President Truman decided to use the atomic bomb against Japan because he thought

A) American patriotism was waning.

B) the bomb would save hundreds of thousands of American lives.

C) the Soviet Union lacked the resources to continue fighting.

D) American naval forces were too weak to invade Japan.

47. As a result of the United States atomic bombing of Hiroshima and Nagasaki,

A) the Soviet Union allied with Japan.

B) Allied powers divided Japan into peace-keeping zones.

C) the Japanese surrendered.

D) the United Nations was created to end global war.

48. All of the following were effects of nuclear technology EXCEPT:

A) radioactive dust from nuclear testing contaminating food and water.

B) stopping development of conventional weapons.

C) increasing tension between the United States and the Soviet Union.

D) building nuclear power plants to produce electricity.

Chapter 24

Test Bank Questions

Use the map of Europe During WWII to answer the following questions.

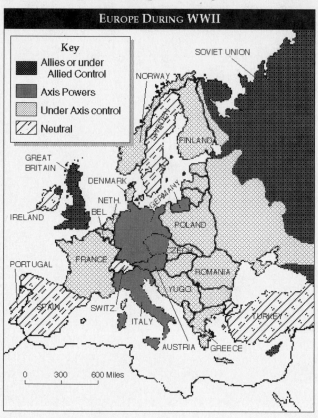

49. By 1942, what parts of Europe were under Axis control?

50. Why do you think Great Britain was able to remain free of Axis control?

51. What role did Spain, Sweden, and Turkey play in World War II?

Answer the following questions.

52. What similar strategies did fascist leaders in Germany, Italy, and Japan use to transform their nations into strong world powers?

53. What were some alternatives to using the atomic bomb against Japan? Explain whether or not you think dropping the atomic bomb was the best strategy.

54. How might the events of World War II have been different if Germany had honored its non-aggression pact with the Soviet Union?

© Prentice-Hall, Inc.

Test Bank Answer Key

[1] h _____

[2] a _____

[3] c _____

[4] e _____

[5] g _____

[6] f _____

[7] b _____

[8] i _____

[9] D _____

[10] A _____

[11] B _____

[12] D _____

[13] A _____

[14] D _____

[15] C _____

[16] B _____

[17] B _____

[18] C _____

[19] C _____

[20] C _____

[21] C _____

[22] Turkey, Sweden, Ireland, Spain, and Portugal

[23] Britain was separated from the mainland by the North Sea, so a ground invasion of Britain was impossible.

[24] By breaking the non-aggression pact, Germany had to fight along both the eastern and western fronts.

Test Bank Answer Key

[25] Many Germans and Italians resented the terms of the Treaty of Versailles and felt humiliated by the outcome of World War I. Japanese military leaders resented their dependence on other nations for resources such as petroleum and iron. In addition, all three nations suffered from weak economies and viewed aggression as a means of becoming a strong world power.

[26] Although France and Great Britain tried to avoid war by following a policy of appeasement, their proximity to Germany made them vulnerable to attack, and they soon declared war against Germany. The geographic location of the United States, however, protected the nation against invasion and made it easier for Americans to pursue a policy of isolationism.

[27] The Allies would probably not have won the war without the help of the American armed forces. When the United States entered the war, Britain was the last Allied nation to remain unconquered. The combined military genius and strength of British and American forces made possible the liberation of Europe. On the Pacific front, U.S. Marines and naval forces regained control of strategic islands, and the dropping of the atomic bomb forced the surrender of Japan.

[28] f

[29] h

[30] a

[31] b

[32] d

[33] c

[34] e

[35] g

[36] D

[37] C

[38] A

[39] B

[40] D

[41] D

[42] A

Test Bank Answer Key

[43] C

[44] C

[45] C

[46] B

[47] C

[48] B

[49] Except for Great Britain, Ireland, and Sweden, Europe from France east to the Soviet Union was under Axis control.

[50] The North Sea protected Great Britain from a ground invasion.

[51] They were neutral countries, siding neither with the Axis nor the Allies.

[52] Fascist leaders in Germany, Italy, and Japan ruled as dictators and transformed their nations into strong world powers by strengthening the military and by invading, occupying, or annexing neighboring lands. All used aggression to bolster national pride and improve their economies.

[53] The United States could have softened its insistence on "unconditional surrender," used a naval blockade against Japan, continued its island-hopping strategy and bombing of Japan, or demonstrated to Japanese diplomats the awesome power of the bomb. Pro: The atomic bomb was probably the best alternative at the time because it may have saved as many as one million American lives. In retrospect, given the devastating effects of the bombing, this alternative should have been considered only after all other options failed to bring about the surrender of Japan. Con: Dropping the bomb on Japanese cities was not the best strategy because it resulted in the deaths of innocent civilians. Instead, the United States should have demonstrated to the Japanese the awesome power of such a weapon by dropping an atomic bomb on an isolated region.

[54] If Germany had honored its non-aggression pact with the Soviet Union, the Soviet Union might not have joined the war on the side of the Allies, and Germany would not have been weakened by fighting along its eastern front. A stronger Germany would have prolonged the war.

World War II at Home (1941-1945)

Test Bank Questions

Match the terms below with the following descriptions. Write the letter of the correct answer. You will not use all the terms.

a. internment camps
b. braceros
c. March on Washington
d. "Double V" campaign
e. wildcat strikes
f. cost-plus system
g. rationing
h. Congress of Racial Equality (CORE)

1.   laborers brought from Mexico to work temporarily on American farms

2.   centers built to house Japanese Americans evacuated from their homes on the West Coast

3.   program created as an incentive for businesses to convert to wartime production

4.   work stoppages not endorsed by the unions

5.   effort launched to win both the war overseas against the Axis and the war at home against racial injustice

6.   distribution of goods in fixed amounts by using coupons

Write the letter of the correct answer.

7.   Why did President Franklin Roosevelt create the Office of War Mobilization?

    A) to encourage business executives to work in wartime government agencies

    B) to coordinate the production of war materials

    C) to create new markets for American-made consumer goods

    D) to create job opportunities for women

8.   Why did Henry Ford build the Willow Run bomber plant?

    A) to produce automobiles and bombers in the same plant

    B) to avoid the high cost of converting existing plants to wartime production

    C) to fight unemployment and end the Great Depression

    D) to build aircraft using assembly-line techniques

Test Bank Questions

Write the letter of the correct answer.

9. What was one consequence of the union strikes in the coal fields?
    A) passage of the Smith-Conally Act limiting future strike activity
    B) decrease in union membership
    C) agreement between labor and management to refrain from strikes and lockouts
    D) formation of the United Mine Workers

10. Which of the following best reflects people's wartime optimism?
    A) a "baby boom"
    B) 1941 March on Washington
    C) popularity of paperback books
    D) heavy attendance at movies and baseball games

11. Which of the following is an example of deficit spending?
    A) launching bond drives to borrow money to finance the war
    B) freezing prices to head off inflation
    C) raising taxes to finance government programs
    D) collecting tax revenues early to pay for war costs

12. How did major league baseball clubs fill their ranks during the war?
    A) visited high schools and colleges to recruit players
    B) recruited players from other countries
    C) placed want ads in newspapers
    D) used players from the All-American Girls Softball League

13. What prevented Americans from spending the high wages they earned in wartime jobs?
    A) desire to build up savings after the hardships of the Depression
    B) inflated prices of consumer goods
    C) fear of going into debt
    D) shortages of consumer items

14. Why did the Office of Price Administration create a rationing program?
    A) to revitalize international trade
    B) to head off inflation
    C) to help finance the war
    D) to encourage patriotism and inspire optimism

Test Bank Questions

Write the letter of the correct answer.

15. Why did the government launch campaigns asking Americans to save items such as rubber hoses, razor blades, and shoes?

    A) all of these reasons

    B) to use these items to produce war materials

    C) to foster a sense of home front participation in the war effort

    D) to conserve resources

16. Which of the following best describes women who went to work during wartime?

    A) white and middle class

    B) young and unmarried

    C) of all ages, ethnic, and economic groups

    D) primarily African American

17. How did most employers view women who joined the work force during wartime?

    A) with resentment because women refused to perform certain chores

    B) with anger because working women ignored household and child care responsibilities

    C) with fear because women often filed job discrimination lawsuits

    D) with pleasure because they believed women could do certain jobs more effectively than men

18. How did most women view their employment?

    A) with hostility because of job discrimination

    B) with delight because they were able to earn their own money

    C) with guilt because they took jobs away from men with families

    D) with fear because working conditions were intimidating

19. Which statement best describes the effect of the war on racial conditions in the U.S.?

    A) brought about an end of the Jim Crow system

    B) improved conditions for Mexican Americans and Navajos only

    C) improved racial conditions in northern and western cities

    D) highlighted the injustice of racism in the country

20. For what reason did Japanese Americans suffer the worst discrimination?

    A) refusal of Japanese immigrants to become American citizens

    B) festering anti-Japanese prejudice reinforced by the bombing of Pearl Harbor

    C) all of these answers

    D) terrorist attacks by Japanese living on the West Coast

Test Bank Questions

Write the letter of the correct answer.

21. How did most Japanese Americans respond to the policy of internment?
    A) challenged the policy in court
    B) refused to report to centers
    C) demanded reparation payments
    D) abided by the policy

Use the poster of Housewives to answer the following questions.

22. What is the purpose of the poster?

23. Why is the message in the poster targeted to housewives only?

24. What symbol does the artist use to represent "kitchen fats?"

25. Why does the artist include a battle scene in the poster?

Answer the following questions.

26. Secretary of War Henry L. Stimson stated that "if you are going to try to go to war, or to prepare for war in a capitalist country, you have to let business make money out of the process or business won't work." Was Stimson's assumption correct? Explain.

27. What were the short- and long-term effects of World War II on social conditions in the United States?

28. Was the image of Rosie the Riveter a false or accurate representation of working women during World War II? Why? If you had been asked to create a poster to attract women into the work force, what image(s) would you have used?

Test Bank Questions

Identify each term or key person below.

29. internment camps

30. braceros

31. A. Philip Randolph

32. John L. Lewis

33. wildcat strikes

34. rationing

35. Rosie the Riveter

36. cost-plus system

Write the letter of the correct ending.

37. When the Depression finally ended, most businesses
    A) started producing consumer items again.
    B) agreed to refrain from lockouts.
    C) converted immediately to wartime production.
    D) raised their prices.

38. Henry Ford contributed to wartime production by
    A) creating new markets overseas.
    B) introducing mass production to the shipbuilding industry.
    C) organizing the Office of Production Management.
    D) applying the assembly line to aircraft production.

39. During the war, union membership increased primarily as a result of
    A) the decline in average weekly wages.
    B) passage of the Smith-Conally Act.
    C) increasing numbers of people entering the work force.
    D) worker resentment over soaring industry profits.

40. Financing the war with borrowed money is an example of
    A) the gross national product.   B) wartime conversion.
    C) the cost-plus system.   D) deficit spending.

41. On the home front, the mood was generally one of
    A) pessimism and fear.   B) weariness and low-spirits.
    C) resentment and hostility.   D) cooperation and optimism.

42. Americans spent the high wages they earned in wartime jobs in all of
    the following ways EXCEPT by
    A) buying paperback books.
    B) investing in war bonds.
    C) going to baseball games and movies.
    D) buying new cars.

Chapter 25

Test Bank Questions

Write the letter of the correct ending.

43. To head off inflation, the government
    A) hired "dollar-a-year men."
    B) withheld taxes from monthly paychecks.
    C) created a rationing program.
    D) revitalized international trade.

44. The government asked Americans to collect items such as bathing caps, razor blades, and scrap metal in order to
    A) create job opportunities.
    B) distribute these materials more equally without rationing.
    C) foster a sense of home front participation in the war effort.
    D) send these items to servicemen overseas.

45. Before World War II, most women who worked were
    A) young and unmarried.
    B) white and middle class.
    C) of all ages, economic, and ethnic groups.
    D) African American.

46. Many employers were pleased to have women working for them because they believed women would
    A) perform certain jobs more effectively than men.
    B) complain less than male workers.
    C) refuse to join unions.
    D) be content with low-paying domestic service jobs.

47. During wartime, women in the work force were paid
    A) higher wages than men to cover child care costs.
    B) high wages only in defense plants.
    C) significantly less than men doing the same job.
    D) the same wages as men doing the same jobs.

48. On the home front during the war years,
    A) African Americans began taking direct action to promote racial equality.
    B) racial discrimination disappeared in employment practices.
    C) the Jim Crow system was banned by executive order.
    D) racial conditions improved in urban areas.

Test Bank Questions

Write the letter of the correct ending.

49. After the war ended, many working women returned to being full-time homemakers because they were

    A) offered only part-time jobs.

    B) worried about leaving their children.

    C) unskilled and unprepared for peacetime jobs.

    D) pressured to give up their jobs to returning soldiers.

50. As a result of their experiences during the war, thousands of Native Americans

    A) incited race riots.

    B) assimilated into the larger society.

    C) used sit-ins to end discrimination.

    D) returned to their reservations.

51. Anti-Japanese sentiment intensified in the United States as a result of

    A) Japanese demands for reparation payments.

    B) the refusal of Japanese immigrants to become American citizens.

    C) terrorist attacks by Japanese living on the West Coast.

    D) the Japanese attack on Pearl Harbor.

Use the poster of the man in overalls to answer the following questions.

52. What is the main idea of the poster?

53. In what way are overalls like a military uniform?

Test Bank Questions

Use the poster of the man in overalls to answer the following questions.

"Those overalls are your UNIFORM, bud."

54. What assumption do you think the artist has made about farmers in creating this poster?

Answer the following questions.

55. Why do you think most Japanese Americans neither protested nor challenged their relocation to internment camps?

56. What were the short- and long-term effects of World War II on economic conditions in the United States?

57. Were America's goals overseas consistent or inconsistent with its goals on the home front? Give reasons to support your answer.

Test Bank Answer Key

[1] b _____

[2] a _____

[3] f _____

[4] e _____

[5] d _____

[6] g _____

[7] B _____

[8] D _____

[9] A _____

[10] A _____

[11] A _____

[12] C _____

[13] D _____

[14] B _____

[15] A _____

[16] C _____

[17] D _____

[18] B _____

[19] D _____

[20] B _____

[21] D _____

[22] to encourage housewives to save and recycle kitchen fats

[23] The artist assumes that only housewives cook.

[24] a frying pan

[25] The battle scene is the symbol for the "explosives" that the kitchen fats will be used to produce.

[26] Stimson's assumption was correct. When the Depression ended, most businesses were reluctant to convert to wartime production and preferred instead to produce more profitable consumer goods. After the government instituted the cost-plus system, enabling businesses to profit from wartime production, many industries promptly converted.

[27] In the short term, the war created greater employment opportunities for women as well as for minorities. In the long term, however, many of these workers lost their jobs to returning servicemen. The war highlighted the racial injustices in American society, such as race riots and job discrimination. It also gave rise to civil disobedience strategies and anti-discrimination orders that would lead to long-term positive social changes.

[28] The image was accurate in depicting a woman as working in a defense-related job while her husband or boyfriend was in the military. The image was misleading in depicting the female worker as young and white; in reality, women of all ages, ethnic, and economic groups worked in the defense industry. One might have selected images that emphasized the diversity of the female work force and of the jobs they performed.

[29] centers housing Japanese Americans forced to evacuate their homes on the West Coast

[30] laborers brought in from Mexico to work on American farms during wartime

[31] head of the Brotherhood of Sleeping Car Porters who proposed a massive march on Washington to demand an end to racial discrimination.

[32] head of United Mine Workers who called strikes in the coal fields

[33] work stoppages organized by workers without union authorization

[34] distributing goods in a fixed amount using coupons

[35] fictional young woman who represented the "typical" American woman working in a defense job

[36] incentive program in which government paid businesses development and production costs plus a certain percentage as profit for all wartime materials produced

[37] A

[38] D

[39] C

[40] D

Test Bank Answer Key

[41] D

[42] D

[43] C

[44] C

[45] A

[46] A

[47] C

[48] A

[49] D

[50] B

[51] D

[52] Farmers, like soldiers, have an important role to play in the war effort.

[53] Both a military uniform and farm overalls symbolize one's patriotic duty during wartime.

[54] The artist assumes that many farmers are young men who would prefer to be fighting overseas in battle.

[55] Because Japanese Americans comprised a tiny minority, were loyal citizens, and aware of anti-Japanese sentiment, many chose not to challenge their relocation orders.

[56] In the short-term, the war ended the Depression and created job opportunities for women and other groups. In the long-term, deficit spending introduced to finance the war created a huge national debt.

[57] American goals overseas and on the home front were inconsistent. The American military fought against the injustices and racial policies of the Axis powers overseas while American politics ignored the continuing injustices of racism at home. African Americans, Mexican Americans, and Native Americans continued to experience discrimination in employment, housing, and in public places.

The Cold War and American Society (1945-1960)

Test Bank Questions

Complete each of the following sentences by selecting the appropriate term from the choices listed in parentheses.

1. After World War II, (NATO, NSC-68) recommended that the United States quadruple its defense budget to withstand the threat of communism.

2. At the end of World War II, the (17th parallel, 38th parallel) became the boundary between communist North Korea and democratic South Korea.

3. The term (cold war, containment) was used to describe the American foreign policy of stopping the spread of communism.

4. The (Truman Doctrine, Marshall Plan) pledged American aid to Greece and Turkey.

5. In 1959, revolutionary leader (Ho Chi Minh, Fidel Castro) overthrew the Cuban dictatorship.

6. Secretary of State (George C. Marshall, Joseph R. McCarthy) drafted a plan to aid European nations after World War II.

7. The (HUAC, Federal Employee Loyalty Program) imprisoned ten Hollywood personalities for sympathizing with the Communist party.

8. The execution of (Alger Hiss, Julius and Ethel Rosenberg) in 1953 intensified anticommunist sentiment in the United States.

9. France had long controlled (Indochina, satellite nations), nations in Southeast Asia that had fallen to the Japanese during World War II.

Write the letter of the correct answer.

10. Which of the following showed that the United States did not completely trust the Soviet Union during World War II?

    A) the formation of a democratic Polish government

    B) the North Africa campaign

    C) the delayed opening of a western front in Europe

    D) the secret development of the atomic bomb

11. After World War II, which of the following worsened U.S.-Soviet relations and led eventually to the cold war?

    A) the clash over Poland

    B) the discovery of Russian spies in New Mexico

    C) Soviet sympathy for Nazi Germany

    D) the United Nations charter

Test Bank Questions

Write the letter of the correct answer.

12. What greatly limited the effectiveness of the United Nations in the early postwar years?

    A) limited communist representation

    B) lack of a charter

    C) the veto power of Security Council members

    D) disputes among members of the General Assembly

13. How did the Soviet Union respond when France, Britain, and the United States merged their zones and formed West Germany?

    A) It blockaded all ground and water routes to West Berlin.

    B) It made East Germany a satellite nation.

    C) It formed a military alliance with Mao Tse-tung.

    D) It put up an iron curtain to divide East Germany from West Germany.

14. Which of the following events encouraged the drafting of NSC-68?

    A) Soviet soldiers crushed an uprising in Hungary.

    B) Civil war broke out in China.

    C) The Soviet Union developed nuclear weapons.

    D) The Soviet Union opposed the Truman Doctrine.

15. What was the outcome of the Korean War?

    A) Korea was unified under a communist government.

    B) North Korea surrendered after the threat of atomic warfare.

    C) China controlled North Korea while South Korea remained independent.

    D) Korea remained divided almost exactly the same as before the war.

16. Why did the United States first become involved in the conflict in Vietnam?

    A) to help the North Vietnamese fight communism

    B) to help France withstand the Vietnamese battle for independence

    C) to counter Soviet aid to North Vietnam with aid to South Vietnam

    D) to unify North and South Vietnam

17. After World War II, why did the United States become involved in foreign affairs in the Middle East?

    A) to end dictatorships in oil-rich Arab nations

    B) to create a homeland for European Jews

    C) to prevent the Soviet Union from gaining a foothold in Arab nations

    D) to help end religious tensions in the Middle East

Test Bank Questions

Write the letter of the correct answer.

18. Which of the following was NOT a result of the anticommunist crusade in the United States after World War II?

A) Truman created the Federal Employee Loyalty Program.

B) The Democratic party gained more followers in the late 1940s.

C) Alger Hiss was accused of espionage.

D) Many Hollywood personalities were blacklisted.

19. What impact did Joseph R. McCarthy have on American society?

A) He encouraged Americans to stand up for their civil rights.

B) He created opposition to U.S. involvement in Latin American affairs.

C) He strengthened the U.S. Army.

D) He encourged a widespread fear of communism.

Test Bank Questions

Use the map of Postwar Military Alliances to answer the following questions.

POSTWAR MILITARY ALLIANCES IN EUROPE, 1955

Key
NATO countries
Warsaw Pact countries

20. What was the Warsaw Pact?

21. What four Western European nations were not members of NATO in 1955?

22. What was the military status of Germany after World War II?

Answer the following questions.

23. Explain how U.S. foreign policy was consistent in Southeast Asia, Latin America, and the Middle East in the late 1940s and early 1950s. Use examples to support your answer.

24. What assumptions did many Americans make in the early 1950s about communist sympathizers, based on the way suspects were treated in the United States?

25. How do you think the Soviet Union viewed the formation of NATO and the Marshall Plan? Give reasons to support your answer.

Test Bank Questions

Complete each sentence below by selecting the correct word from the list. You will not use all the words.

a. NATO   h. containment
b. Marshall Plan   i. Truman Doctrine
c. 38th parallel   j. HUAC
d. iron curtain   k. cold war
e. domino theory   l. NSC-68
f. 17th parallel   m. satellite nation
g. Berlin airlift

26. The _____ was the imaginary line that divided the capitalist West from the communist East.

27. A _____ in Eastern Europe was controlled politically and economically by the Soviet Union.

28. The _____ provided vital supplies to a region blockaded by the Soviet Union.

29. The term _____ refers to the indirect conflict between the United States and the Soviet Union that began at the end of World War II.

30. After World War II, American leaders developed a policy of _____ to resist and stop Soviet aggression.

31. According to the _____, if one country in Indochina fell to communism, others would soon follow.

32. In the late 1940s, the _____ investigated the motion picture industry for left-wing activities.

33. The _____ divided Vietnam into communist North Vietnam and anticommunist South Vietnam.

34. The _____ pledged American financial aid to all European nations following World War II.

Write the letter of the correct ending.

35. All of the following increased tensions between the United States and the Soviet Union EXCEPT the

A) formation of the United Nations.

B) creation by Stalin of a totalitarian state.

C) delayed opening of a western front in Europe.

D) exclusion of the Soviet Union from the Manhattan Project.

36. Shortly after World War II, the first major disagreement between the United States and the Soviet Union involved

A) the Polish government.

B) establishing worldwide markets.

C) the role of Britain in postwar problems.

D) the division of Palestine into an Arab and a Jewish state.

Test Bank Questions

Write the letter of the correct ending.

37. In the early postwar years, the United Nations was largely
    ineffective because
    A) the UN charter was too limited.
    B) Security Council members exercised their veto power.
    C) the Soviet Union refused to sit on the Security Council.
    D) the General Assembly had too little power.

38. The Truman Doctrine and the Marshall Plan were examples of
    A) Kennan's containment policy.
    B) Eisenhower's domino theory.
    C) the arms race.
    D) communist ideology.

39. NSC-68 recommended that the United States
    A) quadruple its defense budget.
    B) support freedom fighters in East Germany and Hungary.
    C) recognize the communist government of China.
    D) pursue treaties with the Soviet Union for arms reductions.

40. During the Korean War, the United States succeeded in
    A) keeping South Korea free from communism.
    B) ending communism in Southeast Asia.
    C) pushing Chinese troops out of North Korea.
    D) unifying Korea under a democratic government.

41. In the early years of the war in Vietnam, the United States
    A) boycotted both North and South Vietnam.
    B) invaded North Vietnam.
    C) sent aid to France.
    D) sent aid to Ho Chi Minh.

42. After World War II, the United States became involved in the affairs
    of Latin American nations in order to
    A) prevent Fidel Castro from overthrowing the Cuban dictatorship.
    B) protect U.S. financial investments in Latin America.
    C) prevent Cuba from developing ties with the Soviet Union.
    D) protect U.S. interests in the large oil reserves of those
       nations.

Test Bank Questions

Write the letter of the correct ending.

43. Both Truman's Federal Employee Loyalty Program and Joseph McCarthy's hearings

    A) defended Americans' civil liberties.

    B) questioned the American economic system.

    C) fought against discrimination in government.

    D) worked to prevent communism from infiltrating American society.

44. Like Julius and Ethel Rosenberg, Alger Hiss was accused of

    A) falsely accusing government officials.

    B) blacklisting communist Americans.

    C) racism and anti-Semitism.

    D) espionage.

Use the map of Postwar Military Alliances to answer the following questions.

45. What was the political status of Germany after World War II?

Chapter 26

Test Bank Questions

Use the map of Postwar Military Alliances to answer the following questions.

POSTWAR MILITARY ALLIANCES IN EUROPE, 1955

46. By 1955, into what two military camps was Europe divided?

47. Name four European countries that belonged to neither camp.

Answer the following questions.

48. How did the fear of communism after World War II result in violations of civil liberties in the United States?

49. How were the Truman Doctrine and the Marshall Plan relevant to American foreign policy during the cold war?

50. Explain why the political and economic ideologies of the Soviet Union and the United States caused division after World War II.

Test Bank Answer Key

[1] NSC-68

[2] 38th parallel

[3] containment

[4] Truman Doctrine

[5] Fidel Castro

[6] George C. Marshall

[7] HUAC

[8] Julius and Ethel Rosenberg

[9] Indochina

[10] D

[11] A

[12] C

[13] A

[14] C

[15] D

[16] B

[17] C

[18] B

[19] D

[20] a military alliance of the Soviet Union and Eastern European nations

[21] Spain, Switzerland, Ireland, Austria, Sweden, Finland

[22] West Germany was a member of NATO, and East Germany belonged to the Warsaw Pact.

[23] The United States pursued its policy of containment in all three regions. In Southeast Asia, the United States fought to prevent the unification of Korea under the communist government of North Korea; in Latin America, the United States helped overthrow communist activity in Guatemala; and in the Middle East, the United States forced Soviet troops to pull back from the Iranian border.

Test Bank Answer Key

[24] Many Americans assumed that communist sympathizers were traitors to the American way of life and were either plotting a communist takeover or selling secrets to the Russians. Individuals suspected of communist involvement were assumed to be guilty as charged and considered dangerous and untrustworthy.

[25] The Soviet Union viewed the Marshall Plan and NATO as vehicles for American intervention into European affairs. The Soviet Union feared that the United States would benefit greatly from the economic and military recovery of Western Europe and that a strong Europe would be a threat to its satellite nations in Eastern Europe.

[26] d

[27] m

[28] g

[29] k

[30] h

[31] e

[32] j

[33] f

[34] b

[35] A

[36] A

[37] B

[38] A

[39] A

[40] A

[41] C

[42] B

[43] D

[44] D

[45] Germany had been divided into democratic West Germany and communist East Germany.

Test Bank Answer Key

[46] Most Western European nations were members of NATO, a mutual defense alliance, while the Soviet Union and its Eastern European satellite nations were members of the Warsaw Pact.

[47] Yugoslavia, Spain, Austria, Switzerland, Sweden, Finland, Ireland

[48] Fear of communism led to the creation of the Federal Employee Loyalty Program and HUAC, both of which tarnished the names of many innocent people through their investigations. HUAC investigations also encouraged blacklisting, which destroyed many people's careers. In addition, anticommunist crusaders such as McCarthy encouraged the suppression of both freedom of speech and honest debate.

[49] Both the Truman Doctrine and the Marshall Plan provided financial aid for the economic recovery of European nations, in the hope that communist movements in those nations would lose momentum once their economies improved. U.S. foreign policy aimed to bolster struggling nations so that they would not be vulnerable to communist infiltration or financial assistance from the Soviet Union.

[50] The Soviet Union's communist ideology held that the workers of the world would one day unite and create a state in which men and women worked together for the common good and shared all resources. By contrast, the United States was a democratic, capitalist nation that valued representative government and private enterprise. After the war, both the Soviet Union and the United States sought to promote their incompatible ideologies, which caused great division in world politics.

The Postwar Years at Home (1945-1960)

Test Bank Questions

Complete each sentence below by selecting the correct word from the list. You will not use all the words.

a. agribusiness
b. franchise
c. termination policy
d. per capita income
e. modern republicanism

f. baby boom
g. real purchasing power
h. diversified conglomerate
i. Fair Deal

1. A giant corporation became a _____ by investing in a wide range of businesses that produced different kinds of goods and services.

2. President Eisenhower called his conservative approach to government _____.

3. From 1945 to 1960, the average income per person, or _____, nearly doubled.

4. The consolidation of small farms into large income-producing units was known as _____.

5. The Eisenhower administration adopted a _____ to eliminate Native American reservations.

6. A _____ gives a group or individual the right to market a company's goods or services.

7. During the postwar years, an increase in _____ enabled Americans to acquire more consumer goods.

Write the letter of the correct ending.

8. All of the following spurred economic growth in the 1950s EXCEPT
   A) the computer industry.   B) a decrease in government spending.
   C) consumer credit.   D) major corporate expansion.

9. One effect of business expansion after World War II was
   A) the weakening of labor unions.
   B) a shift in the work force from blue-collar to white-collar jobs.
   C) lower wages for most workers.
   D) a major decline in working conditions for most Americans.

Test Bank Questions

Write the letter of the correct ending.

10. William J. Levitt promoted suburban growth in the 1950s by
    A) developing commercial nuclear power plants.
    B) using mass-production techniques in home-building.
    C) encouraging agribusiness.
    D) opening franchises along major highways.

11. Unlike Betty Friedan, pediatrician Benjamin Spock and politician Adlai Stevenson believed that women should
    A) be well-informed about political and economic affairs.
    B) stay home with their children.
    C) explore creative roles.
    D) contribute to the family income.

12. The beatniks of the 1950s promoted
    A) family values.
    B) equal rights for African Americans.
    C) spontaneity and individuality.
    D) traditional social patterns.

13. One of President Truman's greatest challenges in reconverting to a peacetime economy was
    A) encouraging mass production of consumer goods.
    B) keeping inflation in check.
    C) appeasing women who lost their jobs to returning soldiers.
    D) securing passage of the Taft-Hartley Act.

14. Unlike Truman, President Eisenhower favored programs that
    A) increased the power of the federal government.
    B) called for liberal spending.
    C) aided big business.
    D) secured economic justice for all citizens.

15. The 1957 launching of Sputnik
    A) plunged the United States into a series of three recessions.
    B) greatly increased Eisenhower's popularity.
    C) proved the superiority of American technology.
    D) made many Americans feel insecure.

Test Bank Questions

Write the letter of the correct ending.

16. Jackie Robinson, Thurgood Marshall, and Martin Luther King, Jr., were alike in that they

 A) were the first African Americans to play professional sports.

 B) fought the government's termination policy.

 C) stood up against racial segregation.

 D) helped ignite a religious revival in the 1950s.

17. In 1954 the Supreme Court ruled in <u>Brown v. Board of Education</u> that

 A) the government must provide loans to low-income college students.

 B) segregation was no longer permissible in public schools.

 C) the government must provide grants for science and foreign-language facilities.

 D) bus segregation was unconstitutional.

18. President Eisenhower placed the Arkansas National Guard under federal command in order to

 A) end segregation in the armed forces.

 B) protect Mexican American rights.

 C) integrate Central High School.

 D) end the bus boycott.

Use the table of Work to answer the following questions.

	WORK STOPPAGES	WORKERS INVOLVED (IN THOUSANDS)	PERCENT OF TOTAL WORKERS EMPLOYED
1945	4,750	3,470	8.2
1946	4,985	4,600	10.5
1947	3,693	2,170	4.7
1948	3,419	1,960	4.2
1949	3,606	3,030	6.7
1950	4,843	2,410	5.1
1951	4,737	2,220	4.5
1952	5,117	3,540	7.3
1953	5,091	2,400	4.7
1954	3,468	1,530	3.1
1955	4,320	2,650	5.2
1956	3,825	1,900	3.6

19. Based on the data in the chart, why did Congress pass the Taft-Hartley Act in 1947?

Test Bank Questions

Use the table of Work to answer the following questions.

	WORK STOPPAGES	WORKERS INVOLVED (IN THOUSANDS)	PERCENT OF TOTAL WORKERS EMPLOYED
1945	4,750	3,470	8.2
1946	4,985	4,600	10.5
1947	3,693	2,170	4.7
1948	3,419	1,960	4.2
1949	3,606	3,030	6.7
1950	4,843	2,410	5.1
1951	4,737	2,220	4.5
1952	5,117	3,540	7.3
1953	5,091	2,400	4.7
1954	3,468	1,530	3.1
1955	4,320	2,650	5.2
1956	3,825	1,900	3.6

20. Explain whether you think the Taft-Hartley Act was successful or unsuccessful in curbing labor strikes.

21. How would you describe the labor situation in the United States in 1952?

Answer the following questions.

22. What effect did developments in technology have on the American way of life in the 1950s?

23. How was the government's termination policy consistent with the American trend toward conformity in the 1950s?

24. In what way was President Eisenhower's approach in government in keeping with the ideology of his Republican predecessors? How did this approach differ from the Republican ideology of the 1920s?

Match the terms below with the following descriptions. Write the letter of the correct answer. You will not use all the terms.

a. Richard M. Nixon
b. Adlai Stevenson
c. William J. Levitt
d. Jackie Robinson
e. Betty Friedan
f. Benjamin Spock
g. Thurgood Marshall
h. J.D. Salinger
i. Martin Luther King, Jr.
j. Ray Kroc

25. Eisenhower's vice presidential running-mate in the 1952 election

26. developer who mass-produced new communities in the suburbs

27. first African American to play major league baseball

28. spokesperson for the Montgomery bus boycott

Test Bank Questions

Match the terms below with the following descriptions. Write the letter of the correct answer. You will not use all the terms.

a. Richard M. Nixon
b. Adlai Stevenson
c. William J. Levitt
d. Jackie Robinson
e. Betty Friedan
f. Benjamin Spock
g. Thurgood Marshall
h. J.D. Salinger
i. Martin Luther King, Jr.
j. Ray Kroc

29. Democratic candidate for president in 1952 and 1956

30. African American lawyer who fought segregation in America's schools

31. author of <u>The Feminine Mystique</u>

Write the letter of the correct answer.

32. How did per capita income and real purchasing power change in the 1950s?
    A) Both per capita income and real purchasing power plummeted.
    B) Both per capita income and real purchasing power increased dramatically.
    C) Per capita income kept pace with inflation while real purchasing power decreased.
    D) Per capita income decreased while real purchasing power increased.

33. What effect did diversified conglomerates and the franchise system have on the American economy in the 1950s?
    A) They promoted diversity and individualism within the business world.
    B) They eliminated thousands of service-oriented, white-collar jobs.
    C) They created countless new jobs across the country.
    D) They inadvertantly slowed industrial growth.

34. Which of the following was NOT a factor in suburban growth during the postwar period?
    A) the social movement of the beatniks
    B) mass-production of affordable homes
    C) the GI bill
    D) the baby boom

35. What role were most American women expected to fulfill in the 1950s?
    A) second income earners
    B) leaders of social causes
    C) full-time mothers
    D) political participants

Test Bank Questions

Write the letter of the correct answer.

36. Which of the following best describes the beatniks of the 1950s?
    A) They worked to revive organized religion.
    B) They rebelled against conformity and traditional social patterns.
    C) They valued American middle-class culture above diverse cultural heritage.
    D) They fought against racial injustices.

37. Why did Congress pass the Taft-Hartley Act in 1947?
    A) to increase employment compensation
    B) to restrict labor strikes that threatened national interest
    C) to protect union officials against undue invasion of privacy
    D) to raise the minimum wage

38. Why did President Truman expect to lose the election of 1948?
    A) He had received illegal gifts.
    B) He had required union leaders to take loyalty oaths.
    C) He had been unable to check postwar inflation.
    D) He was not supported by the right and left wings of the Democratic party.

39. What was the aim of President Eisenhower's modern republicanism?
    A) to promote social welfare programs
    B) to increase government spending to promote economic growth
    C) to encourage corporate expansion without dismantling New Deal programs
    D) to increase presidential power

40. What impact did Sputnik have on most Americans?

    A) It increased confidence in American education.
    B) It made them question America's technological supremacy.
    C) It reinforced America's faith in capitalism.
    D) It promoted national pride.

41. What was the significance of the Supreme Court ruling in Brown v. Board of Education?

    A) It declared that the African American protest movement was unconstitutional.
    B) It ended segregation in America's public schools.
    C) It stated that all public institutions must provide separate but equal facilities for African Americans.
    D) It forced the federal government to provide educational grants to lower-income families.

Test Bank Questions

Write the letter of the correct answer.

42. What did the Eisenhower administration's termination policy seek to eliminate?

    A) the nation's fear of communism

    B) segregation in Little Rock, Arkansas

    C) poverty in the United States

    D) Native American reservations

Use the table of Work to answer the following questions.

	WORK STOPPAGES	WORKERS INVOLVED (IN THOUSANDS)	PERCENT OF TOTAL WORKERS EMPLOYED
1945	4,750	3,470	8.2
1946	4,985	4,600	10.5
1947	3,693	2,170	4.7
1948	3,419	1,960	4.2
1949	3,606	3,030	6.7
1950	4,843	2,410	5.1
1951	4,737	2,220	4.5
1952	5,117	3,540	7.3
1953	5,091	2,400	4.7
1954	3,468	1,530	3.1
1955	4,320	2,650	5.2
1956	3,825	1,900	3.6

43. What data might Senator Taft have used to convince other members of Congress to support the Taft-Hartley Act in 1947?

44. Use the information in the table to agree or disagree with the following statement: Workers were more content during Eisenhower's first term (1953–1956) than during the Truman years (1945–1952).

45. How do the work stoppages in 1952 and 1953 compare to the work stoppages in 1946? Why were the stoppages in 1946 more harmful to the economy?

Answer the following questions.

46. How did technological advances during the post–World War II years affect the work force?

47. Compare Truman's and Eisenhower's concepts of the responsibilities of the federal government.

48. Support the following statement from your text about American life in the 1950s: "Conformity seemed the order of the day."

Test Bank Answer Key

[1] h

[2] e

[3] d

[4] a

[5] c

[6] b

[7] g

[8] B

[9] B

[10] B

[11] B

[12] C

[13] B

[14] C

[15] D

[16] C

[17] B

[18] C

[19] In 1946, a record number of workers--4.6 million--went on strike, more than 10 percent of the total work force.

[20] The act appears to have been successful; the work stoppages in the early 1950s involved fewer workers and a lower percentage of the total work force than did the 1946 strikes.

[21] There was a dramatic increase in the number of work stoppages and the percentage of workers on strike, the highest since passage of the Taft-Hartley Act.

[22] Technological advances created more white-collar jobs and introduced computers into the workplace and television into the home. Innovations such as affordable mass-produced housing, an interstate highway system, and affordable automobiles encouraged Americans to settle in the suburbs.

Test Bank Answer Key

Following years of war and depression, middle-class Americans embraced conformity in an effort to preserve their new-found comfort and security. The media promoted the middle-class lifestyle and encouraged many ethnic groups to abandon their cultural heritages in favor of American culture. This widespread conformity was consistent with the termination policy to eliminate reservations and assimilate [23] Native Americans into the mainstream American society.

Modern republicanism was consistent with traditional Republican ideology in that it favored decreasing the power of the federal government and limiting government interference in big business. Unlike his Republican predecessors, however, Eisenhower accepted the New Deal principle of government responsibility for the social [24] welfare of its citizens.

[25] a

[26] c

[27] d

[28] i

[29] b

[30] g

[31] e

[32] B

[33] C

[34] A

[35] C

[36] B

[37] B

[38] D

[39] C

[40] B

[41] B

[42] D

Test Bank Answer Key

[43] Taft might have stressed that, in 1946, the percentage of workers involved in strikes reached a record level, posing a threat to national security.

[44] Agree. During Eisenhower's first term, no more than 2,650 workers, or 5.2 percent of all workers, were on strike in any given year. This percentage was exceeded four times during Truman's presidency.

[45] Although there were more work stoppages in 1952 and 1953 than in 1946, more workers were involved in the 1946 stoppages, encompassing a greater percentage of the labor force, and posing a threat to the health of a postwar economy.

[46] New developments in technology eliminated many blue-collar jobs and created new white-collar jobs. For the first time, more Americans were employed in service jobs rather than in manufacturing jobs. In addition, technological advances transformed farming into a profitable big business, forcing many small farmers to seek jobs in urban areas.

[47] Truman wanted to expand the social welfare programs of the New Deal by adopting a national health insurance program and other legislation to promote economic justice. By contrast, Eisenhower accepted the New Deal programs, but did not work to expand them. Eisenhower focused on aiding big business and reducing government spending.

[48] In the 1950s, there was widespread acceptance of the American dream--a house in the suburbs, one or two cars, an office job, and a family in which the husband worked and the wife kept house. Americans of different ethnic backgrounds appeared to have abandoned their cultural heritages to pursue the middle-class ideals of comfort and security.

The Kennedy and Johnson Years (1960-1968)

Test Bank Questions

Use each term below in a sentence which shows the meaning of the term.

1. Warren Commission

2. Great Society

3. Immigration Act of 1965

4. Limited Test Ban Treaty

Write the letter of the correct ending.

5. When President Kennedy took office, the liberal consensus was that
   A) the elimination of poverty should be the nation's most important goal.
   B) capitalism was a failing economic system.
   C) domestic problems were destroying the fabric of American society.
   D) communism posed the greatest threat to the United States.

6. An important factor in Kennedy's 1960 election was his
   A) public image, particularly as seen on television.
   B) extensive experience as a legislative leader in Congress.
   C) promise to ensure the survival of liberty.
   D) pledge to end the cold war with the Soviet Union.

7. President Kennedy's New Frontier program was most successful in
   A) restoring economic prosperity.
   B) increasing funding for space programs.
   C) improving public education.
   D) eliminating poverty.

8. Most of Kennedy's proposals were defeated in Congress because he
   A) made too many enemies in Congress.
   B) misunderstood the needs of low-income families.
   C) lacked a popular mandate to push his proposals through.
   D) was accused of catering to business interests.

9. Unlike Kennedy, President Johnson
   A) opposed civil rights and spending cuts.
   B) was a strong legislative leader.
   C) believed military commanders should use nuclear bombs.
   D) was more concerned with foreign than domestic policy.

Test Bank Questions

Write the letter of the correct ending.

10. Each of the following was a major part of Johnson's Great Society EXCEPT

A) health care legislation.

B) a tax-cut.

C) land conservation.

D) aid to education.

11. In general, the actions of the Supreme Court under Chief Justice Earl Warren

A) supported the Great Society.

B) ignored the Great Society.

C) contradicted the Great Society.

D) rendered the Great Society ineffective.

12. Critics complained that the Great Society

A) spent too many tax dollars on poverty programs.

B) gave local communities too much power.

C) helped only the middle class.

D) gave the federal government insufficient authority.

13. President Kennedy promoted the Peace Corps as a program to

A) prevent procommunist revolutions in Latin America.

B) help people in developing nations.

C) help immigrants become United States citizens.

D) rebuild poor neighborhoods in the nation's cities.

14. Kennedy's reputation and the prestige of the United States both suffered as a result of the

A) Alliance for Progress.

B) Cuban missile crisis.

C) Bay of Pigs invasion.

D) Limited Test Ban Treaty.

15. After Kennedy authorized a military buildup to show that the United States would not be intimidated, the Soviets

A) tried to invade West Germany.

B) forced UN troops from East Germany.

C) began construction of the Berlin Wall.

D) enacted a blockade of West Berlin.

16. As a result of the Cuban missile crisis,

A) the United States increased investments in Cuba.

B) Fidel Castro was removed from power.

C) the Soviets removed their missiles from Cuba.

D) the United States increased investments in Cuba.

Test Bank Questions

Use the table of Social Welfare to answer the following questions.

SOCIAL WELFARE EXPENDITURES IN THE UNITED STATES, 1950–1975					
	Expenditures per capita (in constant 1984 dollars)			Expenditures as percentage of GNP		
Fiscal Year	All social welfare programs	Social insurance	Public welfare	All social welfare programs	Social insurance	Public welfare
1950	630	133	75	8.2	1.7	1.0
1960	984	346	94	10.3	3.8	1.0
1965	1189	432	119	11.2	4.1	1.1
1970	1773	660	229	14.7	5.5	1.9
1975	2424	1026	389	19.0	8.1	2.9

Note: Social insurance includes all social security programs, including Medicare, public employee retirement, and unemployment insurance. Public welfare includes cash public assistance, Medicaid, food stamps, and public housing. Health and education expenditures are included in "All social welfare programs."

Source: Ann Kallman Bixby, "Public Welfare Expenditures, Fiscal Year 1984," Social Security Bulletin 50, no. 6 (June 1987).

17. In 1975, which type of social welfare program was the most costly?

18. President Johnson launched the "War on Poverty" in 1964. In its first decade, how did the program affect expenditures per capita for all social welfare programs?

19. How can you tell from the table that the Great Society programs affected many different groups of people?

Answer the following questions.

20. In what way was President Johnson's Great Society a continuation of Kennedy's New Frontier?

21. How was President Kennedy's foreign policy consistent with the United States' cold war pledge to contain communism?

22. Based on events during Kennedy's presidency, what predictions can you make about U.S.-Soviet relations in the late 1960s?

Use each term below in a sentence which shows the meaning of the term.

23. Volunteers in Service to America (VISTA)

24. Medicare

Test Bank Questions

Use each term below in a sentence which shows the meaning of the term.

25. Peace Corps

26. Berlin Wall

Write the letter of the correct answer.

27. When Kennedy first became President, what was the liberal consensus view within the government of the United States?

A) Racial injustice was weakening the nation.

B) Public education needed to be reformed.

C) Communism posed the greatest threat to the United States.

D) Capitalism was creating widespread poverty.

28. Which of the following was NOT a goal of the New Frontier program?

A) to empower big business

B) to provide aid to the poor

C) to cut taxes

D) to promote the space program

29. Which of the following best describes Kennedy's domestic program?

A) The few measures that Congress passed did not relieve major problems.

B) He launched a remarkable reform program that altered American society.

C) He had won a popular mandate to win passage of radical new programs.

D) Congress supported nearly all of his programs, but most were failures.

30. What did the Warren Commission decide about the Kennedy assassination?

A) Kennedy was killed by a single man who had worked alone.

B) Communist sympathizers had helped plan the assassination.

C) Industrial leaders had plotted the murder.

D) The assassination had been authorized by the CIA.

31. How did the Great Society differ from the New Frontier?

A) Most Great Society programs were passed in Congress.

B) The Great Society was concerned with poverty.

C) The Great Society was largely ineffective.

D) Education was not a part of the Great Society.

Test Bank Questions

Write the letter of the correct answer.

32. What was the effect of the tax-cut bill that Johnson pushed through Congress?

    A) The nation suffered from high inflation.

    B) The federal deficit grew quickly.

    C) The Gross National Product rose steadily.

    D) The unemployment rate increased.

33. What was the intent of the Immigration Act of 1965?

    A) to eliminate quotas that discriminated against immigrants from certain areas

    B) to reduce the total annual number of immigrants to the United States

    C) to increase the number of immigrants from northern and western Europe

    D) to stem the flow of political refugees to the United States

34. Which criticism of the Great Society was most common among middle-class citizens?

    A) The program spent too much tax money on poor people.

    B) The program weakened the federal government.

    C) The program gave local communities too much financial power.

    D) The program fundamentally altered the distribution of wealth.

35. What was the Alliance for Progress?

    A) a program to promote economic development and social reform in Latin America

    B) a program to send missionaries abroad to help developing nations

    C) a federal work program to create jobs for the unemployed

    D) a domestic program to help the poor participate in policy-making decisions

36. Which event helped President Kennedy decide to authorize an invasion of Cuba at the Bay of Pigs?

    A) Fidel Castro interfered with U.S. shipping off the coast of Florida.

    B) Supporters of Fidel Castro threatened to attack opponents in Guatemala.

    C) Fidel Castro seized U.S. property in Cuba.

    D) The United States learned that Cuba was developing atomic weapons.

Test Bank Questions

Write the letter of the correct answer.

37. Which of the following brought the United States and the Soviet Union to the brink of nuclear war?

    A) the Cuban missile crisis

    B) the Panamanian riot

    C) the signing of a Limited Test Ban Treaty

    D) the construction of the Berlin Wall

38. His handling of which of the following improved President Kennedy's prestige?

    A) the Bay of Pigs invasion

    B) the Cuban missile crisis

    C) the Berlin crisis

    D) a rebellion in the Dominican Republic

Use the table of Social Welfare to answer the following questions.

SOCIAL WELFARE EXPENDITURES IN THE UNITED STATES, 1950–1975					
	Expenditures per capita (in constant 1984 dollars)			Expenditures as percentage of GNP		
Fiscal Year	All social welfare programs	Social insurance	Public welfare	All social welfare programs	Social insurance	Public welfare
1950	630	133	75	8.2	1.7	1.0
1960	984	346	94	10.3	3.8	1.0
1965	1189	432	119	11.2	4.1	1.1
1970	1773	660	229	14.7	5.5	1.9
1975	2424	1026	389	19.0	8.1	2.9

Note: Social insurance includes all social security programs, including Medicare, public employee retirement, and unemployment insurance. Public welfare includes cash public assistance, Medicaid, food stamps, and public housing. Health and education expenditures are included in "All social welfare programs."

Source: Ann Kallman Bixby, "Public Welfare Expenditures, Fiscal Year 1984," Social Security Bulletin 50, no. 6 (June 1987).

39. Which type of social welfare program increased most dramatically from 1950 to 1975?

Test Bank Questions

Use the table of Social Welfare to answer the following questions.

SOCIAL WELFARE EXPENDITURES IN THE UNITED STATES, 1950–1975					
	Expenditures per capita (in constant 1984 dollars)			Expenditures as percentage of GNP		
Fiscal Year	All social welfare programs	Social insurance	Public welfare	All social welfare programs	Social insurance	Public welfare
1950	630	133	75	8.2	1.7	1.0
1960	984	346	94	10.3	3.8	1.0
1965	1189	432	119	11.2	4.1	1.1
1970	1773	660	229	14.7	5.5	1.9
1975	2424	1026	389	19.0	8.1	2.9

Note: Social insurance includes all social security programs, including Medicare, public employee retirement, and unemployment insurance. Public welfare includes cash public assistance, Medicaid, food stamps, and public housing. Health and education expenditures are included in "All social welfare programs."

Source: Ann Kallman Bixby, "Public Welfare Expenditures, Fiscal Year 1984," Social Security Bulletin 50, no. 6 (June 1987).

40. What information from the table might some Americans use to support their claim that social welfare programs were a drain on the economy?

41. President Johnson launched the "War on Poverty" in 1964. How did this program affect expenditures on public welfare programs from 1965–1975?

Answer the following questions.

42. In what way was President Johnson's Great Society program consistent with Kennedy's New Frontier?

43. Why was President Johnson more successful than Kennedy in pushing his measures through Congress?

44. What assumptions do you think Kennedy and Johnson made about economic and political instability in other nations, especially those in Latin America?

Test Bank Answer Key

[1] The Warren Commission was formed to investigate the Kennedy assassination.

[2] The Great Society was President Johnson's domestic program that included aid to education, medical care for the elderly, and the War on Poverty programs.

[3] The Immigration Act of 1965 eliminated discrimination quotas against immigrants from all areas outside of northern and western Europe.

[4] The Limited Test Ban Treaty banned nuclear testing above the ground.

[5] D

[6] A

[7] B

[8] C

[9] B

[10] C

[11] A

[12] A

[13] B

[14] C

[15] C

[16] C

[17] social insurance programs

[18] Expenditures for all social welfare programs increased significantly from 1965–1975.

[19] In addition to welfare programs, which benefited the poor, social insurance programs––which had higher expenditures than welfare––included programs such as social security and Medicare which benefited middle- and upper-class people.

[20] The Great Society promoted many of the same programs that Kennedy had pushed in his New Frontier. For example, Johnson pushed Kennedy's tax-cut and civil rights bills through Congress. Johnson also revised Kennedy's bill to aid public education and adopted Kennedy's poverty program as the basis for the Great Society's War on Poverty.

Test Bank Answer Key

[21] Kennedy used both money and military strength to try to contain and weaken communist influence throughout the world. For example, the Alliance for Progress was designed to create allies for the United States and counter procommunist revolutionary movements in Latin America. Other events, such as the Bay of Pigs invasion, the Cuban missile crisis, and the rejection of a treaty to divide Berlin, demonstrated Kennedy's willingness to risk nuclear war to contain communism.

[22] U.S.–Soviet relations will continue to deteriorate in the late 1960s. The Cuban missile crisis and the crisis over Germany showed that neither the United States nor the Soviet Union trusted each other. The crises also demonstrated the U.S. willingness to risk war to protect itself from the communist threat.

[23] VISTA was a domestic version of the Peace Corps; volunteers helped the nation's poor communities.

[24] Medicare was designed to provide health care for the elderly.

[25] The Peace Corps was a program in which volunteers helped developing nations around the world.

[26] The Soviets built the Berlin Wall to keep East Germans from entering West Germany through Berlin.

[27] C

[28] A

[29] A

[30] A

[31] A

[32] C

[33] A

[34] A

[35] A

[36] C

[37] A

[38] B

[39] social insurance programs

Test Bank Answer Key

[40] From 1950 to 1975, expenditures as a percent of the GNP increased more than 10 percent.

[41] Per capita expenditures on public welfare programs targeted at the poor more than tripled.

[42] Johnson incorporated many of Kennedy's New Frontier ideas and programs into his Great Society. For example, Johnson's War on Poverty was the program that Kennedy had begun to consider. Johnson also pushed Kennedy's civil rights, tax-cut, and education bills through Congress.

[43] Johnson had been an effective majority leader in the Senate and was experienced in dealing with recalcitrant senators. Where Kennedy was afraid to make enemies in Congress because he wanted their support on matters of foreign policy, Johnson was more concerned with accomplishments than with maintaining friendships.

[44] Kennedy and Johnson may have assumed that economic and political instability would harm U.S. relations with those countries, even when a rebel movement seemed to be more democratic than the existing government. Kennedy and Johnson also assumed that the Soviet Union was either supporting or instigating communist revolutions worldwide; every instance of instability was viewed as some type of communist plot.

The Civil Rights Movement (1960-1968)

Test Bank Questions

Match the terms below with the following descriptions. Write the letter of the correct answer. You will not use all the terms.

a. sit-in
b. de jure segregation
c. Black Power
d. Freedom Rides

e. March on Washington
f. Nation of Islam

g. Congress of Racial Equality (CORE)

h. Albany Movement
i. de facto segregation
j. Civil Rights Act of 1964
k. Southern Christian Leadership Conference (SCLC)
l. Voting Rights Act of 1965
m. (SNCC) Student Nonviolent Coordinating Committee

1. African American group founded by Elijah Muhammad

2. the idea that African Americans should unite, take pride in their heritage, and control their own organizations

3. actual, as opposed to legal, separation of whites and African Americans

4. legislation that enabled more African Americans to register to vote

5. a year-long campaign of protest marches against racial injustices in Georgia

6. civil rights workers traveling on interstate buses to protest segregation at terminals

7. legislation that banned discrimination in all public facilities

8. protest technique in which African Americans occupied a segregated establishment and demanded service

9. civil rights organization founded in 1942 and dedicated to effecting change through peaceful confrontation

10. civil rights organization founded by African American ministers in 1957

Write the letter of the correct ending.

11. The NAACP appealed primarily to

A) radical, young students.

B) middle- and upper-class African Americans.

C) African American religious groups.

D) white activists.

Write the letter of the correct ending.

12. SNCC was formed to enable students to

A) establish a more interracial organization.

B) use more peaceful tactics than the SCLC used.

C) make their own decisions about priorities and tactics.

D) shift the civil rights movement to the North.

13. Southerners responded to the Freedom Rides with

A) compassion and understanding.   B) peaceful boycotts.

C) disinterest and boredom.   D) violence.

14. The Albany Movement failed largely because

A) activists used violent tactics.

B) the police chief's tactic of nonviolent opposition failed to stir up sympathy for the movement.

C) Martin Luther King, Jr., refused to support the movement.

D) local policymakers ignored the movement.

15. One aim of civil rights activists in the Birmingham campaign was to

A) register African Americans to vote.

B) integrate all-white social clubs.

C) improve African American schools.

D) end discriminatory hiring practices.

16. The statement that best describes President Kennedy's reaction to the civil rights movement is:

A) He boldly supported the movement and alienated most of Congress.

B) He condemned the movemnent and the violence that it aroused.

C) He refused to take sides and ignored civil rights legislation.

D) He slowly lent his support to the cause and introduced civil rights legislation.

17. The Mississippi Freedom Democratic Party was organized to

A) push passage of the Civil Rights Act of 1964.

B) represent African Americans at the 1964 Democratic National Convention.

C) prevent the reelection of President Johnson.

D) protest injustices during the Freedom Rides.

18. After Congress passed the Voting Rights Act of 1965,

A) violence between whites and African Americans was eliminated.

B) white Southerners launched a campaign to prevent African Americans from voting.

C) many African Americans were elected to office at all levels.

D) the civil rights movement fizzled out.

Test Bank Questions

Write the letter of the correct ending.

19. In his essays, James Baldwin warned Americans that
    A) African American voters would change the course of the nation's history.
    B) the Nation of Islam would undermine the Constitution.
    C) desegregation would only lead to greater problems.
    D) continued discrimination against African Americans would result in widespread violence.

20. The Nation of Islam and the Black Power movement both taught that African Americans should
    A) emigrate to Africa.
    B) use peaceful, nonviolent protest as a means of effecting change.
    C) separate themselves from white communities.
    D) strive to integrate themselves with white society.

Use the maps of African American Registration to answer the following questions.

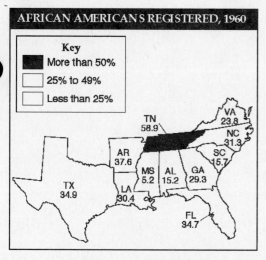

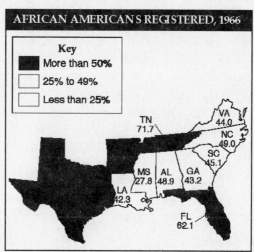

21. Which state experienced the lowest registration turnout of African Americans in the 1960s?

22. In which states would the federal government be LEAST likely to supervise voter registration in 1966?

23. Based on the maps, would you say that the civil rights movement was successful in the 1960s? Explain.

Answer the following questions.

24. Which civil rights leader--Martin Luther King, Jr., or Malcolm X--do you think was more popular among white Americans? Give reasons for your choice.

Test Bank Questions

Answer the following questions.

25. Explain how SNCC both potested and practiced discrimination in the late 1960s.

Complete each sentence below by selecting the correct word from the list. You will not use all the words.

a. Freedom Rides
b. de facto segregation
c. sit-in

d. Black Power
e. March on Washington
f. de jure segregation
g. Civil Rights Act of 1964

h. Nation of Islam
i. Congress of Racial Equality (CORE)
j. Southern Christian Leadership conference (SCLC)
k. Voting Rights Act of 1965
l. Albany Movement
m. (SNCC) Student Nonviolent Coordinating Committee

26. Civil rights activists used the _____ technique to force segregated establishments to serve African Americans.

27. The _____ banned discrimination in all public facilities.

28. Founded in 1942, the _____ used peaceful confrontation to effect social change.

29. In August 1963, more than 200,000 joined the _____ in support of civil rights.

30. In 1957 Martin Luther King, Jr., and other ministers founded the _____.

31. During the _____, civil rights activists used interstate buses to protest segregation at terminals.

32. As a result of the _____ the number of elected African American public officials increased.

33. The _____ gave young African Americans a greater voice in the civil rights movement.

34. The rigid pattern of separation dictated by law in the South was known as _____.

35. Stokely Carmichael called on African Americans to support _____.

Write the letter of the correct answer.

36. How did the National Urban League help African Americans?

    A) by providing them with good medical care
    B) by providing legal support to defend them in court
    C) by helping them to integrate lunch counters
    D) by helping newcomers to large cities find homes and jobs

Test Bank Questions

Write the letter of the correct answer.

37. In what way were the SCLC and CORE alike?
    A) Both relied on militant tactics.
    B) Both promoted nonviolent protest.
    C) Both deferred to church leaders.
    D) Neither was interracial.

38. Which of the following best describes the effects of sit-ins?
    A) They were very ineffective and usually increased discrimination.
    B) They were applauded by most white people throughout the South.
    C) They usually brought an end to segregation in the facilities they targeted.
    D) They were illegal and forced local governments to resort to violence.

39. Where did Freedom Riders encounter the greatest resistance?
    A) in the Midwest   B) in the Southwest
    C) in the Deep South   D) in the Northeast

40. Why was the Birmingham campaign more successful than the Albany Movement?
    A) The Albany Movement was not supported by the SCLC.
    B) The Birmingham campaign garnered more white sympathy.
    C) The Birmingham campaign used more militant tactics.
    D) The Albany Movement was unorganized.

41. How did President Kennedy respond to the riot over James Meredith's admission to the University of Mississippi?
    A) He blamed civil rights activists for the riot.
    B) He sent army troops to restore order and protect Meredith.
    C) He ignored the riot.
    D) He condemned the university but did not interfere with local officials.

42. Which was true of the Civil Rights Act of 1964?
    A) It prohibited discriminatory hiring on the basis of race, sex, religion, or nationality.
    B) It brought an end to de facto segregation.
    C) It marked the end of the civil rights movement.
    D) It made lynching illegal and greatly reduced violence.

Test Bank Questions

Write the letter of the correct answer.

43. What was the significance of the Mississippi Freedom Democratic Party?

   A) It helped pass legislation to ban public housing discrimination.

   B) It nearly cost President Johnson his reelection in 1964.

   C) It alerted President Johnson to the need to protect voting rights for African Americans.

   D) It marked the beginning of compromise between southern whites and African Americans.

44. What message did Malcolm X preach to African Americans?

   A) to fight for greater integration with white society

   B) to abandon violent, militant tactics in favor of civil disobedience

   C) to completely separate themselves from white society

   D) to love and pray for white people

45. Which of the following was NOT a result of the civil rights movement?

   A) The federal government rebuilt the nation's ghettos.

   B) Segregation became illegal.

   C) African Americans were assured the right to vote.

   D) African Americans served in local, state, and federal politics.

Use the maps of African American Registration to answer the following questions.

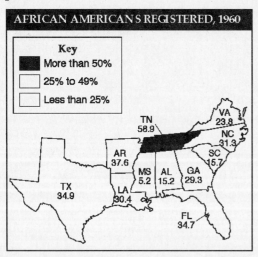

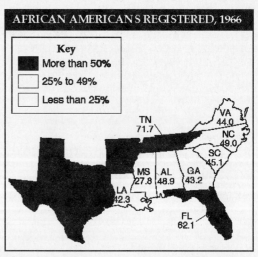

46. In which state did African Americans seem to encounter the least amount of resistance to voter registration in the 1960s?

47. What appears to have been the immediate effect of the Voting Rights Act of 1965?

Test Bank Questions

Use the maps of African American Registration to answer the following questions.

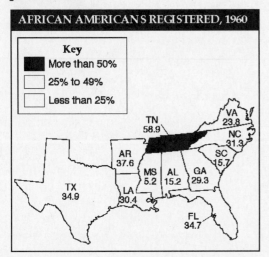

AFRICAN AMERICANS REGISTERED, 1960

Key
More than 50%
25% to 49%
Less than 25%

TN 58.9
VA 23.8
NC 31.3
AR 37.6
SC 15.7
MS 5.2
AL 15.2
GA 29.3
TX 34.9
LA 30.4
FL 34.7

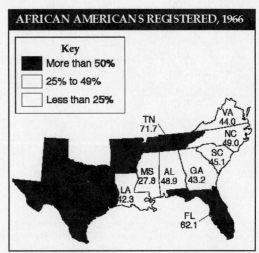

AFRICAN AMERICANS REGISTERED, 1966

Key
More than 50%
25% to 49%
Less than 25%

TN 71.7
VA 44.0
NC 49.0
SC 45.1
MS 27.8
AL 48.9
GA 43.2
LA 42.3
FL 62.1

48. What evidence on the maps supports the argument made by some African Americans that the civil rights movement did not make enough progress in the 1960s?

Answer the following questions.

49. In your opinion, which civil rights tactic--King's nonviolent protest or Stokely Carmichael's militant style--was more effective? Explain.

50. How did the focus of the civil rights movement shift with the founding of new groups such as the SCLC, SNCC, and the Black Panthers?

Test Bank Answer Key

[1]   f

[2]   c

[3]   i

[4]   l

[5]   h

[6]   d

[7]   j

[8]   a

[9]   g

[10] k

[11] B

[12] C

[13] D

[14] B

[15] D

[16] D

[17] B

[18] C

[19] D

[20] C

[21] Mississippi

[22] Texas, Arkansas, Tennessee, Florida

[23] Yes, many more African Americans had registered to vote in 1966 than in 1960. No, in most southern states fewer than 50 percent of eligible African Americans had registered to vote in 1966.

[24] Most white Americans probably preferred King. He preached nonviolence and unity, whereas Malcolm X preached separation from white society and that whites were the enemy. Malcolm X's message encouraged more militant tactics, greater violence, and fear.

Test Bank Answer Key

[25] In the beginning, SNCC was an interracial organization that protested racial discrimination against African Americans. As SNCC became more radical and began to preach separation from white people, it discriminated against its white members. SNCC also maintained its independence from other civil rights groups led by church leaders who were committed to gradual change.

[26] c

[27] g

[28] i

[29] e

[30] j

[31] a

[32] k

[33] m

[34] f

[35] d

[36] D

[37] B

[38] C

[39] C

[40] B

[41] B

[42] A

[43] C

[44] C

[45] A

[46] Tennessee

[47] It greatly increased the number of African Americans registered to vote in southern states in 1966.

Test Bank Answer Key

[48] In 1966, fewer than 50% of eligible African Americans had registered to vote in seven southern states.

[49] King's nonviolent protest appears to have been more effective. He was able to gain white sympathy and political support for important civil rights legislation while Carmichael encouraged riots and further alienated African Americans from white communities. Carmichael's tactic may have been effective in forcing the government to act in order to keep the peace; however, his techniques may also have resulted in greater de facto discrimination.

[50] When the SCLC was founded by African American ministers, the movement used boycotts and other nonviolent tactics to end racial discrimination in the South. The creation of SNCC shifted the focus away from church leaders, giving young African Americans a greater voice and making the movement more militant. The Black Panthers caused division in the movement by promoting separation from whites and increasingly violent tactics. Overall the movement became more militant, angry, and radical.

Continuing Social Revolution (1960-1975)

Test Bank Questions

Explain the goal(s) of each of the following.

1. United Farm Workers (UFW)

2. Equal Rights Amendment (ERA)

3. Japanese American Citizens League (JACL)

4. American Indian Movement

5. Environmental Protection Agency (EPA)

Write the letter of the correct ending.

6. In the 1960s, the growth of the feminist movement was influenced by
    A) the publication of Ladies' Home Journal.

    B) the Roe v. Wade decision.

    C) Betty Friedan's book The Feminine Mystique.

    D) the activities of Phyllis Schlafly.

7. The National Organization for Women (NOW) promoted all of the following in the 1960s and 1970s EXCEPT
    A) the exemption of women from military combat.

    B) the legalization of abortion.

    C) equal job opportunities for women.

    D) an end to gender discrimination.

8. In the 1960s, both Mexican American and Native American activists argued that the federal government
    A) denied them equal opportunities in many aspects of life.

    B) should grant them American citizenship.

    C) should compensate their wartime internment.

    D) had passed unfair immigration laws against their groups.

9. César Chávez became a national hero for his efforts to
    A) establish the Mexican American Legal Defense and Educational Fund.

    B) increase federal funding for public schools in barrios.

    C) improve working conditions for migratory farm workers.

    D) fund community action groups in East Los Angeles.

Test Bank Questions

Write the letter of the correct ending.

10. Hawaiian statehood was important for Asian Americans because it
A) increased their employment opportunities.
B) increased public support for their equal rights movement.
C) increased their political representation.
D) ended racial discrimination toward their group.

11. Dennis Banks and Russell Means were
A) the founders of the Bureau of Indian Affairs.
B) founders of the Brown Berets.
C) leaders of the American Indian Movement (AIM).
D) Native American lawmakers.

12. In the 1960s, most Native American activists wanted
A) more self-determination.
B) to dissolve centuries-old treaties with the federal government.
C) to make reservations a part of mainstream society.
D) protection against the police and other authorities.

13. The 1973 occupation of Wounded Knee by AIM activists was most successful in
A) encouraging industries to relocate there.
B) pressuring the federal government to reexamine treaty rights.
C) improving Native Americans' public image.
D) gaining full citizenship rights for Native Americans.

14. Rachel Carson's <u>Silent Spring</u> focused on the

A) harmful effects of chemical pesticides.
B) problems of nuclear power plants.
C) proper disposal of toxic wastes.
D) health hazards caused by air pollution.

15. In the 1960s, Ralph Nader became well known for
A) setting up the Food and Drug Administration.
B) lobbying for conservation legislation.
C) his campaign to block ratification of the ERA.
D) making car manufacturers more responsible.

Chapter 30

Test Bank Questions

Use the table of Median Earnings to answer the following questions.

MEDIAN EARNINGS OF MEN AND WOMEN IN THE UNITED STATES, 1960–1990				
Year	Women	Men	Women's earnings as a percent of men's	Earnings gap in constant 1990 dollars
1960	$ 3,257	$ 5,368	60.7	$ 8,569
1970	5,323	8,966	59.4	11,529
1980	11,197	18,612	60.2	11,776
1990	19,822	27,678	71.6	7,856

Source: Bureau of the Census

16. How can you tell that women made little progress toward fair pay during the 1970s, despite the fact that their earnings more than doubled?

17. Which decade would equal rights activists label as the "best" decade for women? Explain.

18. Based on the information above, what conclusion can you draw about the earnings of working men and women?

Answer the following questions.

19. In the 1960s, what kind of image of women did NOW activists consider "false"? What kind of image would NOW have considered "accurate"?

20. How did the civil rights movement influence the movements of other minorities and women?

21. What did the Native American, Mexican American, Asian American, and women's movements have in common in the 1960s and 1970s?

Match the terms below with the following descriptions. Write the letter of the correct answer. You will not use all the terms.

a. Gloria Steinem   f. Phyllis Schlafly

b. César Chávez   g. Anglos
c. Dennis Banks   h. Chicanos
d. Rachel Carson   i. Betty Friedan

e. Latinos   j. Henry González

22. conservative political activist who led a national campaign to block ratification of the Equal Rights Amendment (ERA)

23. leader of the Native American activist movement in the late 1960s and early 1970s

24. founder of the United Farm Workers (UFW)

25. journalist who helped found Ms. Magazine for women interested in feminist issues

26. marine biologist who wrote <u>Silent Spring</u>

Test Bank Questions

Match the terms below with the following descriptions. Write the letter of the correct answer. You will not use all the terms.

a. Gloria Steinem   f. Phyllis Schlafly

b. César Chávez   g. Anglos
c. Dennis Banks   h. Chicanos
d. Rachel Carson   i. Betty Friedan

e. Latinos   j. Henry González

27. English-speaking, non-Latinos

28. Spanish-speaking Americans

Write the letter of the correct answer.

29. In what way did the civil rights movement help the women's movement of the 1960s?

    A) It led to the creation of the Equal Employment Opportunity Commission.

    B) It paved the way for ratification of the Equal Rights Amendment.

    C) It taught feminists effective militant tactics.

    D) It taught women the value of political pressure and direct action.

30. Which of the following was NOT a goal of the National Organization for Women (NOW) in the 1960s and 1970s?

    A) right of women to have an abortion

    B) improved wages for women

    C) equal job opportunities for women

    D) exemption of women from military combat

31. Why was ratification of the Equal Rights Amendment (ERA) important to NOW members?

    A) It would prohibit discrimination based on race.

    B) It would guarantee equal opportunities for women.

    C) It would legalize "consciousness-raising" groups.

    D) It would outlaw sexual harassment.

32. What popular tactic did the United Farm Workers (UFW) use in their fight for higher wages and improved working conditions?

    A) They destroyed crops.

    B) They staged standoffs with the federal government.

    C) They established their own "police" force.

    D) They organized consumer boycotts.

Test Bank Questions

Write the letter of the correct answer.

33. Which of the following was a direct result of the publication of Silent Spring?

A) conservation of farmlands.

B) opposition to nuclear power plants.

C) establishment of tree-planting programs.

D) restrictions on the use of chemical pesticides.

34. Which issue was top priority for Japanese American activists after World War II?

A) citizenship rights.

B) integration into mainstream society.

C) compensation for losses during internment.

D) local control of public schools.

35. Which activist used the most militant tactics?

A) Betty Friedan   B) César Chávez

C) Russell Means   D) Phyllis Schafly

36. What effect did Hawaiian statehood have on most Asian Americans?

A) It weakened their equal rights movement.

B) It ended racial discrimination against their group.

C) It increased their self-pride.

D) It weakened their involvement in politics.

37. How did the demands of the Native American activists differ from those of other minority groups?

A) Native Americans wanted to dissolve all treaties with the federal government.

B) Native Americans did not want U.S. citizenship rights.

C) Native Americans did not want government aid.

D) Native Americans wanted autonomy.

38. Which organization was concerned the most with unfair immigration laws?

A) Japanese American Citizens League

B) United Farm Workers

C) Brown Berets

D) American Indian Movement

39. Which of the following issues made Ralph Nader famous in the 1960s as a "one-man lobby for the public"?

A) oil spills   B) air pollution

C) automobile safety   D) toxic waste

Test Bank Questions

Use the table of Median Earnings to answer the following questions.

MEDIAN EARNINGS OF MEN AND WOMEN IN THE UNITED STATES, 1960–1990				
Year	Women	Men	Women's earnings as a percent of men's	Earnings gap in constant 1990 dollars
1960	$ 3,257	$ 5,368	60.7	$ 8,569
1970	5,323	8,966	59.4	11,529
1980	11,197	18,612	60.2	11,776
1990	19,822	27,678	71.6	7,856

Source: Bureau of the Census

40. How did the income of working women compare with that of working men in the 1960s?

41. During which decade did women make the greatest strides toward equality in the labor force? Explain?

42. Based on the information above, explain whether you think the women's movement has been a failure or a success.

Answer the following questions.

43. Which issues were central to the movements of women and minority groups in the 1960s?

44. Why do you think the Mexican American, Native American, Asian American, and women's movements became much stronger after the civil rights movement?

45. Support the following conclusion from your text about Native Americans in the 1960s and 1970s: "Native Americans were perhaps the country's most troubled non-white group."

Test Bank Answer Key

[1] to prevent migratory farm workers from being exploited by growers

[2] to guarantee equality of rights under the law for women

[3] to win passage of the Japanese American Claims Act and work for changes in anti-Asian immigration laws

[4] to improve conditions for Native Americans living in cities and encourage racial and cultural pride in young people

[5] to monitor and reduce pollution of the environment

[6] C

[7] A

[8] A

[9] C

[10] C

[11] C

[12] A

[13] B

[14] A

[15] D

[16] Women still earned about 60 percent as much as men.

[17] the 1980s; Women's earnings increased by more than $8,000 and women's earnings as a percent of men's gained more than 11 percentage points.

[18] Possible answer: Although working women have made significant gains, they continue to earn less than men.

[19] NOW activists considered the popular image of women only as contented married homemakers as "false" because many married women worked outside the home. They would have portrayed women as well educated, qualified and capable, and politically and socially motivated.

[20] The civil rights movement inspired women and minorities to seek equality and taught these groups the best tactics - direct, nonviolent action, political pressure, and strong publicity - for gaining public and political support. The movement also provided women and minorities with important legislation - the Civil Rights Act - to fight discrimination.

[21] Each group fought against longstanding economic, political, and social injustices in the United States. They used similar political techniques and legal weapons to fight racial and/or gender discrimination, gain respect, and achieve equality of opportunity in all aspects of American Life.

[22] f

[23] c

[24] b

[25] a

[26] d

[27] g

[28] e

[29] D

[30] D

[31] B

[32] D

[33] D

[34] C

[35] C

[36] C

[37] D

[38] A

[39] C

[40] During the 1960s, the gap between the earnings of men and women increased significantly from $8,569 to $11,529.

[41] Women made the greatest strides during the 1980s, when their earnings increased by more than $8,000 and the gap between men's and women's earnings decreased by more than 11 percentage points.

[42] The women's movement has been fairly successful. From 1960 to 1990, women's earnings have gained on men's by more than 10 percent, but inequalities in income still exist.

Test Bank Answer Key

[43] All groups sought equality of opportunity in all aspects of American life and hoped to end discrimination by changing public attitudes.

[44] The civil rights movement inspired these groups by making them more aware of inequalities in American life and teaching them valuable techniques for gaining a more equal role in society. The movement showed women and minorities the value of direct, nonviolent action, the usefulness of political pressure, and the importance of strong publicity in gaining the public's sympathy. The movement also provided activists with an important legal weapon--the Civil Rights Act of 1964.

[45] In the 1960s and 1970s, Native Americans had high rates of unemployment, alcoholism, and suicide, as well as a shorter life expectancy than white Americans. In addition, centuries-old stereotypes and government policies put Native Americans at a great disadvantage. While the government and society sought to erase the traditional lifestyles of Native Americans, they also restricted Native Americans' participation in white American culture.

The Vietnam War and American Society (1960-1975)

Test Bank Questions

Match the terms below with the following descriptions. Write the letter of the correct answer. You will not use all the terms.

a. Tet Offensive
b. Kent State University
c. Saigon
d. Vietnamization
e. Hanoi
f. Woodstock
g. Gulf of Tonkin Resolution
h. My Lai massacre

1. ____ site of counterculture Music and Art Fair

2. ____ incident in which more than one hundred Vietnamese were killed

3. ____ major Viet Cong attack on important cities and towns in South Vietnam

4. ____ policy of replacing American forces with South Vietnamese soldiers

5. ____ congressional act giving the President control over U.S. intervention in Vietnam

6. ____ capital city of South Vietnam

Complete each sentence below by selecting the correct word from the list. You will not use all the words.

a. conscientious objectors
b. New Left
c. (SDS) Students for a Democratic Society
d. escalation
e. psychedelic drugs
f. teach-ins
g. counterculture

7. Members of the _____ believed that radical changes were needed to solve major social problems.

8. Like the Beat Generation of the 1950s, the _____ of the 1960s rejected conventional norms.

9. Civil rights activists were among those who organized the _____.

10. Young men who opposed war on moral grounds were _____.

11. College professors held _____ in which they expressed opinions about the Vietnam War.

Write the letter of the correct ending.

12. John Kennedy's policy in Vietnam was to
    A) gain the loyalty of the Viet Cong.
    B) support Ho Chi Minh.
    C) increase the number of military advisers.
    D) send American troops to Vietnam.

Test Bank Questions

Write the letter of the correct ending.

13. Escalation of the war in Vietnam began with the
    A) formation of the Viet Cong.
    B) My Lai massacre.
    C) passage of the Gulf of Tonkin Resolution.
    D) publication of the Pentagon Papers.

14. American soldiers in Vietnam had to cope with
    A) fighting tropical diseases and infections.
    B) working side by side with communists.
    C) lack of sophisticated equipment.
    D) lack of training.

15. In the United States, television was instrumental in
    A) promoting understanding between Americans and Vietnamese.
    B) bringing the brutality of the war into people's living rooms.
    C) revealing the contents of classified military documents.
    D) developing enthusiasm for the war effort.

16. Student protestors in the 1960s favored
    A) more active CIA recruitment on campuses.
    B) more broad-based membership in ROTC.
    C) American withdrawal from Vietnam.
    D) improved living conditions for college students.

17. Americans questioned the fairness of the draft because
    A) young men who were college students could receive deferments.
    B) only men between the ages of eighteen and twenty-six were drafted.
    C) African Americans had to serve in segregated units.
    D) women were exempt from serving.

18. Resistance to the war took all of the following forms EXCEPT
    A) teach-ins and sympathy strikes.
    B) joining communes.
    C) direct confrontation with police.
    D) marches and demonstrations.

19. Young people who led the "sexual revolution" demanded
    A) publication of books on sexual topics.
    B) more freedom to make personal choices.
    C) the legalization of psychedelic drugs.
    D) a spiritual "inner space."

Test Bank Questions

Write the letter of the correct ending.

20. After Woodstock and Altamont, many conservative older Americans
    A) rejected traditional living patterns.
    B) were shocked by the new attitudes toward traditional values.
    C) applauded the experimentation with relationships, drugs, and music.
    D) joined communes.

21. At the same time that President Nixon was implementing his Vietnamization policy, he was also
    A) engaging in peace talks in Cambodia.
    B) sending the National Guard to Kent State University.
    C) evacuating the American embassy in Saigon.
    D) moving troops into Cambodia.

22. When the war finally ended in 1975, the
    A) North Vietnamese controlled Vietnam.
    B) U.S. government built the Vietnam Veterans Memorial.
    C) North Vietnamese had surrendered.
    D) economy was on the upswing.

Use the chart of US Military Personnel to answer the following questions.

U.S. MILITARY PERSONNEL ASSIGNED IN VIETNAM AS OF DECEMBER 31		
Year	Total	Net Change
1964	23,300	+7,000
1965	184,300	+161,000
1966	385,300	+201,000
1967	485,600	+100,300
1968	536,100	+50,500
1969	475,200	-68,200
1970	334,600	-140,600
1971	156,800	-177,800
1972	24,200	-132,600

Source: DOD/OASD

23. In which year was there the greatest number of American troops in Vietnam? How had that number changed from the previous year?

24. How many additional personnel were sent to Vietnam from 1965 to 1966?

25. In which year did the policy of Vietnamization begin? How can you tell?

Answer the following questions.

26. What do you think was the most lasting effect of the counterculture of the 1960s on the country? On members of the baby boomer generation? Support your answer.

Test Bank Questions

Answer the following questions.

27. Compare the Vietnam War with World War II in terms of its impact on those who fought and on those on the home front.

28. What factors do you think underlay the widespread student protest movement of the 1960s? Give reasons for your opinion.

Complete each sentence below by selecting the correct word from the list. You will not use all the words.

a. Saigon
b. Kent State University
c. (SDS) Students for a Democratic Society
d. Viet Cong

e. My Lai massacre
f. Woodstock
g. Tet Offensive

h. Vietnamization

29. Americans were horrified when the National Guard opened fire on protestors at _____.

30. More than 300,000 people gathered to attend the Music and Art Fair at _____.

31. The American embassy, located in the South Vietnam capital of _____, was attacked.

32. The _____ was comprised of communist guerrillas in the south.

33. During the _____, mounted during the Vietnamese new year, many cities and military installments were attacked.

34. The brutality of U.S. soldiers killing civilians during the _____ shocked many Americans at home.

Match the terms below with the following descriptions. Write the letter of the correct answer. You will not use all the terms.

a. hippie
b. sexual revolution
c. New Left
d. teach-ins

e. counterculture
f. conscientious objector
g. escalation

35. stepping up of the war effort

36. sector of society believing in radical change as the only cure for major social ills

37. one who resists going to war on moral grounds

38. one who resists conventional norms

39. proceedings during which professors and others aired opinions about the war

Test Bank Questions

Write the letter of the correct answer.

40. What did the United States fear would happen if it did not get involved in Vietnam?

    A) Communists would take over the country.

    B) China would invade Vietnam.

    C) The French would control the country.

    D) Diem would be assassinated.

41. What was President Kennedy's policy in Vietnam?

    A) to create government-run farming communities for Vietnamese peasants

    B) to commit to free elections in South Vietnam

    C) to support the division of Vietnam into two separate nations

    D) to increase the number of American military advisers in Vietnam.

42. Under what authority did President Johnson escalate the war?

    A) the Gulf of Tonkin Resolution

    B) the Geneva Conference decision

    C) the advice of General Westmoreland

    D) the Pleiku retaliation

43. What lesson did American soldiers learn once they arrived in Vietnam?

    A) that they could solve racial problems in the army

    B) that they had to fight a guerrilla war against a hidden enemy

    C) that they needed more extensive bombing to defeat the enemy

    D) that they could work together with the communists

44. What effect did television have on public opinion in America?

    A) brought home the brutality and violence of the war

    B) depicted how the Americans were helping the Vietnamese

    C) showed how effective U.S. weaponry was

    D) encouraged support for the war

45. What was the primary focus of the protest movement in the 1960s?

    A) to do away with ROTC and CIA recruiting

    B) to demand U.S. withdrawal from Vietnam

    C) to hold a series of teach-ins

    D) to ban the use of Agent Orange

46. Which of the following was a stepping stone to the creation of SDS?

    A) the civil rights movement

    B) the Beat Generation of the 1950s

    C) the sexual revolution

    D) the free speech movement at Berkeley

Test Bank Questions

Write the letter of the correct answer.

47. What was the basic philosophy of the counterculture?

   A) to gather with one's peers at Woodstock

   B) to question traditional norms and values and to experiment with new ones

   C) to be politically active and join in protesting the war

   D) to live in communes and become working-class people

48. On what grounds did some people react negatively to the counterculture?

   A) It mocked the working class.

   B) It was not economically sound.

   C) It promoted violence.

   D) It threatened traditional morals and values.

49. What is one reason President Johnson decided not to run for reelection?

   A) He believed he had lost his power base.

   B) He believed that Hubert Humphrey could defeat Richard Nixon.

   C) He thought highly of the campaign of Eugene McCarthy.

   D) He feared being assaulted by angry crowds of protestors.

50. What was the reason for the protest at Kent State University?

   A) the use of Agent Orange in Vietnam

   B) escalation of the war into Cambodia

   C) ROTC activities on campus

   D) presence of the National Guard

Use the chart of US Military Personnel to answer the following questions.

U.S. MILITARY PERSONNEL ASSIGNED IN VIETNAM AS OF DECEMBER 31		
Year	Total	Net Change
1964	23,300	+7,000
1965	184,300	+161,000
1966	385,300	+201,000
1967	485,600	+100,300
1968	536,100	+50,500
1969	475,200	-68,200
1970	334,600	-140,600
1971	156,800	-177,800
1972	24,200	-132,600

Source: DOD/OASD

51. Why are the years 1969 to 1972 characterized by a negative net change in the number of troops in Vietnam?

52. In which year was there the greatest net change in the number of troops in Vietnam? What is the reason for this change?

Test Bank Questions

Use the chart of US Military Personnel to answer the following questions.

U.S. MILITARY PERSONNEL ASSIGNED IN VIETNAM AS OF DECEMBER 31		
Year	Total	Net Change
1964	23,300	+7,000
1965	184,300	+161,000
1966	385,300	+201,000
1967	485,600	+100,300
1968	536,100	+50,500
1969	475,200	-68,200
1970	334,600	-140,600
1971	156,800	-177,800
1972	24,200	-132,600

Source: DOD/OASD

53. How did the Gulf of Tonkin resolution affect the number of personnel assigned in Vietnam? How can you tell?

Answer the following questions.

54. What do you think were some of the consequences of the free speech movement, teach-ins, and other activities on college campuses? Explain your answer.

55. Compare the counterculture movement of the 1960s with the youth culture of today. Give examples to support your statement.

56. What factors do you think underlay the U.S. involvement in Vietnam? Give reasons for your opinion.

Test Bank Answer Key

[1] f

[2] h

[3] a

[4] d

[5] g

[6] c

[7] b

[8] g

[9] c

[10] a

[11] f

[12] C

[13] C

[14] A

[15] B

[16] C

[17] A

[18] B

[19] B

[20] B

[21] D

[22] A

[23] 1968; increased by 50,500

[24] 201,000

[25] 1969; this is the first year there is a negative net change in the number of troops.

Test Bank Answer Key

[26] The sexual revolution in the counterculture had the most lasting impact because it has led to many changes in the definition of "family," new living patterns, and an open discussion of sexual topics in the media.

[27] Both wars were fought on foreign soil and were costly in terms of human life and economic resources. Support on the home front and the wartime morale that characterized World War II were lacking during the Vietnam War. Veterans of World War II returned home as heroes while returning Vietnam veterans were usually met with moral outrage and found it difficult to integrate back into American society.

[28] Members of the baby boomer generation did not have to spend their energies on finding and holding jobs, so they had time for introspection. They may have been bored by suburban lifestyles, dissatisfied with society's conservative values, or motivated by idealism. A widening generation gap and an anti-establishment attitude fueled by an unpopular war led to student activism on many fronts.

[29] b

[30] f

[31] a

[32] d

[33] g

[34] e

[35] g

[36] c

[37] f

[38] a

[39] d

[40] A

[41] D

[42] A

[43] B

[44] A

[45] B

[46] A

[47] B

[48] D

[49] A

[50] B

[51] Nixon was carrying out his policy of Vietnamization.

[52] 1966; After his reelection, President Johnson began a drastic escalation of the war.

[53] The resolution, passed in 1964, resulted in a significant increase in the number of troops sent to Vietnam as evidenced by the net change of 161,000 from 1964 to 1965.

[54] Students achieved a greater freedom in expressing their opinions on a variety of issues, and many university officials became more receptive to and supportive of student demands. In the long term, student demands have led to the creation of programs such as ethnic and women's studies and to changes in living arrangements on college campuses.

[55] In both cultures, music and clothing have been important indicators. Where beads and flowers may have characterized the youth of the 1960s, status sneakers and brand-name jeans are important today. Dylan's music has given way to "gangsta" rap. Members of both cultures share an openness about sexual topics and experiment with drugs.

[56] The United States wanted to support French claims in exchange for French support of U.S. containment policies in Europe. Later, however, the fear of the spread of communism, possibly to the Philippines and then to Hawaii, may have influenced U.S. policy. A sense of pride and faith in U.S. military strength also contributed to an escalation of the war effort.

The Nixon Years (1968-1974)

Test Bank Questions

Match the terms below with the following descriptions. Write the letter of the correct answer. You will not use all the terms.

a. H.R. Haldeman   h. John Mitchell
b. Robert F. Kennedy   i. Eugene McCarthy
c. Bob Woodward   j. George Wallace
d. Hubert Humphrey   k. Daniel Ellsberg
e. Spiro Agnew   l. John Erlichman
f. Henry A. Kissinger   m. John J. Sirica
g. Richard M. Nixon   n. Carl Bernstein

1.   former Vice President and Democratic presidential nominee in 1968

2.   Republican vice presidential nominee in 1968

3.   head of National Security Council and later secretary of state

4.   attorney general under President Nixon

5.   person who gave the Pentagon Papers to the <u>New York Times</u>

6.   former Democratic attorney general and presidential candidate in 1968

7.   President Nixon's chief of staff

8.   judge who sentenced the Watergate burglars

9.   Alabama governor and third-party presidential candidate in 1968

10. President Nixon's chief domestic adviser

11. prominent antiwar Democratic presidential candidate in 1968

Write the letter of the correct ending.

12. One result of the assassination of Martin Luther King, Jr., was
     A) increased political opposition to the Johnson administration.
     B) increased interest in the Poor People's Campaign.
     C) a strong federal campaign to heal the rifts dividing the country.
     D) an erosion of faith in the idea of nonviolent change.

13. Violence erupted at the 1968 Democratic Convention in Chicago when
     A) Mayor Daley made a speech on TV.
     B) police moved in on demonstrators.
     C) Robert Kennedy was assassinated.
     D) George Wallace was nominated.

Test Bank Questions

Write the letter of the correct ending.

14. One reason that Nixon won the election in 1968 was that
    A) disillusioned Democrats did not bother to vote.
    B) he appealed to Northerners and white-collar voters.
    C) he promised to balance the budget.
    D) he was swept in with a majority of Republican representatives.

15. Nixon's administration reflected his attempts to develop
    A) a staff of "El Supremos."
    B) an imperial presidency.
    C) an effete corps of political supporters.
    D) an open presidency.

16. To make good on his promise to restore law and order, Nixon
    A) used economic controls to cut down on crime.
    B) supported the Family Assistance Plan.
    C) condemned the backlash against the counterculture.
    D) discouraged protests and criticized demonstrators.

17. Nixon's "southern strategy" included all of the following EXCEPT
    A) denying federal funding to school districts where segregation persisted.
    B) reducing appropriations needed for enforcing fair housing.
    C) trying to prevent the extension of the Voting Rights Act of 1965.
    D) easing guidelines for desegregation.

18. In foreign affairs, many historians give Nixon credit for
    A) bringing about détente between the superpowers.
    B) abandoning realpolitik, or practical politics.
    C) supporting Israel in the 1973 war against Egypt and Syria.
    D) establishing the People's Republic of China.

19. The SALT I treaty was based on the idea of
    A) the United States achieving superiority over the Soviet Union.
    B) creating deep rifts in the communist world.
    C) balancing nuclear arms development and deployment between the superpowers.
    D) creating a basis for diplomatic ties between the United States and China.

Test Bank Questions

Write the letter of the correct ending.

20. The Plumbers group and CREEP were formed for the purpose of
    A) concealing illegal activities.
    B) ensuring Nixon's victory in the 1972 election.
    C) working with the FBI and CIA.
    D) creating an enemies' list.

21. Attorney General John Mitchell refused to go along with some of the wiretapping activities because
    A) he did not want to commit perjury to shield the President.
    B) he believed these activities should be done by the FBI and the CIA.
    C) they were too risky and he might get caught.
    D) he knew they were illegal.

22. Because Nixon would not give up the tapes that could reveal if he had been involved in the Watergate cover-up,
    A) Haldeman and Erlichman resigned.
    B) Spiro Agnew was accused of tax evasion and taking bribes.
    C) Congress began a process that could have led to impeachment.
    D) Archibald Cox was hired as special prosecutor.

Test Bank Questions

Use the graph of Nixon's Popularity Rating to answer the following questions.

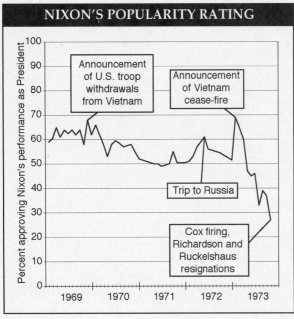

NIXON'S POPULARITY RATING

Announcement of U.S. troop withdrawals from Vietnam

Announcement of Vietnam cease-fire

Trip to Russia

Cox firing, Richardson and Ruckelshaus resignations

Source: Gallup Poll Surveys 1969–1973

23. In which year was Nixon's popularity the highest? The lowest?

24. What percent of the people approved of Nixon's handling of his job as President in January of 1970?

25. When do you think the information about Watergate began to influence public opinion? How can you tell?

Answer the following questions.

26. What foreign policy principles and ideas advocated by Henry Kissinger influenced President Nixon's foreign policy?

27. Was President Nixon consistent or inconsistent in his dedication to a domestic policy of law and order? Cite examples to support your answer.

28. Do you think Nixon was justified in refusing to release the tapes until ordered to do so by the Supreme Court? Explain your response.

Test Bank Questions

Complete each sentence below by selecting the correct word from the list. You will not use all the words.

a. Richard M. Nixon
b. Henry A. Kissinger
c. Eugene McCarthy
d. H.R. Haldeman
e. John J. Sirica
f. Robert F. Kennedy
g. Spiro Agnew
h. Hubert Humphrey
i. Daniel Ellsberg
j. John Erlichman
k. John Mitchell
l. Archibald Cox
m. George Wallace

29. A former attorney general, _____ campaigned for the presidency in 1968.

30. Alabama governor _____ became the third-party candidate in the 1968 race for the presidency.

31. In 1968 the Republicans chose _____ as their presidential candidate.

32. The Democrats chose _____ as their presidential candidate.

33. As head of the National Security Council and later secretary of state, _____ played a major role in shaping foreign policy.

34. The attorney general who approved tapping phones at Democratic National Committee headquarters was _____.

35. _____ was President Nixon's chief of staff.

36. The Republican Vice President who was forced to resign as a result of his illegal activities was _____.

37. The judge who sentenced the Watergate burglars was _____.

38. _____, a former Defense Department official, gave the Pentagon Papers to the New York Times.

39. _____ was a prominent Democratic antiwar candidate.

Write the letter of the correct answer.

40. What was an important effect of the assassinations of Martin Luther King, Jr., and Robert Kennedy?
    A) led to greater unity in the country
    B) led to the creation of a White House enemies' list
    C) resulted in a public loss of confidence in nonviolent protest
    D) increased pressure to restrict armaments in the SALT talks

Write the letter of the correct answer.

41. Why did Hubert Humphrey fail to win total support from the Democratic party?

    A) He had supported President Johnson's policies on Vietnam.

    B) He had failed to maintain law and order in Chicago.

    C) He had resisted Eugene McCarthy's support as too far from the mainstream.

    D) He had ordered police to clear out protestors at a rally.

42. To which groups did George Wallace target his campaign?

    A) campus radicals and antiwar forces

    B) professors and editorial writers

    C) southerners and blue-collar workers

    D) Republicans and left-leaning Democrats

43. How did Nixon deal with the problems of rising inflation and unemployment?

    A) established long-term wage and price controls

    B) considered deficit spending

    C) increased federal spending to provide jobs

    D) imposed an embargo on oil shipped from OPEC nations

44. Which domestic policy helped Nixon win voter support in the South?

    A) enforcing the Supreme Court decision on school busing

    B) refusing to support a Family Assistance Plan

    C) strengthening guidelines for desegregation

    D) trying to prevent extension of the Voting Rights Act of 1965

45. What was Henry Kissinger's role in shaping U.S. foreign policy?

    A) provided briefing papers that gave Nixon options for decision making

    B) insisted on reducing nuclear weapons after the SALT I treaty

    C) introduced the War Powers Act

    D) helped Nixon practice <u>realpolitik</u> in Cambodia

46. What was Nixon's greatest accomplishment with the Soviets?

    A) bringing about a détente and reversing direction of foreign policy

    B) visiting Moscow and meeting with Premier Brezhnev

    C) mending rifts between China and the Soviet Union

    D) recognizing the communist government in the Soviet Union

Test Bank Questions

Write the letter of the correct answer.

47. What did Nixon do to change U.S.-Chinese relations?
    A) visited China and met with Mao Zedong
    B) gave China's seat in the UN to the People's Republic
    C) established trade regulations with China
    D) gave diplomatic recognition to the People's Republic of China

48. Why was the Plumbers group formed?
    A) to stop information leaks that could be politically detrimental to Nixon
    B) to break into the Democratic National Committee's office
    C) to raise money to fund campaign activities and "dirty tricks"
    D) to coordinate the intelligence activities of the FBI and CIA

49. What was Nixon's role in Watergate?
    A) He tapped the phones at the Democratic National Committee headquarters.
    B) He helped collect secret funds at CREEP and spent them on a sabotage campaign.
    C) He appointed a special prosecutor to investigate the charges.
    D) He saw to it that the FBI did not investigate the Watergate break-in and was involved in the cover-up.

50. Why did Nixon resign?
    A) to avoid possible impeachment
    B) to prove his loyalty to his staff
    C) to restore confidence in government
    D) to avoid turning over his tapes

Test Bank Questions

Use the graph of Nixon's Popularity Rating to answer the following questions.

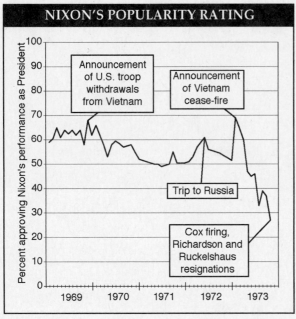

Source: Gallup Poll Surveys 1969–1973

51. What was Nixon's approval rating when he announced the Vietnam cease-fire?

52. When was Nixon's approval rating at its lowest? What percent of the people approved of the way he handled his job as President at that time?

53. According to this graph, how did Nixon's trip to Russia affect his popularity? Use dates and percents to support your answer.

Answer the following questions.

54. How did the course of American history change as a result of Nixon's election in 1968? Explain your answer.

55. If Nixon had not chosen to resign, what do you think might have happened? Give evidence to support your predictions.

56. Do you think Nixon made significant contributions to world peace in terms of his foreign policy? Explain.

Test Bank Answer Key

[1] d

[2] e

[3] f

[4] h

[5] k

[6] b

[7] a

[8] m

[9] j

[10] l

[11] i

[12] D

[13] B

[14] A

[15] B

[16] D

[17] A

[18] A

[19] C

[20] B

[21] C

[22] C

[23] 1973; 1973

[24] about 65 percent

[25] right after the cease-fire announcement; popularity rating dropped
sharply

Test Bank Answer Key

Kissinger's admiration for <u>realpolitik</u>, his belief that a limited
nuclear war could be fought successfully, and his recognition of deep
rifts within the communist world influenced Nixon's foreign policy
[26] decisions.

Nixon was inconsistent. He supported strong actions to promote law
and order, discouraged any kind of protest, and lashed out at
demonstrators. However, Nixon, Attorney General Mitchell, and other
Nixon staff members used illegal measures more serious than the
activities they meant to control. They had phones tapped, proposed
investigations that were far outside the law, and organized a unit to
[27] stop government leaks.

It is possible to argue that he believed that the information on the
tapes would threaten national security. However, Nixon was
obstructing justice and violating the system of checks and balances
by refusing to obey a congressional order to turn over the tapes. On
the other hand, Nixon probably recognized that the tapes were
incriminating and that it was his constitutional right to protect
[28] himself from self-incrimination.

[29] f _____

[30] m _____

[31] a _____

[32] h _____

[33] b _____

[34] k _____

[35] d _____

[36] g _____

[37] e _____

[38] i _____

[39] c _____

[40] C _____

[41] A _____

[42] C _____

[43] B _____

[44] D _____

Test Bank Answer Key

[45] A

[46] A

[47] A

[48] A

[49] D

[50] A

[51] about 69 percent

[52] November 1973; about 28 percent

[53] It boosted his popularity; at the beginning of 1972, his popularity rating was about 50 percent and it rose to slightly above 60 percent as a result of the trip.

[54] The Nixon election signaled a reversal of Great Society programs, less attention to civil rights, a fragmentation of the Democratic party, and a redirection of U.S. foreign policy.

[55] He might have been impeached. The House Judiciary Committee had already voted for impeachment and chances were good that the full House and Senate would have voted for impeachment also. An impeachment hearing would have intensified political divisions in the country and further eroded public morale. In the end, however, the country's "long national nightmare" would be over and there would be a constitutional transition of power.

[56] Yes; Nixon's policies opened the door to establishing relations with China, reduced tensions between the U.S. and the Soviet Union, and established the first steps toward nuclear disarmament.

The Post-Watergate Period (1974-1980)

Test Bank Questions

Match the terms below with the following descriptions. Write the letter of the correct answer. You will not use all the terms.

a. amnesty   e. deregulation
b. Three Mile Island   f. dissident
c. Helsinki Accords   g. stagflation
d. Camp David Accords

1.   condition in which unemployment and inflation rise while the economy stays flat

2.   series of agreements made by thirty-five nations

3.   site of an accident at a nuclear power plant

4.   general pardon, in this case granted to draft evaders

5.   activist who opposes the actions of government

6.   reduction or removal of government controls

Complete each sentence below by selecting the correct word from the list. You will not use all the words.

a. Nelson Rockefeller   e. Cyrus Vance
b. Menachem Begin   f. James Earl Carter, Jr.
c. Ayatollah Khomeini   g. Gerald R. Ford
d. Anwar el-Sadat

7.   _____ was governor of Georgia before being elected President in 1976.

8.   _____, who had been appointed Vice President, inherited the presidency when Nixon resigned.

9.   The Secretary of State who invited Egyptian and Israeli leaders to meet at Camp David was _____.

10. The Egyptian leader who negotiated a peace treaty with the Israeli prime minister was _____.

11. _____, a fundamentalist Islamic leader, was aggressively anti-Western.

Write the letter of the correct ending.

12. One of Gerald Ford's first acts as President was to

     A) deregulate several industries.

     B) rescue the crew of the Mayaguez.

     C) curb inflation and increase employment.

     D) pardon his predecessor.

Test Bank Questions

Write the letter of the correct ending.

13. Ford tried to restore public confidence in the economy by
    A) promoting a WIN campaign.
    B) raising interest rates.
    C) pushing for fewer unemployment benefits.
    D) asking Congress to approve a tax increase.

14. Ford's domestic policy was characterized by his
    A) belief in limited government.
    B) preoccupation with Watergate.
    C) lack of skill in creating a managed economy.
    D) reluctance to veto any popular measure.

15. In the area of foreign policy, President Ford
    A) signed a new SALT agreement on nuclear disarmament.
    B) sent troops to Southeast Asia to prevent communists from taking over Vietnam.
    C) continued forging ties with China.
    D) attempted to intervene in Turkey and Angola.

16. One of Jimmy Carter's major problems as President was that he
    A) appointed too many women and minorities to his staff.
    B) failed to set human rights standards for foreign policy.
    C) lacked the ability to deal with Congress.
    D) adopted a formal and aloof presidential style.

17. President Carter took a bold step in foreign policy when he
    A) got the leaders of Israel and Egypt to negotiate a peace accord.
    B) returned the Panama Canal to Panama.
    C) signed the second Strategic Arms Limitation Treaty.
    D) visited China to continue Nixon's policies toward that country.

18. Iranian students seized the U.S. embassy and took Americans hostage to protest
    A) the failure of the United States to modernize Iran.
    B) Carter's letting the shah enter the United States for medical treatment.
    C) the ayatollah's insistence on a return to Muslim fundamentalism.
    D) Shah Mohammad Reza Pahlavi's return to power in Iran.

19. As a result of President Carter's inconsistent economic policy,
    A) inflation rose.   B) interest rates fell.
    C) unemployment fell.   D) deficit spending decreased.

Test Bank Questions

Write the letter of the correct ending.

20. One result of the Carter energy conservation crusade was the creation of

   A) the Nuclear Regulatory Commission.

   B) a federal Department of Energy.

   C) the MEOW program.

   D) the Three Mile Island nuclear power plant.

21. Because the Vietnam War still divided Americans, reaction was mixed when Carter

   A) sent marines to Cambodia.

   B) granted amnesty to those who had evaded the draft.

   C) restored diplomatic relations with the People's Republic of China.

   D) opened up an investigation of the dangers of Agent Orange.

22. The significance of the Bakke case was that it

   A) rejected race as a factor in admission decisions.

   B) signaled the start of a white backlash against affirmative action.

   C) legalized racial quotas for admission to medical and law schools.

   D) encouraged African Americans to apply to medical school.

Use the table of World Crude Oil Production to answer the following questions.

WORLD CRUDE OIL PRODUCTION			
(Thousand Barrels Per Day)			
Year	Total World Production	OPEC Production	OPEC Percentage
1974	56,088.4	30,729.2	54.8
1975	53,384.0	27,155.0	50.9
1976	57,883.2	30,737.7	53.1
1977	59,862.8	31,253.4	52.2
1978	60,396.8	29,805.3	49.3
1979	62,819.9	30,928.8	49.2
1980	59,826.0	26,879.2	44.9

Source: The Secretariat, Organization of Petroleum Exporting Countries

23. How much crude oil was produced in the world in 1976? Of this amount, what percent was produced by the OPEC nations?

24. What overall trend do you observe in the percent of the world's crude oil production supplied by the OPEC nations from 1974 to 1980?

Test Bank Questions

Use the table of World Crude Oil Production to answer the following questions.

WORLD CRUDE OIL PRODUCTION			
(Thousand Barrels Per Day)			
Year	Total World Production	OPEC Production	OPEC Percentage
1974	56,088.4	30,729.2	54.8
1975	53,384.0	27,155.0	50.9
1976	57,883.2	30,737.7	53.1
1977	59,862.8	31,253.4	52.2
1978	60,396.8	29,805.3	49.3
1979	62,819.9	30,928.8	49.2
1980	59,826.0	26,879.2	44.9

Source: The Secretariat, Organization of Petroleum Exporting Countries

25. In 1977, President Carter called on Americans to conserve energy and reduce their dependence on imported oil. Can you tell from the information presented in this table if Americans complied with the President's request? Explain.

Answer the following questions.

26. The Carter presidency has been criticized on the grounds that the President saw only parts of an issue, and never the big issue or main idea. Do you think this is true? Support your answer.

27. In what ways was the Iranian hostage crisis a defining point for President Carter?

28. President Ford concluded that pardoning Nixon would heal the wounds caused by Watergate. Do you think his conclusion was valid? Explain.

Match the terms below with the following descriptions. Write the letter of the correct answer. You will not use all the terms.

a. stagflation
b. Camp David Accords
c. amnesty
d. deregulation
e. shuttle diplomacy
f. Helsinki Accords
g. dissidents

29. In the _____, eastern and western European nations (and the United States) pledged economic cooperation.

30. The _____ resulted in a treaty defining a framework for Middle East peace.

31. Carter's support of Soviet _____ led to a worsening of relations between the U.S. and the USSR.

32. Carter granted _____ to draft evaders.

33. Critics of _____ argued that companies would cut service in less profitable situations.

Test Bank Questions

Match the terms below with the following descriptions. Write the letter of the correct answer. You will not use all the terms.

a. James Earl Carter, Jr.   e. Ayatollah Khomeini
b. Menachem Begin   f. Cyrus Vance
c. Gerald Ford   g. Nelson Rockefeller
d. Shah Mohammad Reza Pahlavi

34. Vice President appointed by a nonelected President

35. Secretary of State in the Carter administration

36. anti-Western Islamic leader

37. Iranian leader supported by the United States

38. Israeli prime minister who negotiated peace terms with Egyptian leader

39. former governor of Georgia who became President

Write the letter of the correct answer.

40. What was one effect of President Ford's pardon of Nixon?

   A) It removed the ugliness of Watergate.

   B) It smoothed the actual transition between Nixon and Ford.

   C) It increased Ford's popular support.

   D) It made people suspect Ford and Nixon had made a bargain.

41. What was President Ford's program to overcome stagflation?

   A) He tried to restore public confidence through the WIN campaign.

   B) He proposed a multibillion dollar tax increase.

   C) He provided financial incentives for people to save rather than spend.

   D) He increased the money supply.

42. Which of the following statements characterizes President Ford's foreign policy?

   A) He followed the direction set by President Nixon and Henry Kissinger.

   B) He refused to recognize the governments of newly independent African nations.

   C) He thwarted congressional attempts to play a strong role in foreign affairs.

   D) He initiated no foreign policy actions.

43. What was an important theme in Jimmy Carter's election in 1976?

   A) He was an experienced businessman.

   B) He was an expert in nuclear energy.

   C) He believed that the Soviets did not want to dominate Eastern Europe.

   D) He was a Washington outsider and could be trusted.

Test Bank Questions

Write the letter of the correct answer.

44. Which statement best describes President Carter's approach to the presidency?
   A) He used the presidency as a pulpit for his religious beliefs.
   B) He assumed the ceremonial style of the presidency.
   C) He kept his administration scandal-free.
   D) He found it difficult to bargain with Congress to pass legislation.

45. What was a significant consequence of the Helsinki Accords?
   A) worldwide promotion of human rights
   B) the establishment of diplomatic relations with the People's Republic of China
   C) an agreement on a framework for peace in the Middle East
   D) a boycott of the summer Olympic games in Moscow

46. What factors complicated President Carter's relations with the Soviet Union?
   A) Carter's commitment to human rights and support of dissidents
   B) Carter's move to close the Panama Canal to Soviet ships
   C) Carter's program to build additional nuclear weapons
   D) Carter's rejection of SALT II

47. What did President Carter do to try to get the U.S. hostages released from Iran?
   A) He sent Cyrus Vance to Teheran to talk to the Iranian captors.
   B) He brought the shah to the United States for medical treatment.
   C) He released Iranian assets in the United States.
   D) He attempted a commando rescue of the hostages.

48. Why was President Carter's energy program ineffective?
   A) It caused an accident at Three Mile Island.
   B) Congress blocked the goals of the program.
   C) The Department of Energy was unable to enforce energy-saving regulations.
   D) The United States could import oil from the OPEC countries.

49. Why did Carter take steps to deregulate some transportation industries?
   A) to increase competition and decrease costs
   B) to improve safety
   C) to lower interest rates
   D) to help conserve oil

Test Bank Questions

Write the letter of the correct answer.

50. What was one important result of the <u>Bakke</u> case?

   A) It ruled out consideration of race as a factor in admissions decisions.

   B) It encouraged African Americans to apply to medical schools.

   C) It legalized racial quotas for admission to medical schools.

   D) It signaled the start of a white backlash against affirmative action.

Use the table of World Crude Oil Production to answer the following questions.

WORLD CRUDE OIL PRODUCTION			
(Thousand Barrels Per Day)			
Year	Total World Production	OPEC Production	OPEC Percentage
1974	56,088.4	30,729.2	54.8
1975	53,384.0	27,155.0	50.9
1976	57,883.2	30,737.7	53.1
1977	59,862.8	31,253.4	52.2
1978	60,396.8	29,805.3	49.3
1979	62,819.9	30,928.8	49.2
1980	59,826.0	26,879.2	44.9

Source: The Secretariat, Organization of Petroleum Exporting Countries

51. In which year did OPEC countries produce the lowest percentage of oil? What percent of the world's oil did OPEC countries produce that year?

52. What was the total world oil production in 1979?

53. What additional information would you need to determine whether President Carter's energy conservation program was at all effective?

Answer the following questions.

54. What do you think was Gerald Ford's main problem as President? Support your answer.

55. In what ways were Carter's religious beliefs and high moral principles stumbling blocks to his effectiveness as President?

56. How valid was President Carter's conclusion that pardoning Vietnam draft evaders would help heal the nation's wounds? Explain.

Test Bank Answer Key

[1] g

[2] c

[3] b

[4] a

[5] f

[6] e

[7] f

[8] g

[9] e

[10] d

[11] c

[12] D

[13] A

[14] A

[15] C

[16] C

[17] A

[18] B

[19] A

[20] B

[21] B

[22] B

[23] 57,883.2 thousand barrels per day; 53.1

[24] In general, with the exception of 1975 to 1976, there has been a slight downward trend in the percent of oil produced by OPEC, relative to total world production. For the years 1978-1980, OPEC countries produced less than half of the world's crude oil.

[25] No. The table provides no information on the number of barrels exported to the United States.

Test Bank Answer Key

It is probably true. For example, Carter looked at the hostage crisis from the standpoint of the life of each hostage rather than thinking about what--if any--action would be in the country's best interests. Additionally, his commitment to human rights and his public support of Soviet dissidents undermined efforts to relax tensions between the [26] superpowers.

Nightly newscasts turned the hostage crisis into a national debate, and the public became frustrated and impatient. President Carter's inability to secure the hostages' freedom lowered his popularity to the point where he could not possibly be reelected. When a commando rescue mission that he authorized ended in disaster, he was further [27] humiliated.

No, the pardon did not heal the wounds caused by Watergate. It saved the country from going through the ugliness of an impeachment trial, but it clouded the facts that should have been made public. Most Americans could not understand why Nixon had paid no penalty for his [28] involvement in Watergate.

[29] f

[30] b

[31] g

[32] c

[33] d

[34] g

[35] f

[36] e

[37] d

[38] b

[39] a

[40] D

[41] A

[42] A

[43] D

[44] D

[45] A

Test Bank Answer Key

[46] A

[47] D

[48] B

[49] D

[50] D

[51] 1980; 44.9 percent

[52] 62,819.9 thousand barrels

[53] You would need to know how much oil was produced in the United States in each of the years shown and how much was imported.

[54] He lacked administrative experience, direction, foresight, and other leadership qualifications to serve as President. For example, he did not understand the connection between the youngster who needed a jacket and a population that needed public assistance or some plan to help them enter the economic mainstream. He also believed in a limited role for government at a time when government action was needed, particularly in economic matters.

[55] They affected his ability to "wheel and deal" with Congress to get his legislative program passed. In foreign affairs, his commitment to finding ethical solutions to complex issues undermined efforts to improve relations between the United States and the Soviet Union.

[56] The pardon did not heal the wounds caused by Vietnam. Although it resolved problems for many who had evaded the draft, it created feelings of hostility among those who had served in the war. In his concern for moral values, Carter failed to realize that the Vietnam War continued to divide Americans.

High Tide of the Conservative Movement (1980-1992)

Test Bank Questions

Match the terms below with the following descriptions. Write the letter of the correct answer. You will not use all the terms.

a. Saddam Hussein
b. Boris Yeltsin
c. Ronald Reagan
d. Henry Cisneros
e. Sandra Day O'Connor
f. Mikhail Gorbachev
g. Clarence Thomas
h. George Bush

1. "Teflon President" and skillful communicator

2. conservative Supreme Court justice, appointed by George Bush

3. Latino who was elected mayor of San Antonio

4. Soviet leader who proposed <u>perestroika</u> and <u>glasnost</u>

5. president of Russia during the period when the Soviet Union fell apart

6. dictator of Iraq

Complete each sentence below by selecting the correct word from the list. You will not use all the words.

a. supply-side economics
b. Strategic Defense Initiative (SDI)
c. New Right
d. Sandinista
e. Iran-contra affair
f. new federalism
g. televangelism
h. Persian Gulf War
i. S&L scandal
j. Intermediate-Range Nuclear Forces (INF) Treaty

7. By 1980, a broad coalition of conservative groups had formed the _____.

8. To focus the efforts of religious conservatives, Jerry Falwell and others used _____ to raise funds.

9. A theory that calls for lower taxes to put more money in the hands of businesses and investors is called _____.

10. In Nicaragua, the United States tried to undermine the Marxist _____ government.

11. In the _____, profits from the illegal sale of weapons were used to support the group trying to overthrow the government of Nicaragua.

12. Reagan proposed the _____ to intercept Soviet missiles, though many scientists questioned its value.

Test Bank Questions

Write the letter of the correct ending.

13. The conservative coalition was concerned with
    A) eliminating regulations that limited economic competition.
    B) reducing defense expenditures.
    C) fighting runaway inflation.
    D) establishing new federal programs to target social problems.

14. Conservatives used all of these techniqes effectively EXCEPT
    A) spin doctors.
    B) television appeals for money.
    C) frequent press conferences.
    D) direct-mail campaigns.

15. President George Bush reached the peak of his popularity as a result of his
    A) efforts to extend the Voting Rights Act of 1965.
    B) appointments to the federal courts and the Supreme Court.
    C) sending troops to fight the Persian Gulf War.
    D) support of the Nicaraguan rebels.

16. One important result of President Reagan's tax reform measure was
    A) deregulation of the S&Ls.
    B) reduced taxes paid by the people with the highest incomes.
    C) an increase in revenues spent by the states.
    D) an increase in the amount of tax revenues collected.

17. Presidents Reagan and Bush endorsed the conservative policy of
    A) protecting consumers through regulation of industry.
    B) maintaining federally insured bank accounts.
    C) having government pay a larger share of Medicare.
    D) supporting pro-life efforts and school prayer.

18. A significant result of the Reagan-Bush policies was
    A) a more activist Supreme Court that helped shape social policy.
    B) a decrease in the annual deficit and the national debt.
    C) a decrease in real poverty as a result of higher family incomes.
    D) a wider gap between the rich and the poor.

19. President Reagan worked to slow down the civil rights movement by
    A) abolishing the Civil Rights Commission.
    B) supporting affirmative action.
    C) appointing conservative judges.
    D) excluding minorities from his cabinet.

Test Bank Questions

Write the letter of the correct ending.

20. The women's movement suffered a setback when
    A) women introduced the issue of sexual harassment.
    B) women began to compete for traditionally "male" jobs.
    C) women were drafted into the armed forces.
    D) ratification of the Equal Rights Amendment was defeated.

21. Ronald Reagan's defense policy included
    A) reducing the size of conventional military forces.
    B) abandoning the SALT II plan.
    C) refusing to sign the INF treaty in 1987.
    D) reducing budget deficits by limiting the military budget.

22. The United States and its allies went to war against Iraq when Iraq
    A) invaded Kuwait.   B) attacked Israel and Bahrain.
    C) invaded Saudi Arabia.   D) bombed the U.S. embassy in Lebanon.

Use the table of Election Results to answer the following questions.

ELECTION RESULTS, 1980–1988				
Year	Candidates	Popular Vote	Percent of total vote	Electoral Vote
1980	Ronald Reagan (R)	43,899,248	52	489
	Jimmy Carter (D)	35,481,435	42	49
	John B. Anderson (Ind.)	5,719,437	06	——
1984	Ronald Reagan (R)	54,281,858	59	525
	Walter F. Mondale (D)	37,457,215	41	13
1988*	George Bush (R)	48,881,221	54	426
	Michael S. Dukakis (D)	41,805,422	46	111

*A majority of 270 electoral votes out of 538 are needed to win. In 1988, one vote was cast for Senator Lloyd Bentsen (D-TX).

23. In which election did the winning candidate receive the most popular votes?

24. Did John Anderson affect the outcome of the 1980 election? Explain.

25. In what ways does this table show that the Republican candidates received a huge mandate in the elections of 1980, 1984, and 1988?

Answer the following questions.

26. President Reagan remained committed to his "Star Wars" venture despite its enormous cost and the fact that some scientists did not believe it would work. Why do you think he took this position?

27. Compare the gains and setbacks of the Native American and Latino movements of the 1980s and 1990s.

28. From what groups in American society did Presidents Reagan and Bush draw their support? What specific policies or conservative ideology appealed to each group and why?

Test Bank Questions

Complete each sentence below by selecting the correct word from the list. You will not use all the words.

a. Ronald Reagan   e. Henry Cisneros
b. George Bush   f. Boris Yeltsin
c. Mikhail Gorbachev   g. Sandra Day O'Connor
d. Saddam Hussein

29. A former actor and California governor, _____ was President for two terms.

30. The first woman Supreme Court justice was _____.

31. The Iraqi leader who invaded Kuwait was _____.

32. The election of _____ as mayor of San Antonio, Texas, was an example of Latino political gains in the 1980s.

33. Vice President _____ was elected President in 1988.

34. Soviet leader _____ proposed a program of glasnost.

Match the terms below with the following descriptions. Write the letter of the correct answer. You will not use all the terms.

a. Strategic Defense   e. Iran-contra affair
   Initiative (SDI)
b. new federalism   f. S&Ls
c. New Right   g. televangelism
d. supply-side economics

35. broad coalition of conservative groups

36. Nixon's term for a plan to encourage local governments to take the lead in meeting community needs

37. "thrift institutions" that historically concentrated on making home mortgage loans to individuals

38. use of the media by the religious right to raise funds

39. Reagan's proposed new program of missile defense

40. incident involving illegal sale of weapons

Write the letter of the correct answer.

41. What was the primary goal of the New Right?

     A) to bring the hostages home

     B) to overturn liberal programs of the New Deal and Great Society

     C) to promote women's rights

     D) to reduce military spending

Test Bank Questions

Write the letter of the correct answer.

42. What was an advantage of using direct-mail campaigns for political fundraising?
    A) The campaigns provided employment for conservative activists.
    B) The audience for the letters could be carefully selected or targeted.
    C) No religious affiliation was needed for this type of fundraising.
    D) The letters contained useful sound bites written by spin doctors.

43. Which factor contributed significantly to Reagan's popularity?
    A) his support of the middle class
    B) his ability to delegate authority wisely
    C) his fear of communism
    D) his skill at communicating through television

44. What were the two major components of Reagan's economic plan?
    A) consumer protection and limited competition
    B) increased money supply and banking regulations
    C) higher taxes and fewer government-supported social programs
    D) lower taxes and reduced government spending

45. What was Reagan's viewpoint on social issues such as legalized abortion?
    A) He wanted to increase Medicare and Social Security payments.
    B) He endorsed the goals of the Moral Majority.
    C) He assumed a neutral position, thus earning the nickname "Teflon President."
    D) He supported deregulation to protect the public.

46. What was one result of the Reagan-Bush judicial appointments?
    A) The courts endorsed the theory of supply-side economics.
    B) Sexual harassment disappeared after the Clarence Thomas hearings.
    C) The Supreme Court overturned Roe v. Wade.
    D) The judiciary took a less active role in social policy.

47. What stand did President Reagan take in the area of civil rights?
    A) He worked to promote affirmative action programs.
    B) He strengthened the Civil Rights Commission.
    C) He opposed busing as a policy to achieve racial balance in schools.
    D) He tried to prevent extension of the Voting Rights Act of 1965.

Test Bank Questions

Write the letter of the correct answer.

48. How did Native Americans fare during the 1980s?

A) They benefited from government-funded colleges set up on reservations.

B) They made considerable gains in politics only.

C) They failed to win back long-ignored treaty rights.

D) They made progress in education, business, and the law on their own.

49. What was one important objective of Reagan's defense policies?

A) to continue SALT II

B) to increase the supply of nuclear weapons

C) to create "a new world order"

D) to reduce conventional military forces

50. What was a result of the Persian Gulf War?

A) The Soviet Union was dismantled and the Berlin Wall came down.

B) The President's popularity fell to its lowest point.

C) Iraq secretly bought weapons from the United States.

D) The Iraqis left Kuwait but Saddam Hussein remained in power.

Use the table of Election Results to answer the following questions.

ELECTION RESULTS, 1980–1988				
Year	Candidates	Popular Vote	Percent of total vote	Electoral Vote
1980	Ronald Reagan (R)	43,899,248	52	489
	Jimmy Carter (D)	35,481,435	42	49
	John B. Anderson (Ind.)	5,719,437	06	——
1984	Ronald Reagan (R)	54,281,858	59	525
	Walter F. Mondale (D)	37,457,215	41	13
1988*	George Bush (R)	48,881,221	54	426
	Michael S. Dukakis (D)	41,805,422	46	111

*A majority of 270 electoral votes out of 538 are needed to win. In 1988, one vote was cast for Senator Lloyd Bentsen (D-TX).

51. In which election did Reagan win his most resounding victory? How can you tell?

52. Did the independent candidate, John Anderson, affect the results of the 1980 election? Explain.

53. Can you tell from the information presented here where Michael Dukakis's support came from? Explain your answer.

Answer the following questions.

54. President Reagan did little to ease poverty in the United States, despite the increasing numbers of poor and homeless people. Why do you think he did not respond more positively to the poor?

Test Bank Questions

Answer the following questions.

55. Imagine yourself as a reporter interviewing President Bush on his foreign policy for a newspaper article. What questions might you ask him? How might he answer these questions?

56. What conclusions can you draw about the effects of supply-side economics? Justify your answer.

Test Bank Answer Key

[1] c

[2] g

[3] d

[4] f

[5] b

[6] a

[7] c

[8] g

[9] a

[10] d

[11] e

[12] b

[13] A

[14] C

[15] C

[16] B

[17] D

[18] D

[19] C

[20] D

[21] B

[22] A

[23] 1984

[24] No; Reagan still won more than 50 percent of the popular vote and well over the required 270 electoral votes.

[25] In each election, the Republican candidate received a definite majority of popular votes and won at least 150 more electoral votes than was needed to be elected.

Test Bank Answer Key

President Reagan was intent on defending the United States against the Soviet Union which he viewed as the "evil empire." When he assumed office in 1981, he was determined to defend the interests of the United States no matter what the cost. To achieve this goal, he proposed not only building up conventional military forces but
[26] increasing the supply of nuclear weapons as well.

Latinos made significant gains in politics and higher education but continued to face serious problems as evidenced by the high dropout rate of high school students and the small percentage of students completing college. Native Americans, on their own, made progress in education and in developing their business and legal skills. Native American lawyers successfully argued for tribal jurisdiction in cases concerning reservations and won long-ignored treaty rights. However, Native Americans, many of them at the poverty level, were adversely
[27] affected by the cutbacks in social welfare programs in the 1980s.

Reagan and Bush drew their support from the New Right, a coalition of groups with a wide range of political, economic, and social concerns. The economic policies of Bush and Reagan were of greatest benefit to business people, investors, and those with high incomes. Social policies, such as endorsing school prayer and rejecting affirmative action, were popular with the Moral Majority, who wanted to restore Christian values to society, and with blue-collar workers, who felt
[28] threatened by "reverse discrimination."

[29] a _____

[30] g _____

[31] d _____

[32] e _____

[33] b _____

[34] c _____

[35] c _____

[36] b _____

[37] f _____

[38] g _____

[39] a _____

[40] e _____

[41] B _____

Test Bank Answer Key

[42] B _____

[43] D _____

[44] D _____

[45] B _____

[46] D _____

[47] D _____

[48] D _____

[49] B _____

[50] D _____

[51] In 1984 he captured 59 percent of the popular vote and about 97 percent of the electoral vote.

[52] His candidacy did not affect the outcome. If his votes had been added to Carter's, Carter still would not have won 50 percent of the popular vote. In addition, Reagan won well over the required 270 electoral votes.

[53] The table does not provide any information to make that determination. A table showing the breakdown of votes by states would be needed.

[54] He was committed to the idea that anyone who really tried could succeed in the United States. He subscribed to the theory of supply-side economics, believing that prosperity would "trickle down" from the top to those at the lower levels of the economy such as the homeless and unemployed. He also thought that his program provided a safety net for the "truly needy."

[55] Question: For what foreign policy achievement do you think you will be remembered?
Response: I will be remembered for the Persian Gulf War and the creation of a "new world order."
Question: What was your role in the Iran-contra affair?
Respnose: Oliver North made the arrangements on his own without my knowledge or the approval of President Reagan.
Question: How do you justify U.S. intervention in Latin American affairs?
Response: Because of the proximity of Latin America to the United States, we intervene to protect American interests and to undermine forces that threaten our security.

Test Bank Answer Key

In the short term, supply-side economics brought an end to the recession and ushered in the prosperous, materialistic decade of the 1980s. In the long term, the policy further polarized the society into rich and poor. The nation's wealth was more unevenly shared than at any time since the end of World War II, and real poverty
[56] increased, hitting women and children the hardest.

The Promise of Change (1992-Present)

Test Bank Questions

Match the terms below with the following descriptions. Write the letter of the correct answer. You will not use all the terms.

a. Hillary Rodham Clinton   f. Frederik W. De Klerk
b. Maya Angelou   g. Nelson Mandela
c. Yitzhak Rabin   h. Bill Clinton
d. Al Gore   i. Slobodan Milosevic
e. Yasir Arafat

1. presiding officer of the Senate who cast tie-breaking vote mandating budget cuts

2. former Arkansas governor who became President

3. head of PLO who signed Middle East peace agreement

4. South African prime minister committed to ending apartheid

5. head of task force to devise new national health insurance plan

6. Serb leader who backed siege of Sarajevo and ethnic cleansing to eliminate Croats and Muslims

7. Israeli prime minister who signed peace accord in Washington

Write the letter of the correct ending.

8. In 1992, in contrast to his Republican opponent, the Democratic presidential candidate proposed
    A) doing away with party politics.
    B) a more active role for the federal government.
    C) an all-out campaign to resist communism.
    D) reducing taxes and government spending.

9. The 1992 presidential campaign was fought largely
    A) by a network of volunteers who canvassed voters door-to-door.
    B) through direct-mail campaigns to targeted groups.
    C) on television talk shows and interview programs.
    D) through newspaper and magazine ads.

10. Bill Clinton did not receive a strong popular mandate because
    A) the third-party candidate won 19 percent of the popular vote.
    B) he won less than half of the electoral vote.
    C) the Republicans kept control of both houses of Congress.
    D) he won less than half of the total popular vote cast.

Test Bank Questions

Write the letter of the correct ending.

11. Clinton's economic stimulus package
    A) cut the deficit significantly.
    B) was defeated by Congress.
    C) was effective in stimulating the economy.
    D) affected only the wealthiest Americans.

12. Clinton believed that his health-care reform package would meet with public approval because it
    A) could be funded by existing revenues.
    B) covered all citizens.
    C) would create a national health alliance to pay health claims.
    D) would improve the quality of medical care.

13. Although the United States supported Boris Yeltsin, he faced serious difficulties at home because
    A) the Russian economy was unstable and the people resisted reforms.
    B) he refused to share power with Vladimir Zhirinovsky.
    C) he supported rigid economic controls.
    D) he favored an aggressive foreign policy.

14. After Clinton pledged to send U.S. troops to Bosnia as part of a peacekeeping force,
    A) Muslims in Bosnia were wiped out through an ethnic cleansing campaign.
    B) he had to retract his pledge because Americans did not want to become involved.
    C) Bosnia Herzegovina seceded from Yugoslavia.
    D) the international community acted together and crafted a peace treaty.

15. Although the parties had engaged in secret negotiations, the United States took an active role in developing an agreement between
    A) the white minority and African majority in South Africa.
    B) Jean-Bertrand Aristide and military leaders in Haiti.
    C) Boris Yeltsin and Vladimir Zhirinovsky.
    D) Palestinians and Israelis.

16. As a result of famine and violent civil war, the UN sent troops to
    A) Eastern Europe.   B) South Africa.
    C) the Gaza Strip.   D) Somalia.

Test Bank Questions

Write the letter of the correct ending.

17. The purpose of NAFTA was to

   A) oppose unionization of industries in the United States, Canada, and Mexico.

   B) promote free trade among the United States, Canada, and Mexico.

   C) make the Western Hemisphere the most cooperative in the world.

   D) remove barriers to world trade.

18. The concept of multiculturalism arose in response to a

   A) gay and lesbian march on Washington, D.C.

   B) need for all students to develop self-esteem.

   C) recognition that history should make people feel good about themselves.

   D) desire to teach awareness and tolerance of cultural differences.

Use the table of Estimate of US Refugee Admissions to answer the following questions.

ESTIMATE OF U.S. REFUGEE ADMISSIONS, 1991		
Region	Authorized levels	Estimated arrivals
Africa	4,900	4,000
East Asia	52,000	53,500
Eastern Europe	5,000	7,000
Latin America/Caribbean	3,100	2,500
Near East/South Asia	6,000	5,000
Soviet Union	50,000	38,000
Subtotal	121,000	110,000
Privately funded	10,000	2,300
Total	131,000	112,300

Source: U.S. Department of State *Dispatch*, September 30, 1991

19. From which two regions did most refugee admissions actually come in 1991?

20. What was the maximum number of refugees authorized from Latin America and the Caribbean? About how many refugees arrived from this region?

21. Why do you think the United States was willing to accept so many refugees from the Soviet Union and East Asia in 1991?

Answer the following questions.

22. President Clinton recognized the diversity that increasingly characterized the U.S. population. What facts support this conclusion?

23. Reducing the federal deficit and enacting a national health insurance plan were two priorities of the Clinton administration. Do you think these two objectives are related to one another? Give reasons to support your answer.

24. What are some social and economic effects of the surge in immigration to the United States in the 1980s and 1990s?

Test Bank Questions

Complete each sentence below by selecting the correct word from the list. You will not use all the words.

a. Slobodon Milosevic   f. Al Gore
b. Yitzhak Rabin   g. Yasir Arafat
c. Ben Nighthorse Campbell h. Hillary Rodham Clinton
d. Bill Clinton   i. Frederik W. de Klerk
e. Nelson Mandela

25. _____, former governor of Arkansas, won the presidency in 1992 with 43 percent of the popular vote.

26. Vice President _____ cast the tie-breaking vote in the Senate to pass the President's budget.

27. _____, the Serbian leader, wanted to ensure that the Serbs had a powerful voice in the government.

28. _____, a leader in the antiapartheid struggle, spent more than a quarter century in prison.

29. _____, Israeli prime minister, signed a peace agreement providing for Palestinian self-rule in the Gaza Strip.

30. _____ headed a task force to devise a plan for national health insurance.

31. Radical groups within the PLO challenged the authority of their leader _____.

Write the letter of the correct answer.

32. Which was the dominant theme in the 1992 presidential election?
    A) It was time to turn the government over to the postwar baby boomers.
    B) The government should take a more active role in solving economic and social problems.
    C) The nations should abandon party politics in order to reduce the deficit.
    D) Government policies should promote traditional free enterprise to solve economic problems.

33. Which of the following was the most significant reason why television was important in the campaign?
    A) It was an effective way to create an active corps of volunteers.
    B) It reduced the need for direct-mailings.
    C) It played an important role in molding public opinion.
    D) It was an inexpensive way to solicit funds.

Test Bank Questions

Write the letter of the correct answer.

34. What position did Janet Reno hold in the Clinton administration?
    A) Secretary of Transportation
    B) first woman attorney general
    C) Supreme Court justice
    D) head of Children's Defense Fund

35. Which of the following did NOT occur during the first few months of Clinton's presidency?
    A) His program for health reform was defeated.
    B) His first budget barely squeaked by Congress.
    C) He chose women, African Americans, and Latinos for his political team.
    D) His economic stimulus package was defeated in the Congress.

36. What did Clinton see as the most important feature of his health-care reform package?
    A) It would eliminate the medical bureaucracy.
    B) It would create a health alliance in each state.
    C) It would provide universal coverage.
    D) It would not require new taxes.

37. Why did Boris Yeltsin face difficulties in Russia, despite United States support?
    A) Transition to a market economy was difficult and unpopular.
    B) He had not been elected democratically.
    C) The voters refused to approve a new constitution.
    D) He lost support when he blamed Russia's woes on foreigners and Jews.

38. Why did Clinton back off from his pledge to send U.S. troops to Bosnia?
    A) European nations decided to intervene.
    B) The siege of Sarajevo had ended.
    C) UN negotiators were able to craft a peace treaty to resolve the issue.
    D) American public opinion would not support the move.

Test Bank Questions

Write the letter of the correct answer.

39. What was the role of the United States in promoting peace in the Middle East?
    A) It helped remove occupying forces from the war zones along the West Bank.
    B) It supported Israel's right to exist.
    C) It assisted in final negotiations for a peace treaty between the PLO and Israel.
    D) It sent troops to the Gaza Strip.

40. What did the United States attempt to do in Haiti?
    A) implement economic sanctions
    B) remove Jean-Bertrand Aristide from power
    C) bring about an end to poverty
    D) return Jean-Bertrand Aristide to power

41. What was the purpose of the North American Free Trade Agreement (NAFTA)?
    A) to reduce unemployment in the United States
    B) to prevent further uprisings in the Western Hemisphere
    C) to promote free trade among Canada, the United States, and Mexico
    D) to create a free-trade zone in Europe

42. Which factor led to the concept of multiculturalism?
    A) the desire to discover the truth about the past
    B) sensitivity to gay and lesbian rights
    C) the need to develop pride in the United States
    D) the desire to embrace, not exclude, minority cultures

Use the table of Estimate of US Refugee Admissions to answer the following questions.

ESTIMATE OF U.S. REFUGEE ADMISSIONS, 1991		
Region	Authorized levels	Estimated arrivals
Africa	4,900	4,000
East Asia	52,000	53,500
Eastern Europe	5,000	7,000
Latin America/Caribbean	3,100	2,500
Near East/South Asia	6,000	5,000
Soviet Union	50,000	38,000
Subtotal	121,000	110,000
Privately funded	10,000	2,300
Total	131,000	112,300

Source: U.S. Department of State *Dispatch*, September 30, 1991

43. From which region did the least number of refugees come? The greatest number?

Test Bank Questions

Use the table of Estimate of US Refugee Admissions to answer the following questions.

ESTIMATE OF U.S. REFUGEE ADMISSIONS, 1991		
Region	Authorized levels	Estimated arrivals
Africa	4,900	4,000
East Asia	52,000	53,500
Eastern Europe	5,000	7,000
Latin America/Caribbean	3,100	2,500
Near East/South Asia	6,000	5,000
Soviet Union	50,000	38,000
Subtotal	121,000	110,000
Privately funded	10,000	2,300
Total	131,000	112,300

Source: U.S. Department of State *Dispatch*, September 30, 1991

44. What was the authorized level of refugee admissions for the Soviet Union in 1991? How many refugees are estimated to have arrived?

45. Why do you think there was such a relatively large number of immigrants from East Asia in 1991?

Answer the following questions.

46. New patterns and policies of immigration in the 1980s and 1990s have brought many changes to American life. What facts support this conclusion?

47. The United States continues to play a role in the affairs of Russia, the former Yugoslavia, the Middle East, and Haiti. Do you think America's foreign policy objectives in each instance are related to one another? Give reasons to support your answer.

48. How was Clinton's first year in office similar to President Franklin Roosevelt's first year? How did it differ?

Test Bank Answer Key

[1] d

[2] h

[3] e

[4] f

[5] a

[6] i

[7] c

[8] B

[9] C

[10] D

[11] B

[12] B

[13] A

[14] B

[15] D

[16] D

[17] B

[18] D

[19] East Asia, Soviet Union

[20] 3,100; 2,500

[21] The United States may have accepted many refugees from these areas for humanitarian reasons as many of these immigrants were victims of political or religious persecution.

[22] His cabinet appointments reflected "the face of America," and included members of minority groups. He appointed a woman to the Supreme Court and asked his wife to head a task force to develop the administration's health-care package.

Test Bank Answer Key

The two objectives are related in the long-term. Clinton maintains that the health-care system is "too expensive, too bureaucratic and too wasteful." If his proposed health-care reforms are passsed, government spending will eventually be reduced, and in turn, the deficit will be cut. On the other hand, critics of Clinton's health-care program predict that it would result in higher costs and [23] create a deficit of at least $918 billion in its first six years.

New immigrants have strained the social services and educational facilities of several states, particularly Florida, Texas, and California, and according to some, have taken jobs away from native-born Americans, particularly those at the lower levels. As with previous waves of immigrants, recent waves have added ideas, [24] values, and culture to the "American mixture."

[25] d

[26] f

[27] a

[28] e

[29] b

[30] h

[31] g

[32] B

[33] C

[34] B

[35] A

[36] C

[37] A

[38] D

[39] C

[40] D

[41] C

[42] D

[43] Latin America/Caribbean; East Asia

Test Bank Answer Key

[44] 50,000; 38,000

[45] Many people may have been forced to leave their homes because of political pressures; others may have sought a way out of poverty, particularly in Laos and Cambodia.

[46] Clinton's appointments--as well as political gains made by various minority groups--reflect the new ethnic and cultural diversity resulting from changes in immigration patterns. Education has been particularly affected by the new wave of immigration. Many new students do not speak English and the perspective of school curriculums has been refocused to highlight the contributions of a wide variety of cultures.

[47] American foreign policy goals in each of these instances are related. The overall goals are to support democratic government, to cooperate with international organizations such as the United Nations to promote peace, and to provide humanitarian relief when needed.

[48] Both Presidents began their administrations on a wave of positive feelings and hope at a time when the economy needed help. Both moved aggressively at the start to create a momentum and be productive. Unlike Clinton, however, Roosevelt was able to push a great deal of legislation through Congress with minimal opposition.

Unit 1

Test Bank Questions

Complete each of the following sentences by selecting the appropriate term from the choices listed in parentheses.

1. The author of the Declaration of Independence was (Thomas Jefferson, Benjamin Franklin).

2. George Grenville began a series of changes in British policies designed to pay off debts resulting from the (French and Indian War, War for Independence).

3. The (Intolerable Acts, Proclamation of 1763) forbade American colonists to settle west of the Appalachian Mountains.

4. The Virginia Company was an example of a (<u>congregacion</u>, joint-stock company), an enterprise supported by investors who expected to share a profit.

5. Most European households in the 1400s were examples of a (cousinocracy, patriarchal society), or male-dominated social organization.

6. According to the theory of (salutary neglect, mercantilism), the thirteen colonies existed to serve the interests of Great Britain.

7. (Marquis de Lafayette, Samuel de Champlain) founded the town of Quebec.

8. (Metacom, Powhatan) was a sachem who led Native Americans in King Philip's War.

9. The Spanish (<u>encomienda</u> system, enclosure movement) required Native Americans to work for the profit of an individual Spaniard.

10. Enslaved Africans endured great hardships during the journey to the Americas, known as the (Middle Passage, Great Migration).

11. The idea that ordinary people can and should govern themselves is known as (natural rights, popular sovereignty).

12. Native Americans relied on (religious toleration, oral tradition) as a way to preserve their spiritual beliefs.

Test Bank Questions

Write the letter of the correct answer.

13. What did almost all Native American societies have in common in the 1400s?

    A) They relied on buffalo for food and clothing.

    B) They refused to trade outside of their groups.

    C) They depended on kinship networks for most social needs.

    D) They lived as hunter-gatherers.

14. How did the European encounter with the Americas affect West Africans?

    A) Most West Africans became wealthy as a result of increased trade.

    B) West Africans developed strong kinship networks.

    C) Millions of West Africans were enslaved and shipped to the Americas.

    D) The West African population was decimated by diseases.

15. What crop became the foundation of the Jamestown colony's economy in the early 1600s?

    A) cotton   B) tobacco   C) rice   D) indigo

16. Which statement best describes the French approach to Native American cultures?

    A) French settlers tried to transform Native American societies.

    B) French fur traders became business partners with Native Americans.

    C) The French forced Native Americans to migrate from the Northeast.

    D) French settlers adopted the Native American way of life.

17. Why did the Puritans emigrate to North America in the 1600s?

    A) to escape religious persecution

    B) to serve as Catholic missionaries in Native American villages

    C) to explore and conquer the North American continent

    D) to develop trading opportunities for Britain

18. Which of the following was true of colonial American society in the early 1700s?

    A) Colonists were dedicated to the belief that men and women were equal.

    B) Colonists preserved the natural rights of all people.

    C) Colonial society rejected the European model of a hierarchy.

    D) Power belonged solely to those men who owned land.

19. In which colonies were enslaved Africans more likely to preserve their cultural traditions in the 1700s?

    A) Middle Colonies   B) South Carolina and Georgia

    C) New England Colonies   D) Virginia and Maryland

Test Bank Questions

Write the letter of the correct answer.

20. Which of the following influenced the colonists' decision to declare their independence?

    A) Pontiac's Rebellion, the Treaty of Paris

    B) the Intolerable Acts, <u>Common Sense</u>

    C) the Navigation Acts, the Great Awakening

    D) the Boston Tea Party, the triangular trade

21. What made the final American victory at Yorktown possible?

    A) the desertion of most Loyalists

    B) George Washington's military genius

    C) French troops and military supplies

    D) Iroquois attacks on the British

22. Which of the following was true of the American Revolution?

    A) The Revolution had little effect on civilians.

    B) The Revolution improved American–Native American relations.

    C) As a result of the Revolution, African Americans gained greater freedom.

    D) As a result of the Revolution, all white men were granted equal rights.

Test Bank Questions

Use the map of North America to answer the following questions.

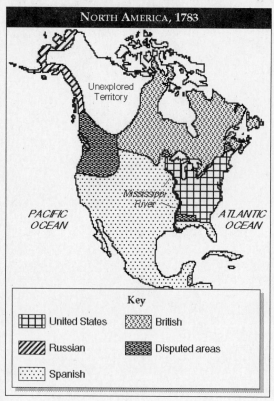

NORTH AMERICA, 1783

Unexplored Territory

Mississippi River

PACIFIC OCEAN

ATLANTIC OCEAN

Key

▦ United States   British

▨ Russian   ▨ Disputed areas

Spanish

23. As a result of the Treaty of 1783, what land did the United States gain?

24. (a) What country claimed most of the land west of the Mississippi River?
    (b) What other foreign countries had land claims in North America in 1783?

25. What conflicting land claims would the new nation have to resolve?

Answer the following questions.

26. Explain why Native American and English societies were often in conflict from the early 1500s to the late 1700s.

27. Compare the way American colonists viewed the British prior to the American Revolution with the way many Native Americans viewed the colonists.

28. How were the principles of the American Revolution inconsistent with the realities of American society?

Test Bank Questions

Complete each of the following sentences by selecting the appropriate term from the choices listed in parentheses.

29. During the (Great Awakening, Reformation) of the early 1500s, new Christian churches developed in protest against the Catholic church.

30. A Native American clan was a type of (kinship network, cousinocracy).

31. General (Thomas Jefferson, George Washington) led the Patriots during the War for Independence.

32. Europeans in the 1400s explained the economic contrasts within society as part of a (hierarchy, division of labor).

33. King Ferdinand and Queen Isabella supported the venture of navigator (Christopher Columbus, John Smith) to sail westward across the Atlantic Ocean.

34. After the Boston Tea Party, the British passed the (Intolerable Acts, Proclamation of 1763) to punish the colony of Massachusetts.

35. During a series of struggles known as (the French and Indian War, Pontiac's Rebellion), Native Americans rebelled against British rule.

36. The (Treaty of Paris, Declaration of Independence) granted the American colonies complete sovereignty in 1783.

37. Under the (encomienda system, enclosure movement), Native Americans were forced to work for the profit of an individual Spaniard.

38. According to the theory of (mercantilism, salutary neglect), the American colonies existed to serve the interests of Great Britain.

39. In 1680 (Powhatan, Popé) led the Pueblos and some Apaches in a full-scale revolt against Spanish control of New Mexico.

40. The wave of English settlers across the Atlantic Ocean in the early 1600s is referred to as the (Middle Passage, Great Migration).

Write the letter of the correct ending.

41. Both Native American and West African societies in the 1400s
    A) practiced the Islamic faith.
    B) developed extensive trading networks.
    C) supported themselves primarily through farming.
    D) believed that land should be shared by all.

42. The goal of most European explorers in the 1400s and 1500s was to
    A) drive the Muslims out of the Americas.
    B) increase the labor supply.
    C) conquer West African kingdoms.
    D) find new markets for trade.

Test Bank Questions

Write the letter of the correct ending.

43. The Europeans were able to conquer the Americas so quickly largely because many Native American groups
    A) suffered a population decline due to starvation and malnutrition.
    B) died of deadly diseases brought from Europe.
    C) were constantly at war with one another.
    D) lacked any form of social organization.

44. The European nation that believed in remaking the Native American cultures that it conquered was
    A) Spain.   B) the Netherlands.
    C) France.   D) England.

45. The Puritans who founded the Massachusetts Bay Colony did not believe in the principle of
    A) popular sovereignty.   B) natural rights.
    C) religious toleration.   D) a patriarchal society.

46. Colonial American society in the early 1700s was
    A) set up as a classless society.
    B) based on the principle that men and women were created equal.
    C) dedicated to preserving the natural rights of all people of European descent.
    D) dominated by white, wealthy landowners.

47. Many enslaved Africans living in South Carolina and Georgia in the 1700s
    A) adopted European customs.   B) became skilled artisans.
    C) preserved their traditions.   D) gained their freedom.

48. British–American relations worsened after the French and Indian War when the British
    A) refused to protect the colonists from further Native American uprisings.
    B) restricted the colonies' participation in the triangular trade.
    C) began to practice salutary neglect.
    D) imposed taxes on the American colonies.

49. The Declaration of Independence promoted all of the following ideas EXCEPT
    A) natural rights.   B) equal rights.
    C) popular sovereignty.   D) abolition of slavery.

50. The American Revolution improved the legal and political status of
    A) white men.   B) women.
    C) African Americans.   D) Native Americans.

Test Bank Questions

Use the map of North America to answer the following questions.

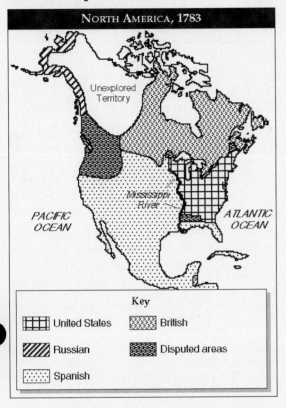

NORTH AMERICA, 1783

Unexplored Territory

PACIFIC OCEAN

Mississippi River

ATLANTIC OCEAN

Key

United States   British

Russian   Disputed areas

Spanish

51. (a) What foreign nations had land holdings in North America in 1783?
    (b) Which nation had the most extensive land claims?

52. About how much of its North American territory did Britain lose when the thirteen colonies became an independent nation in 1783?

53. With what two countries might the new nation encounter problems over conflicting land claims?

Answer the following questions.

54. What effects did the European encounter with the Americas have on Native American and West African societies?

55. What did the Native Americans who fought in King Philip's War have in common with the American colonists who fought in the American Revolution?

56. Why were Native Americans allied with the French rather than with the British in the 1600s and 1700s?

Test Bank Answer Key

[1]   Thomas Jefferson

[2]   French and Indian War

[3]   Proclamation of 1763

[4]   joint-stock company

[5]   patriarchal society

[6]   mercantilism

[7]   Samuel de Champlain

[8]   Metacom

[9]   encomienda system

[10] Middle Passage

[11] popular sovereignty

[12] oral tradition

[13] C

[14] C

[15] B

[16] B

[17] A

[18] D

[19] B

[20] B

[21] C

[22] D

[23] most of the land east of the Mississippi River to the Atlantic Ocean and south of the Great Lakes to Florida

[24] (a) Spain
      (b) Britain and Russia

[25] The United States would have to resolve the dispute with Britain over its northern borders and a dispute with Spain over its southern border.

Test Bank Answer Key

[26] Native Americans and English societies were often in conflict as a result of differing attitudes and ways of life. The English felt superior to the Native Americans and tried to impose their culture on Native American groups. The English believed in private ownership of land, while Native Americans shared land in common. The English way of life, which altered the environment for farming, threatened the Native American lifestyle of hunting and gathering.

[27] Prior to the American Revolution, many American colonists felt that the British were curtailing their freedoms and treating them unfairly. Likewise, many Native Americans felt the American colonists were encroaching on their freedom to use the land and to practice their traditional way of life.

[28] The principles of the American Revolution, such as equality and natural rights, were inconsistent with the way in which women, enslaved African Americans, and Native Americans were treated in American society. Each group had few rights, was considered inferior, and was exploited and subjected to the control of others.

[29] Reformation

[30] kinship network

[31] George Washington

[32] hierarchy

[33] Christopher Columbus

[34] Intolerable Acts

[35] Pontiac's Rebellion

[36] Declaration of Independence

[37] encomienda system

[38] mercantilism

[39] Popé

[40] Great Migration

[41] B

[42] D

[43] B

[44] D

Test Bank Answer Key

[45] C

[46] D

[47] C

[48] D

[49] D

[50] A

[51] (a) Britain, Spain, Russia
(b) Spain

[52] about one third

[53] Spain and Britain

[54] The European encounter with the Americas caused the collapse of many Native American and West African societies. European diseases decimated Native American populations and enabled the Europeans to conquer many Native American groups. The demand for labor on colonial plantations encouraged the trading of guns for enslaved West Africans, resulting in widespread warfare and the decline of many West African societies.

[55] Native Americans who fought in King Philip's War resented English settlers for destroying forests and creating pastures. They viewed white encroachment as a serious threat to their livelihood and their way of life. American colonists viewed the British as power-hungry and corrupt and feared that British policies such as the Stamp Act would curtail their freedoms. Like the Native Amercians, American colonists fought to protect their way of life and their land.

[56] The French, seeking to trade with Native Americans rather than to conquer them, did not usually interfere with Native American cultures. By contrast, British colonists posed a direct threat to Native American cultures. They tried to force Native Americans to adopt European lifestyles, and wanted to turn their hunting grounds into farms and communities.

Unit 2

Test Bank Questions

Match the terms below with the following descriptions. Write the letter of the correct answer. You will not use all the terms.

a. Andrew Jackson
b. Eli Whitney
c. James Madison
d. Gabriel Prosser
e. Tecumseh
f. Samuel Slater
g. Alexander Hamilton
h. John Marshall
i. John Ross
j. Handsome Lake
k. Richard Allen
l. Susanna Haswell Rowson
m. Daniel Shays

1.   helped found the African Methodist Episcopal Church

2.   became a national hero as a result of the Battle of New Orleans

3.   was appointed the first Chief Justice of the Supreme Court

4.   invented the cotton gin in 1793

5.   led an uprising over debts and taxes in Massachusetts

6.   helped the Cherokee devise legal and political systems that blended Cherokee and European traditions

7.   was appointed Secretary of the Treasury under President Washington

8.   organized a revolution of enslaved African Americans in Virginia

9.   duplicated the British spinning mill in the United States

10. promoted the Virginia Plan at the Constitutional Convention and later became the fourth U.S. President

Write the letter of the correct answer.

11. Why were the Nationalists dissatisfied with the Articles of Confederation?
    A) They thought the judicial branch wielded too much power.
    B) They felt the Articles placed too little emphasis on popular sovereignty.
    C) They wanted a unicameral, not a bicameral, legislature.
    D) They believed the national government needed more power.

Write the letter of the correct answer.

12. How did the founders of the Constitution restrict the power of the people?

   A) by passing the Great Compromise to resolve the question of representation

   B) by creating an Electoral College to elect the President

   C) by creating a system of checks and balances

   D) by establishing three separate branches of government

13. Which of the following was designed to protect Americans against the power of the national government?

   A) the Preamble   B) the Elastic Clause

   C) the Bill of Rights   D) the Great Compromise

14. With which of the following were Jeffersonian Republicans most concerned in the 1790s?

   A) protecting the power of the national government

   B) maintaining social order

   C) paying off war debts

   D) defending the people's liberty

15. Which of the following restricted many Americans' freedoms?

   A) the Adams-Onís Treaty

   B) the Hartford Convention

   C) the Alien and Sedition Acts of 1798

   D) the Whiskey Rebellion

16. What was the significance of Marbury v. Madison?

   A) The Supreme Court banned the appointing of midnight judges.

   B) The case proved the effectiveness of the First American Party System.

   C) The case convinced many Americans that the Supreme Court wielded too much power.

   D) The case established the principle of judicial review.

17. What was the aim of the pan-Indian movement in the early 1800s?

   A) to blend Christianity with traditional Native American beliefs

   B) to promote the assimilation of Native Americans into white culture

   C) to unify Native Americans in their resistance to United States expansion

   D) to encourage the resettlement of Native Americans onto reservations

Test Bank Questions

Write the letter of the correct answer.

18. Which of the following led to a declaration of war against Britain in 1812?

A) the XYZ Affair

B) burning of the Capitol and White House

C) British harassment of U.S. shipping

D) British violation of the terms of the Jay Treaty

19. Which of the following best describes population growth in the United States between 1780 and 1830?

A) doubled every twenty years   B) remained unchanged

C) increased slowly   D) declined significantly

20. What impact did the use of steam power and the system of interchangeable parts have on American society in the early 1800s?

A) They reinforced the concept of the republican woman.

B) They decreased reliance on slave labor.

C) They fueled an industrial revolution.

D) They led to the Panic of 1819.

21. Which of the following was NOT a characteristic of American society in the late 1700s and early 1800s?

A) Many Americans found meaning and community in organized religion.

B) Many family ties were weakened as a result of constant migration.

C) Middle-class women exercised more freedom and caution in selecting spouses.

D) Most white Americans began to question slavery and the unfair treatment of Native Americans.

Test Bank Questions

Use the diagram of the branches of government to answer the following
questions.

EXECUTIVE BRANCH

President is commander in chief of the
  armed forces.
President can propose legislation.
President can veto bills and appeal to
  people in speeches.
President can appeal to Congress in
  messages and can call special sessions.

Can impeach and remove President
  from office.
Can overrule President's veto.
Senate can refuse to ratify treaties.
Senate can refuse to confirm
  appointments.
Can declare war.

LEGISLATIVE BRANCH

Explain the system of checks and balances between the legislature and the
President in each of the following situations.

22. How can the President check the power of the legislative branch?

23. How can Congress check the power of the President in foreign affairs?

24. What check does the Senate have over presidential appointments?

Answer the following questions.

25. Use evidence to support or refute the following conclusion: <u>Slavery
    was one of the most divisive issues during the early years of the
    United States</u>.

26. How did the democratic ideals of the American Revolution spill over
    into religion and societal attitudes toward women in the late 1700s
    and early 1800s?

27. Many Nationalists in the late 1700s viewed American democracy as a
    model for the world. What political events from 1783 to 1830 would
    Nationalists have cited as examples of "democracy in action"?

Test Bank Questions

Match the terms below with the following descriptions. Write the letter of the correct answer. You will not use all the terms.

a. Great Compromise
b. Treaty of Ghent

c. Articles of Confederation
d. Whiskey Rebellion
e. Three-fifths Compromise

f. XYZ Affair
g. Embargo of 1807

h. Adams-Onís Treaty

i. black codes
j. Marbury v. Madison

k. Missouri Compromise
l. Bill of Rights
m. Alien and Sedition
   Acts of 1798
n. Battle of Tippecanoe
o. Hartford Convention

28. placed African Americans in free territories in a subordinate position

29. established the power of judicial review

30. resolved the debate during the Constitutional Convention about whether representation in the legislature should be based on population

  :GPRTBL D3702
31. guaranteed certain basic freedoms for Americans

Match the terms below with the following descriptions. Write the letter of the correct answer. You will not use all the terms.

a. Great Compromise
b. Treaty of Ghent

c. Articles of Confederation
d. Whiskey Rebellion
e. Three-fifths Compromise

f. XYZ Affair
g. Embargo of 1807

h. Adams-Onís Treaty

i. black codes
j. Marbury v. Madison

k. Missouri Compromise
l. Bill of Rights
m. Alien and Sedition
   Acts of 1798
n. Battle of Tippecanoe
o. Hartford Convention

32. transferred Florida to the United States

33. established a formula for counting enslaved African Americans for purposes of representation

34. closed courts and harassed tax collectors in protest of excise tax

35. ended the War of 1812

36. determined whether future states would be free states or slave states

37. gave the President the right to imprison or deport citizens of other countries residing in the United States and restricted freedom of speech

38. shattered Native American morale and shattered confidence in Tenskwatawa

39. halted all commerce with Europeans

Test Bank Questions

Write the letter of the correct ending.

40. James Madison and his Virginia Plan promoted
    A) a bicameral legislature.
    B) a unicameral legislature.
    C) powerful state governments and a weak national government.
    D) equal votes in the legislature for all states.

41. The Anti-Federalists agreed to support the Constitution after the addition of the
    A) Bill of Rights.   B) Preamble.
    C) Electoral College.   D) system of checks and balances.

42. The Nationalists criticized the Articles of Confederation for
    A) making the national government too weak.
    B) giving Congress the power to tax.
    C) making the judicial branch too powerful.
    D) giving state governments too little power.

43. During the Second Great Awakening, revivalists promoted the belief that
    A) good works were a prerequisite to earning salvation.
    B) all people could achieve salvation.
    C) church and state should be joined together.
    D) public education was essential for the survival of democracy.

44. The statement that best describes young Americans in the late 1700s and early 1800s is:
    A) They were idealists who wanted to reform society and make it more democratic.
    B) They were constantly migrating and working to improve their lives.
    C) They were unstable, insecure, and dependent on their parents.
    D) They were rebels who rejected authority and traditional values.

45. The rapid population growth of the United States from 1780 to 1830 was primarily the result of the
    A) mass immigration from Europe.
    B) high birth rate among the white population.
    C) stability and relative peace of the new nation.
    D) great increase in the Native American population.

Test Bank Questions

Write the letter of the correct ending.

46. President Jefferson became immensely popular when he
    A) took steps to reduce the power of the federal government.
    B) created a national bank.
    C) passed the Embargo of 1807.
    D) adopted a loose construction of the Constitution.

47. Most Jeffersonian Republicans were ardent supporters of
    A) the French Revolution.
    B) the Alien and Sedition Acts of 1798.
    C) the Northwest Territory.
    D) Alexander Hamilton's economic program.

48. The election of Thomas Jefferson as President in 1800 was significant because it
    A) demonstrated that political parties threatened national unity.
    B) proved that Americans could transfer power peacefully.
    C) forewarned Americans of the danger of a strong national government.
    D) signaled the beginning of the First American Party System.

49. In the early 1800s, Shawnee brothers Tenskwatawa and Tecumseh encouraged Native Americans to
    A) reclaim their traditions.
    B) assimilate into white European culture.
    C) accept Christianity.
    D) migrate to reservations.

Test Bank Questions

Use the diagram of the branches of government to answer the following questions.

EXECUTIVE BRANCH

President is commander in chief of the
  armed forces.
President can propose legislation.
President can veto bills and appeal to
  people in speeches.
President can appeal to Congress in
  messages and can call special sessions.

Can impeach and remove President
  from office.
Can overrule President's veto.
Senate can refuse to ratify treaties.
Senate can refuse to confirm
  appointments.
Can declare war.

LEGISLATIVE BRANCH

Explain the system of checks and balances between the legislature and the President in each of the following situations.

50. The President appoints an unqualified person as Attorney General.

51. The Congress passes a law that violates a presidential campaign promise.

52. The President negotiates a treaty that is unpopular with most Americans.

53. The Congress ignores an appeal by the President and declares war.

Answer the following questions.

54. What are four questions you would ask a middle-class woman who lived during the early years of the republic to learn about women's lives during that period? How would she most likely respond?

55. What political events that took place during the early years of the new republic could Federalists have used to support their claim that the United States needed a strong national government? Explain.

56. What factors promoted United States expansionism in the late 1700s and early 1800s? How did expansionism in turn affect American society?

Test Bank Answer Key

[1] k _____

[2] a _____

[3] h _____

[4] b _____

[5] m _____

[6] i _____

[7] g _____

[8] d _____

[9] f _____

[10] c _____

[11] D _____

[12] B _____

[13] C _____

[14] D _____

[15] C _____

[16] D _____

[17] C _____

[18] C _____

[19] A _____

[20] C _____

[21] D _____

[22] The President can propose bills, veto legislation, appeal to the people, and call special sessions of Congress.

[23] Congress can declare war; the Senate can refuse to ratify a treaty the President has negotiated.

[24] The Senate can refuse to confirm a presidential appointment.

Test Bank Answer Key

Support: The issue of slavery caused division from the very
beginning, when delegates at the Constitutional Convention argued
over how to count the slave population for purposes of
representation. While the Three-fifths Compromise resolved that
crisis, another one erupted about thirty years later over the
admission of Missouri as a slave state. A second compromise--the
Missouri Compromise--resolved that crisis by restoring the balance of
free and slave states.
Refute: The organization of the new government and how much power it
should have overshadowed any debate over slavery. Only a handful of
Americans spoke out against slavery in the early years of the
republic, and exploitation of African Americans was an accepted
[25] practice in the states and in the new territories.

During the Second Great Awakening, religion became very democratic.
Revivalists preached that salvation was available to all people, and
religion enabled many women and African Americans to assume greater
leadership roles. In society, there existed a spirit of hope and a
belief in liberty, progress, and self-improvement. Many Americans
began to view an educated woman as crucial to the success of the
nation, and women gained status in a new role as republican mothers
[26] and wives.

The Nationalists would have cited as examples the compromises reached
at the Constitutional Convention, the formation of a new government,
the election of 1800 when Americans peacefully transferred power from
one political party to another, and a war fought to protect the
[27] principle of freedom of the seas.

[28] i _____

[29] j _____

[30] a _____

[31] l _____

[32] h _____

[33] e _____

[34] d _____

[35] b _____

[36] k _____

[37] m _____

[38] n _____

[39] g _____

Test Bank Answer Key

[40] A

[41] A

[42] A

[43] B

[44] B

[45] B

[46] A

[47] A

[48] B

[49] A

[50] The Senate refuses to confirm the nominee.

[51] The President vetoes the bill.

[52] The Senate rejects the treaty.

[53] As commander in chief, the President refuses to give the order for the troops to be sent into battle or to engage in war tactics.

[54] Students may ask whether she had attended school and why, what her role was like in the family, what her interests were outside the home, and how she viewed courtship and marriage. She might answer that as a young girl she had attended school to learn basic reading and writing skills, virtue, and self-discipline, that her role as a republican woman was to raise and instill values in her children (she probably had four or five of them), and that she was actively involved in the church community or teaching. Before she married, she enjoyed a long courtship with her future husband as they worked out the terms of their life together.

[55] The Federalists could have pointed to the Whiskey Rebellion and defiance of the Embargo of 1807, two situations in which the government used military force to crush resistance. They might also claim that a strong national government was needed to fight wars against Native Americans, settle land disputes, and resolve crises over expansion and slavery.

Test Bank Answer Key

In the late 1700s and early 1800s, the application of steam power, the invention of the cotton gin, canal building, and land

acquisitions via the Louisiana Purchase and the Adams–Onís Treaty encouraged expansionism and westward migration. The explosive expansion of American society, however, strained family ties and relationships and resulted in a new kind of loneliness. When peoples' high expectations for economic success were dashed, many turned to
[56] alcohol or suicide.

Unit 3

Test Bank Questions

Complete each sentence below by selecting the correct word from the list. You will not use all the words.

a. Nat Turner
b. Sacajawea
c. Stephen Austin

d. John Quincy Adams
e. Charles Grandison Finney
f. Harriet Tubman

g. John C. Frémont
h. Dorothea Dix

i. Brigham Young
j. Horace Mann
k. Narcissa Prentiss Whitman
l. Elizabeth Cady Stanton
m. John C. Calhoun
n. Sojourner Truth

o. Frederick Douglass

1. Lyman Beecher and _____ were among the most successful revivalists of the Second Great Awakening.

2. _____, a Shoshone woman, served as translator and guide for the Lewis and Clark expedition.

3. The first organized group of American settlers into Texas was led by _____.

4. _____ pioneered school reform, establishing uniform curricula and teacher training in Massachusetts.

5. _____ was a missionary who taught Sunday School to Native Americans in Oregon's Willamette Valley.

6. A "conductor" in the underground railroad, _____ helped lead fugitive slaves to freedom.

7. Believing he was acting with divine inspiration, _____ organized a slave rebellion in Virginia in 1831.

8. Both William Lloyd Garrison and _____ published antislavery newspapers in the mid-1800s.

9. In the election of 1824, _____ became President after he was voted in by the House of Representatives.

10. In 1848 Lucretia Mott and _____ organized a convention in Seneca Falls, New York, to discuss women's rights.

11. By 1847 an American expedition commanded by _____ had taken control of California.

12. Mormon leader _____ chose the Great Salt Lake Basin as the Mormons' new home.

Test Bank Questions

Write the letter of the correct ending.

13. President Andrew Jackson opposed
    A) industrialization.
    B) the spoils system.
    C) South Carolina's nullification.
    D) relocating Native Americans to Oklahoma.

14. Like the North, the South in the early 1800s
    A) could barely support the growing population in its cities.
    B) was predominantly agricultural.
    C) had become mostly industrial.
    D) was basically a classless society.

15. The Market Revolution is best described as the period in the early 1800s when
    A) Americans began using cash and credit to acquire goods.
    B) a household economy dominated life in the United States.
    C) factories in the United States began to decentralize manufacturing.
    D) the federal government began issuing paper money.

16. In 1823 the United States warned European nations not to intervene in the Americas in what became known as
    A) the Monroe Doctrine.   B) the Wilmot Proviso.
    C) manifest destiny.   D) the American System.

17. Middle-class reformers in the early 1800s were most interested in
    A) regulating business and industry.
    B) improving working conditions.
    C) reforming national politics.
    D) improving personal behavior.

18. All of the following issues increased tensions between the North and South in the 1840s EXCEPT
    A) abolitionism.   B) the tariff.
    C) patronage.   D) educational reform.

19. Southern representatives fought the antislavery movement by pushing through
    A) a program of gradual emancipation.   B) prohibition.
    C) the Tariff of Abominations.   D) the gag rule.

Test Bank Questions

Write the letter of the correct ending.

20. All of the following statements describe nomadic Native American societies in the mid-1800s EXCEPT:

    A) They depended heavily on skilled riding and hunting.

    B) They tended to be more peaceful than village societies.

    C) Women generally had less influence than in agricultural societies.

    D) They often conducted raids on other Native American groups.

21. The California gold rush had the most devastating impact on

    A) Native Americans.   B) Christian missionaries.

    C) African Americans.   D) Mormons.

22. After the Mexican War, Americans disagreed most over

    A) the annexation of Texas.

    B) the issue of slavery in the territories acquired from Mexico.

    C) the southern boundary of the United States.

    D) how to conduct commercial relations with Mexico.

Use the map of the United States to answer the following questions.

23. How did the United States acquire most of the territory in the Southwest?

Test Bank Questions

Use the map of the United States to answer the following questions.

THE UNITED STATES, 1783-1853

ADJUSTED BY TREATY WITH BRITAIN (1846)
CEDED BY BRITAIN (1818)
CANADA
ADJUSTED BY TREATY WITH BRITAIN (1818)
WEBSTER-ASHBURTON TREATY
OREGON COUNTRY (1846)
LOUISIANA PURCHASE (1803)
UNITED STATES (1783)
MEXICAN CESSION (1848)
TEXAS ANNEXATION (1845)
GADSDEN PURCHASE (1853)
Rio Grande
FLORIDA CESSION (1819)
(1810) (1812–13) ANNEXED BY U.S.
MEXICO

24. (a) What natural feature marks the boundary between the United States and Mexico?
    (b) How were border disputes between the United States and Great Britain settled?

25. How did the United States gain possession of Florida?

Answer the following questions.

26. Why do you think most reform movements in the 1830s and 1840s took place in the North?

27. What problems did westward expansion create for the United States government in the first half of the 1800s?

28. What were some advantages and disadvantages of the Market Revolution in the United States? Who benefited? Who was adversely affected?

Test Bank Questions

Match the terms below with the following descriptions. Write the letter of the correct answer. You will not use all the terms.

a. temperance movement
b. underground railroad
c. commodity
d. American System
e. mountain men
f. manifest destiny
g. nullification
h. secularize

i. capitalists
j. suffrage
k. gag rule
l. Monroe Doctrine
m. Wilmot Proviso
n. Tariff of Abominations
o. spoils system

29. the right to vote

30. idea or belief that favored the United States expansion in the mid-1800s

31. people who provide the money to build factories and start businesses

32. system by which enslaved people were secretly helped to reach the North or Canada

33. action of a state to void a law passed by Congress

34. western fur trappers who discovered Native American trails that led to Oregon and California

35. law that restrained freedom of speech

36. U.S. warning to European nations to stay out of the Americas

37. campaign against manufacturing and selling alcoholic beverages

38. placing religious organizations under the control of the state

39. practice by which public offices are filled by friends or supporters of the victorious political party

40. proposed amendment to outlaw slavery in all territory acquired from Mexico in the 1840s

Write the letter of the correct answer.

41. Which of the following was a result of the Market Revolution in the United States?

    A) The United States developed a household economy.

    B) Industries became decentralized.

    C) Families became more self-sufficient.

    D) More Americans began to use cash and credit.

42. How did the North differ from the South in the early 1800s?

    A) Free blacks could vote in the North.

    B) The North was primarily a classless society.

    C) The North had more urban centers and industry.

    D) The North was much more agricultural.

Test Bank Questions

Write the letter of the correct answer.

43. How did National Republicans differ from Jacksonian Democrats?

A) National Republicans wanted to repeal the Tariff of Abominations.

B) National Republicans opposed the American system.

C) National Republicans supported federal intervention in the economy.

D) National Republicans tried to reform the spoils system.

44. Which of the following did President Andrew Jackson support?

A) the McCulloch v. Maryland decision

B) Georgia's seizure of Native American land

C) the Bank of the United States

D) South Carolina's nullification

45. What contribution did Dorothea Dix make in the 1840s?

A) She pioneered school reform.

B) She was an antislavery spokesperson.

C) She began the temperance movement.

D) She spearheaded prison reform.

46. Which of the following was NOT a reason for opposition to abolitionism?

A) Merchants feared the movement would hurt business with the South.

B) Many families did not want African Americans living in their communities.

C) Many people feared that free blacks would move to Liberia.

D) Labor leaders feared that African American workers would accept low wages.

47. Which movement was organized by Lucretia Mott and Elizabeth Cady Stanton in the mid-1800s?

A) the cult of domesticity

B) women's rights

C) Transcendentalism

D) utopian communities

48. How did nomadic Native American societies differ from agricultural societies in the mid 1800s?

A) Nomadic Native Americans used horses.

B) Nomadic societies were friendlier and more peaceful.

C) Women had more influence in agricultural societies.

D) Agricultural societies depended upon hunting buffalo.

Test Bank Questions

Write the letter of the correct answer.

49. What was the immediate cause of the Mexican War?
    A) Texans' declaration of independence
    B) the Wilmot Proviso
    C) Santa Anna's attack on the Alamo
    D) dispute over Texas's border

50. Why did Lewis and Clark explore the Louisiana Territory in 1804?
    A) to search for gold
    B) to establish reservations for Native Americans
    C) to blaze the Oregon Trail for westward expansion
    D) to gather information about its natural resources

Use the map of the United States to answer the following questions.

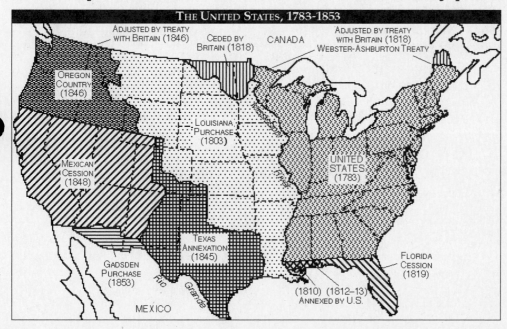

51. (a) With which nation did the United States negotiate its northern borders?
    (b) What natural feature marks the border between Mexico and the United States?

52. (a) What territory did the United States annex during the War of 1812?
    (b) What was the country's single largest territorial acquisition after 1783?

53. What two areas did the United States have to buy?

Test Bank Questions

Answer the following questions.

54. Discuss at least three issues that increased tensions between middle-class northerners and southern whites in the 1830s and 1840s.

55. How did the Market Revolution create social and political divisions in the United States?

56. Why were white immigrants and nomadic Native Americans unable to coexist peacefully on the Great Plains in the mid-1800s?

Test Bank Answer Key

[1] e

[2] b

[3] c

[4] j

[5] k

[6] f

[7] a

[8] o

[9] d

[10] l

[11] g

[12] i

[13] C

[14] B

[15] A

[16] A

[17] D

[18] C

[19] D

[20] B

[21] A

[22] B

[23] Mexico ceded the territory to the United States.

[24] Rio Grande River; by treaty

[25] Western Florida was annexed; Spain ceded the rest of Florida to the United States in 1819.

Test Bank Answer Key

In the early 1800s, the North had become increasingly more urban and industrial. Along with economic growth and a skyrocketing increase in population came a wide range of social problems, including poverty, alcoholism, crime, and poor living conditions. In addition, most evangelical Protestants, who stressed the importance of character and self-improvement, lived in the North as did the Transcendentalists [26] who questioned traditional authority and became active reformers.

As a result of westward expansion, the United States government was confronted with conflicts between eager and adventurous white immigrants and angry Native Americans on the Great Plains. In addition, the government had to resolve the disputes between northerners and southerners over the extension of slavery into the new territories. Westward expansion also led to conflicts and border [27] disputes with other nations, and finally to war with Mexico.

The Market Revolution created thriving industries, economic opportunities for many, and urban growth, but at a cost. As entrepreneurs began to view the relationship between themselves and their employees in strictly economic terms, working conditions deteriorated. Many dissatisfied workers joined labor unions and went out on strike for higher wages and shorter work hours. Living conditions also deteriorated in urban areas, as many cities lacked the facilities needed to support their growing populations. In addition, the Market Revolution widened the gap between rich and poor [28] and intensified regional differences between the North and the South.

[29] j

[30] f

[31] i

[32] b

[33] g

[34] e

[35] k

[36] l

[37] a

[38] h

[39] o

[40] m

[41] D

Test Bank Answer Key

[42] C

[43] C

[44] B

[45] D

[46] C

[47] B

[48] C

[49] D

[50] D

[51] (a) Great Britain
      (b) the Rio Grande

[52] (a) Western Florida
      (b) the Louisiana Purchase

[53] Louisiana Territory and a strip of land in the southwest that is today southern New Mexico and Arizona.

[54] Issues that increased tensions included the Tariff of Abominations, which southerners claimed helped the North but increased the cost of goods in the South; the antislavery movement, which threatened the South's economy and way of life; and social reform movements which southerners resented as northern interference with their society. In addition, the annexation of Texas and the status of slavery in new territories acquired in the Mexican War threatened to upset the balance of power in Congress and the Electoral College.

[55] While the number of wealthy city dwellers increased during the Market Revolution, so did the number of working poor and the unemployed, leading to new divisions in society between rich and poor, employers and employees. The Market Revolution also created a split in national politics, as National Republicans wanted the government to promote economic development and Jacksonian Democrats supported minimal government involvement.

[56] Nomadic Native Americans required a vast expanse of land in order to maintain their way of life which depended on following and hunting the buffalo that crisscrossed the plains. White settlers threatened to carve farms and build communities on Native American hunting grounds. As more Americans migrated West, the United States established military posts further west. By the 1850s, both the U.S. government and the Plains Indians saw military action as the only viable option for settling the conflict of cultures.

Unit 4

Test Bank Questions

Match the terms below with the following descriptions. Write the letter of the correct answer. You will not use all the terms.

a. Robert E. Lee
b. Stephen Douglas
c. George McClellan
d. Jefferson Davis
e. Andrew Johnson
f. Charles Sumner
g. John Brown
h. Ulysses S. Grant

i. Abraham Lincoln
j. Harriet Beecher Stowe
k. William Tecumseh Sherman
l. George Fitzhugh
m. John Wilkes Booth
n. William Henry Seward
o. Rutherford B. Hayes

1. abolitionist who led a raid on Harpers Ferry

2. President of the Union during the Civil War

3. Republican who fell victim to a brutal caning while in the Senate

4. brilliant Confederate general whose war strategy caused the defeat of several Union armies

5. Senator from Illinois who proposed the Kansas-Nebraska Act

6. President during Reconstruction whom Radical Republicans tried to impeach

7. determined Union general who led the seige of Vicksburg

8. southern sympathizer who assassinated President Lincoln

9. Union general who marched his troops from Atlanta to the sea

10. Republican President whose controversial election marked the end of Reconstruction

11. president of the Confederate States of America

12. author of <u>Uncle Tom's Cabin</u>

Write the letter of the correct answer.
13. In what way were the North and South alike in the mid-1800s?
   A) The population in both regions was about the same.
   B) Both subscribed to the theory of states' rights.
   C) Both were capitalist societies.
   D) Both were highly industrial.

Test Bank Questions

Write the letter of the correct answer.

14. Which of the following led to violence and bloodshed between abolitionists and proslavery forces?

    A) the Dred Scott case

    B) the Lincoln-Douglas debates

    C) the Kansas-Nebraska Act

    D) the Compromise of 1850

15. Which political party became the voice of abolitionists in the mid-1850s?

    A) the American party

    B) the Democratic party

    C) the Constitutional Union party

    D) the Republican party

16. Which event convinced the South that secession was its only alternative?

    A) the abolitionist raid on Harpers Ferry

    B) the election of President Lincoln

    C) repeal of the Lecompton constitution

    D) passage of the Fugitive Slave Act

17. How did new technology affect the fighting of the Civil War?

    A) The use of forts continued to be an effective tactic.

    B) Each side was forced to fight a war of attrition.

    C) Advanced weaponry made organization and training less important.

    D) Old strategies that marched masses of men across an open field became suicidal.

18. Which of the following was NOT an action taken by the federal government during the war?

    A) suspension of the writ of habeas corpus

    B) passage of draft laws

    C) suspension of trade with European nations

    D) creation of new forms of taxation

19. Which of the following helped turn the tide of war in favor of the Union?

    A) the battle of Shiloh

    B) the battle of Manassas

    C) the capture of Fort Henry

    D) the siege of Vicksburg

20. What was the main goal of Radical Republicans during Reconstruction?

    A) to end political corruption and reform government

    B) to protect the economy of the North

    C) to put the nation back together after the war

    D) to ensure the rights of African Americans

Test Bank Questions

Write the letter of the correct answer.

21. How did southerners try to regain power over African Americans in the 1860s and 1870s?

   A) by refusing to enforce the black codes

   B) by passing land redistribution laws

   C) by becoming scalawags

   D) by practicing debt peonage

22. Why did Reconstruction seem to fade in the late 1870s?

   A) Many African Americans migrated north where they were guaranteed equal rights.

   B) The women's rights movement began to dominate African American rights.

   C) Republicans became more concerned with promoting industry.

   D) The Supreme Court overturned the congressional plan for Reconstruction.

Use the map of Emancipation in the South to answer the following questions.

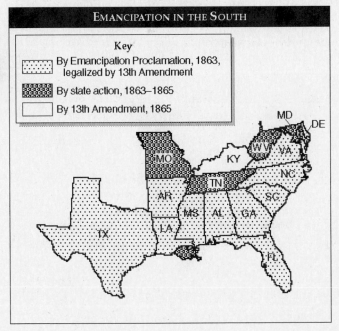

23. Which states took action on their own to end slavery?

24. Which states were neither affected by the Emancipation Proclamation nor took state action to end slavery?

25. How can you tell that the Border States were part of the Union?

Test Bank Questions

Answer the following questions.

26. Why has the Civil War been described as the first modern war in American history?

27. Support the following conclusion from your text about the North and South in the 1850s: <u>Each side saw the other as a threat to the American way of life</u>.

28. What steps did white southerners take to thwart Reconstruction policies? Why do you think so many white southerners resorted to terrorism and violence?

Complete each sentence below by selecting the correct word from the list. You will not use all the words.

a. Freedmen's Bureau

b. Fifteenth Amendment

c. Kansas-Nebraska Act

d. Compromise of 1850

e. Fugitive Slave Act

f. Thirteenth Amendment

g. Gettysburg Address

h. Anaconda Plan

i. Military Reconstruction Act of 1867

j. Emancipation Proclamation

k. writ of <u>habeas corpus</u>

l. Fourteenth Amendment

m. Pacific Railroad Act of 1862

n. Internal Revenue Act of 1862

o. Pickett's Charge

29. The _____ introduced by Senator Stephen Douglas promoted the idea of popular sovereignty with regard to the slave question.

30. After the Civil War, the _____ was established to help African Americans adjust to freedom.

31. The suspension of the _____ freed officers from justifying why prisoners had been imprisoned.

32. In his _____, President Lincoln declared the freedom of all enslaved people in areas of open rebellion against the United States.

33. The _____ stated that no United States citizen could be denied the right to vote.

34. The _____ declared that all persons born or naturalized in the United States were entitled to full citizenship rights.

35. Congress passed the _____ to create new taxes that would help finance the Civil War.

36. In the _____, California was admitted to the Union as a free state while the territories of Utah and New Mexico would decide for themselves the legal status of slavery.

37. Northerners were outraged that the _____ forced them to return runaway slaves to their owners.

Test Bank Questions

Complete each sentence below by selecting the correct word from the list. You will not use all the words.

a. Freedmen's Bureau
b. Fifteenth Amendment
c. Kansas-Nebraska Act
d. Compromise of 1850
e. Fugitive Slave Act
f. Thirteenth Amendment
g. Gettysburg Address
h. Anaconda Plan

i. Military Reconstruction Act of 1867
j. Emancipation Proclamation
k. writ of <u>habeas corpus</u>
l. Fourteenth Amendment
m. Pacific Railroad Act of 1862
n. Internal Revenue Act of 1862
o. Pickett's Charge

38. The _____ ended slavery in the United States.

39. During Reconstruction, Congress passed the _____ to establish districts in the South that would be governed by northern generals.

40. General Scott's recommendation that Union forces surround the Confederacy and squeeze it to death was called the _____.

Write the letter of the correct ending.

41. Many northerners became convinced that slavery would be the ruin of the United States as a result of

 A) John Brown's raid on Harpers Ferry.

 B) publication of <u>Uncle Tom's Cabin</u>.

 C) publication of George Fitzhugh's <u>Cannibals All!</u>

 D) passage of the Fugitive Slave Law.

42. The political party that represented abolitionist views in the mid-1800s was the

 A) Democratic party.   B) Republican party.
 C) Constitutional Union party. D) American party.

43. When Abraham Lincoln was elected President in 1860, southern states

 A) formed the Confederate States of America.

 B) passed the Lecompton constitution.

 C) passed draft laws.

 D) violated the Compromise of 1850.

44. One confederate advantage at the start of the Civil War was

 A) advanced weaponry.   B) greater wealth.
 C) more human resources.   D) bolder and more skillful generals.

Test Bank Questions

Write the letter of the correct ending.

45. During the first two years of the war, Union General Ulysses S. Grant was most successful in
   A) destroying the economy in the eastern region of the Confederacy.
   B) cutting off the northern region of the Confederacy from the southern region.
   C) seizing control of river valleys in the midwestern states.
   D) capturing key cities such as Atlanta and Richmond.

46. The siege of Vicksburg was important because it
   A) persuaded the Confederacy to wage a war of attrition.
   B) boosted the morale of the Confederacy.
   C) gave the Union control of the Mississippi River.
   D) enabled Confederate troops to take the offensive.

47. For most freed African Americans, the most important goal was
   A) owning land and pursuing whatever line of work they chose.
   B) forming their own churches.
   C) getting civil rights legislation passed to protect their rights.
   D) holding high political office.

48. In reaction to President Johnson's Reconstruction policy, Congress
   A) drafted a more moderate plan.
   B) passed measures to limit presidential power.
   C) decided to implement Lincoln's plan instead.
   D) removed the President from office.

49. During Reconstruction, southerners tried to reassert their power over African Americans in all of the following ways EXCEPT
   A) intimidating scalawags and carpetbaggers.
   B) passing black codes.
   C) using the system of debt peonage.
   D) redistributing land.

50. In the late 1870s, Republican governments became less interested in Reconstruction and began to focus more on
   A) eliminating corruption in government.
   B) promoting industry.
   C) women's rights.
   D) breaking the Ku Klux Klan.

Test Bank Questions

Use the map of Emancipation in the South to answer the following questions.

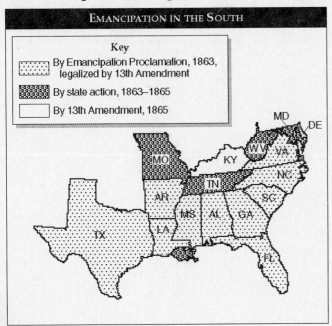

EMANCIPATION IN THE SOUTH

Key
- By Emancipation Proclamation, 1863, legalized by 13th Amendment
- By state action, 1863–1865
- By 13th Amendment, 1865

51. How did emancipation in Tennessee differ from that of other Confederate states?

52. How was slavery abolished in Kentucky and Delaware?

53. Which states were not affected by the Emancipation Proclamation?

Answer the following questions.

54. Discuss three lasting legacies of the Civil War.

55. Your text uses the title "The System Fails" to describe the failure of compromise in resolving the slavery question. Do you think this same title could be used to describe Reconstruction? Explain.

56. Use evidence to support or refute the following conclusion: The question of slavery was the single greatest cause of the Civil War.

Test Bank Answer Key

[1]   g

[2]   i

[3]   f

[4]   a

[5]   b

[6]   e

[7]   h

[8]   m

[9]   k

[10] o

[11] d

[12] j

[13] C

[14] C

[15] D

[16] B

[17] D

[18] B

[19] D

[20] D

[21] D

[22] C

[23] Missouri, Tennessee, West Virginia, and Maryland

[24] Kentucky and Delaware

[25] They were excluded from the Emancipation Proclamation.

Test Bank Answer Key

With the seige of Vicksburg, General Grant ushered in a new age of warfare, one characterized by the use of advanced technologies and a total war strategy. Although technologies change over time--missiles and nuclear weapons have replaced cannons and explosive shells--this type of warfare remains the same. In the Civil War, as well as in many subsequent wars, the mission was one of bringing superior numbers and resources to bear on a well-entrenched enemy. The consequence, more often than not, was massive loss of civilian life [26] and destruction of property.

Northern whites thought slavery violated the basic principles of the Constitution and of the Christian religion and threatened the moral fabric of American society. They feared that slavery would corrupt even those born outside the system as it had the slave owner in Stowe's Uncle Tom's Cabin. Southern whites felt that the abolition of slavery violated Americans' constitutional right to own property. In addition, the abolition of slavery threatened to destroy the economic system of the South and in turn, its way of life. Southerners were determined not to let northerners, whom they regarded as [27] self-righteous, tell them how to live.

Immediately after the war, newly formed southern state governments enacted black codes and vagrancy laws restricting the rights of freed people. To reestablish slavery by another name, southern planters created a debt peonage system under which former slaves signed labor contracts and became trapped in a continuous cycle of accumulating and paying off debts. From 1868 to 1871, many southern whites launched a counterrevolution against radical Reconstruction policies that were transforming the South. They formed the Ku Klux Klan and resorted to terrorism because their social and political status in southern society was threatened and their constitutional rights had [28] been violated.

[29] c

[30] a

[31] k

[32] j

[33] b

[34] l

[35] n

[36] d

Test Bank Answer Key

[37] e

[38] f

[39] i

[40] h

[41] B

[42] B

[43] A

[44] D

[45] C

[46] C

[47] A

[48] B

[49] D

[50] B

[51] Emancipation in Tennessee was a result of state action.

[52] by the 13th Amendment

[53] the Border States and Tennessee

[54] Perhaps the most important legacy was the abolishment of slavery in the United States, as a result of the Thirteenth Amendment, and the transformation of southern society. A second legacy was the introduction of a new age in warfare--the age of total war--a strategy used by General Grant in the seige of Vicksburg. Finally, the war changed the role of the federal government by empowering the government to interfere more in people's lives as well as in the economy. Passage of the Internal Revenue Act of 1862, the Pacific Railroad Act of 1862, and other Republican wartime measures, laid the political and economic foundations for the emergence of the United States as a powerful agricultural and industrial nation.

Test Bank Answer Key

"The System Fails" would be an accurate title to describe the tragic failure of Reconstruction in trying to protect the newly gained civil rights of freed people and helping them achieve economic independence. The inability of the Republican-controlled government to enforce Reconstruction policies in the South, as well as violent southern defiance to those policies, resulted in very few permanent gains for African Americans. In effect, the Reconstruction system
[55] "failed" to free enslaved people from many types of bondage.

While it certainly was true that slavery was the key difference between the North and South, other factors contributed to the outbreak of war. The social, economic, and political concerns of the industrial North differed from and often conflicted with those of the agricultural South. The movement to end slavery confirmed many southerners' fears that the North was gaining too much power, and that southern interests were not being protected. Southerners agreed that they would not allow northerners, whom they regarded as
[56] hypocritical and self-righteous, tell them how to live.

Unit 5

Test Bank Questions

Complete each of the following sentences by selecting the appropriate term from the choices listed in parentheses.

1. (Booker T. Washington, W.E.B. Du Bois) urged blacks to take pride in both their African and American heritages.

2. A widespread rise in the cost of goods is known as (inflation, deflation).

3. Investors known as (speculators, squatters) bought up large tracts of land in the West with the intention of selling them for profit at a later date.

4. In the late 1800s, a social reform movement called (Victorianism, the social gospel movement) developed within religious institutions.

5. The (Homestead Act, Pullman strike) marked a turning point in the federal government's involvement in labor-employer relations.

6. (Chief Sitting Bull, Chief Joseph) was the Sioux leader who fought to keep his people's reservation in the Black Hills.

7. In the late 1800s, many states instituted a system of legal segregation known as (Jim Crow, de facto discrimination).

8. Inventor (Thomas Edison, Alexander Graham Bell) developed the idea of a central electric power station.

9. (William Marcy Tweed, Andrew Carnegie) was the powerful political boss who presided over Tammany Hall.

10. The method of (horizontal consolidation, vertical consolidation) involves bringing together two or more firms in the same business.

11. Proponents of (socialism, laissez-faire) support minimal government interference in economic matters.

12. Many southern states used (literacy tests, blue laws) to prevent African Americans from voting.

Write the letter of the correct ending.

13. One effect of technological changes in the late 1800s was that

   A) factory jobs became harder to find.

   B) more Americans left cities and moved to rural areas.

   C) more Americans could communicate over long distances.

   D) farming became highly profitable.

Test Bank Questions

Write the letter of the correct ending.

14. Most industrialists in the late 1800s supported
    A) nativism.   B) Populism.
    C) socialism.   D) social Darwinism.

15. In order to improve working conditions in the late 1800s, many labor unions promoted
    A) collective bargaining.   B) the system of piecework.
    C) the "gospel of wealth."   D) economy of scale.

16. All of the following encouraged farming in the West EXCEPT
    A) the mining boom.
    B) the business of bonanza farms.
    C) the transcontinental railroad.
    D) improvements in farm implements.

17. Industrialists and farmers in the late 1800s disagreed most over
    A) cooperatives.   B) the Homestead Act.
    C) tariffs.   D) immigration.

18. Unfair business practices in the late 1800s resulted in
    A) government regulation of railroads.
    B) the settlement movement.
    C) nationalization of industries.
    D) reform of the spoils system.

19. In the late 1800s and early 1900s, most immigrants to the United States were from
    A) Asia.
    B) southern and eastern Europe.
    C) northern and western Europe.
    D) Mexico and Central America.

20. Rapid urbanization in the late 1800s resulted in
    A) overcrowded cities, pollution, and crime.
    B) increased farm productivity.
    C) the decline of suburbs.
    D) a higher standard of living for nearly all Americans.

21. Public schools in the late 1800s and early 1900s promoted
    A) agricultural knowledge.
    B) Americanization of immigrant children.
    C) equal educational opportunities for white men and women.
    D) assimilation of Native Americans into the European American way of life.

Test Bank Questions

Write the letter of the correct ending.

22. According to Frederick Jackson Turner's thesis, the American frontier
    A) toughened the bodies and souls of young women.
    B) promoted equal opportunities for African Americans.
    C) helped to form the American character.
    D) destroyed Native American culture.

Use the cartoon about Bryan to answer the following questions.

A Republican view of Bryan -- New York Press, 1986

23. What is the topic of this cartoon?

24. Who has the cartoonist drawn on the coin? What position did this person take on the currency issue?

25. If the cartoonist had wanted to present "a Democratic view," what image might he have used instead?

Answer the following questions.

26. Other names for the Gilded Age, the period from 1877 to 1900, include the Tragic Era and the Dreadful Decades. What events or conditions in the United States may have inspired such labels?

27. In the nation's early years, the United States government viewed Native Americans as "separate nations" and made treaties with them. How did the government appear to view Native Americans in the late 1800s? How did white reformers view them? Cite examples to support your answer.

Test Bank Questions

Answer the following questions.

28. What were some pros and cons of rapid industrial growth in the late 1800s? Who benefited? Who was hurt?

Complete each of the following sentences by selecting the appropriate term from the choices listed in parentheses.

29. The (Interstate Commerce Act, Sherman Antitrust Act) was passed in 1887 to curb railroad company abuses.

30. In 1889 (Jane Addams, Madam C.J. Walker) established a settlement house in Chicago.

31. Many southern states used (grandfather clauses, blue laws) to prevent African Americans from voting.

32. The industrialist who gained a monopoly on the steel industry was (Andrew Carnegie, Henry Bessemer).

33. An example of how white American culture was influenced by African American culture was (vaudeville, the minstrel show).

34. (Booker T. Washington, W.E.B. Du Bois), the first African American to earn a Ph.D. from Harvard, helped found the NAACP.

35. The powerful political machine that controlled New York City's Democratic party in the late 1800s was (the Grange, Tammany Hall).

36. In the 1890s, farmers were more likely to be (Pinkertons, Populists).

37. According to the system of (piecework, economy of scale), those employees who worked fastest earned the most money.

38. The movement to restrict immigration in the 1880s was called (de facto discrimination, nativism).

39. The (Homestead Act, Morrill Land-Grant Act) enabled thousands of American citizens and many immigrants to obtain 160 acres of land for a ten-dollar registration fee.

40. (Socialism, Social Darwinism) is an economic and political philosophy that advocates collective or government ownership of industry and property.

Write the letter of the correct answer.

41. How did big business seek to control competition in the late 1800s?
    A) by preaching the "gospel of wealth"
    B) by forming trusts
    C) by collective bargaining
    D) by using time-and-motion studies

Test Bank Questions

Write the letter of the correct answer.

42. What was the most important impact of the great strikes in the late 1800s?
    A) Employers began to rely on the government for protection against strikes.
    B) The government passed important legislation to protect workers.
    C) Employer-employee relations improved dramatically.
    D) Labor unions gained political and social power.

43. Which of the following did NOT pose a major threat to the Native American way of life in the late 1800s?
    A) Christian missionaries who ran schools on reservations
    B) the settlement movement
    C) the transcontinental railroad
    D) boomers and sooners

44. Which of the following angered farmers in the West the most?
    A) large-scale cooperatives
    B) Frederick Jackson Turner's frontier thesis
    C) farm mechanization
    D) open-range ranching

45. Which of the following issues did most Populists support in the late 1800s?
    A) deflation
    B) lower tariffs
    C) a gold standard
    D) the laissez-faire approach of government

46. How did the American Federation of Labor (AFL) differ from the Knights of Labor?
    A) The AFL was a union of skilled workers.
    B) The AFL refused to engage in collective bargaining.
    C) The AFL engaged in violent tactics.
    D) The AFL actively recruited African Americans.

47. Which of the following did NOT contribute to increased public school enrollment in the early 1900s?
    A) industrialization and urbanization   B) Victorianism
    C) compulsory school laws   D) child labor laws

48. What sparked a revival of nativism and the temperance movement in the late 1800s?
    A) the decline of farming   B) urban problems
    C) corrupt business practices   D) the woman question

Test Bank Questions

Write the letter of the correct answer.

49. Which statement best describes urban workers in the late 1800s?

    A) Many began to attend school at night.

    B) Most found entertainment in saloons.

    C) Most adhered to Victorianism.

    D) Most did not allow themselves much leisure time.

50. What impact did the technological revolution have on women's lives in the late 1800s?

    A) Women found housework more time-consuming and burdensome.

    B) Women qualified for the same jobs as men, and wages greatly improved.

    C) Fewer women needed to work outside the home.

    D) Middle-class women had more time for voluntary activities.

Use the cartoon about Bryan to answer the following questions.

A Republican view of Bryan -- New York Press, 1986

51. What was the primary issue in the presidential election of 1896?

52. What presidential candidate is pictured in this cartoon? What was his position on this issue?

53. If the cartoonist had wanted to present "a Democratic view" of the presidential election, what image of Bryan might he have used instead?

Test Bank Questions

Answer the following questions.

54. The most popular label for the period 1877–1900 was the Gilded Age, coined by Mark Twain. Invent your own label for this period of the United States, and discuss the social, political, and economic conditions or events that inspired your title.

55. In what ways was the federal government consistent in the late 1800s and early 1900s in its approach to economic and social problems? How does the role of government in the economy today compare with its role 100 years ago?

56. Explain how the rapid growth of cities in the late 1800s was both a cause and an effect.

Test Bank Answer Key

[1] W.E.B. Du Bois

[2] inflation

[3] speculators

[4] the social gospel movement

[5] Pullman strike

[6] Chief Sitting Bull

[7] Jim Crow

[8] Thomas Edison

[9] William Marcy Tweed

[10] horizontal consolidation

[11] laissez-faire

[12] literacty tests

[13] C

[14] D

[15] A

[16] A

[17] C

[18] A

[19] B

[20] A

[21] B

[22] C

[23] the presidential election of 1896

[24] William Jennings Bryan is depicted. He supported free silver.

[25] Bryan, or a farmer, could be shown being crucified on a "cross of gold."

Test Bank Answer Key

Widespread corruption in government and business probably inspired these labels. During that period, many industrialists supported politicians with illegal contributions of money, and the spoils system was a common practice in American politics. Other causes for the period's negative reputation include: railroad abuses, the creation of slums and ghettos, the rise of political machines, nativism, wars with Native Americans, and economic hardships for many
[26] farmers and factory workers.

In the late 1800s the government no longer viewed Native Americans as "separate nations" but as local communities threatening the westward expansion. The government laid claim to their homelands, pushed them onto reservations, and used force to ensure that they complied. Some white reformers viewed Native Americans as "savages" who needed to be "civilized," while others tried to break their traditions by forcing
[27] them to become farmers.

Rapid industrial growth brought prosperity to the nation, but widened the economic and social gap between rich and poor. Although industrialization created job opportunities for men and women, the quality of life declined significantly for most laborers--many of them immigrants--who worked long hours under unhealthy conditions and
[28] lived in overcrowded and run-down tenements.

[29] Interstate Commerce Act

[30] Jane Addams

[31] grandfather clauses

[32] Andrew Carnegie

[33] the minstrel show

[34] W.E.B. Du Bois

[35] Tammany Hall

[36] Populists

[37] piecework

[38] nativism

[39] Homestead Act

[40] Socialism

[41] B

[42] A

Test Bank Answer Key

[43] B

[44] D

[45] B

[46] A

[47] B

[48] B

[49] B

[50] D

[51] the currency issue

[52] William Jennings Bryan is pictured. He supported free silver over the gold standard.

[53] He could be depicted as being crucified on a "cross of gold."

[54] Students' labels and reasoning should demonstrate an understanding of social, political, and economic conditions and events of the Gilded Age: widespread corruption in business and politics (e.g., spoils system); poor living conditions in cities; exploitation of labor, widening economic and social gap between rich and poor; the hardships of many farmers; discrimination, nativism, and destructive wars against Native American groups.

[55] The government was consistent by following a laissez-faire approach to both economic and social problems. Today, the government plays a significant role in the economy, regulating the activities of both business and labor and providing for the social welfare of its citizens.

[56] The rapid growth of cities in the late 1800s was an effect of industrialization, new technologies such as skyscrapers, improvements in transportation, and widespread immigration. In turn, urbanization led to overcrowded conditions, spread of disease, creation of ghettos, crime, vice, and corruption in local politics. When people in the middle and upper classes moved from the cities to the suburbs, the economic and social gap between the rich and poor widened.

Unit 6

Test Bank Questions

Complete each sentence below by selecting the correct word from the list. You will not use all the words.

a. self-determination
b. home rule
c. dollar diplomacy
d. muckrakers
e. reparations
f. arbitration
g. Roosevelt Corollary
h. Fourteen Points

i. League of Nations
j. most-favored nation
k. sphere of influence
l. social welfare programs
m. imperialism
n. direct primary
o. Versailles Treaty
p. Open Door Policy

1. By gaining the status of _____ in China, the United States had the same access to trade with China as did any other nation.

2. The _____ to the Monroe Doctrine stated that the United States would intervene in the affairs of neighboring countries to prevent intervention from other powers.

3. Voters in a _____ cast ballots to select nominees for upcoming elections.

4. Under _____, strong nations attempt to create empires by dominating weaker nations.

5. President William Howard Taft's approach to foreign affairs was called _____.

6. Under _____, cities exercise a limited degree of self-rule.

7. President Wilson's _____ called for an end to secret alliances, the restoration of freedom of the seas, and a reduction in armaments.

8. Writers who exposed corruption in business and politics are called _____.

9. The process in which an impartial third party resolves a dispute by deciding on a legally binding solution is called _____.

10. The United States demanded that Austria-Hungary grant _____ to its subject ethnic groups.

11. Progressives believed that _____ would help ensure a basic standard of living for all Americans.

12. Great Britain wanted _____ from Germany for the economic injury it suffered during World War I.

Test Bank Questions

Write the letter of the correct ending.

13. All of the following were results of U.S. expansionism in the late 1800s EXCEPT
    A) increased United States investment in foreign economies.
    B) new markets for American goods.
    C) complicated entanglements with foreign countries.
    D) an economic slowdown in the United States.

14. The United States reaffirmed the Monroe Doctrine in the late 1800s by
    A) forcing Russia to leave Manchuria.
    B) forcing Britain to back down from a territorial dispute with Venezuela.
    C) favoring the annexation of several Caribbean countries.
    D) seeking spheres of influence in Asia.

15. President Theodore Roosevelt is often remembered for
    A) increasing the power of big business.
    B) being a muckraker.
    C) expanding the President's powers.
    D) opposing imperialism.

16. The United States declared war on Spain in 1898 in order to
    A) end Spanish interference with U.S. shipping.
    B) build the Panama Canal.
    C) prevent Spain's annexation of Hawaii.
    D) free Cuba and other territories from Spanish rule.

17. Most progressives in the late 1800s believed that
    A) the government should increase its responsibility for human welfare.
    B) social disorder and even violence were necessary to effect social change.
    C) a laissez-faire approach to business would better the lives of all Americans.
    D) free enterprise in the United States should be eliminated.

18. In the early 1900s, those who promoted woman suffrage, more regulation of business, and a tariff reduction formed the
    A) Socialist Party of America.   B) Federal Trade Commission.
    C) Industrial Workers of the World.   D) Bull Moose party.

19. Carrie Chapman Catt and Alice Paul made the greatest contribution to
    A) abolition of child labor.   B) consumer protection.
    C) woman suffrage.   D) prohibition.

Test Bank Questions

Write the letter of the correct ending.

20. During the early years of World War I, the United States
    A) was an "associate" of the Central Powers.
    B) sent war supplies to the Allies.
    C) built up its armed forces.
    D) struggled to remain neutral.

21. The sinking of the Lusitania and the Zimmerman note encouraged American
    A) outrage at Germany.
    B) opposition to the war.
    C) resentment toward Great Britain.
    D) support of the War Industries Board.

22. After World War I, President Wilson encountered strong opposition in Congress to
    A) U.S. membership in the League of Nations.
    B) the creation of a Committee on Public Information.
    C) making Germany sign a war guilt clause.
    D) the desegregation of the American Expeditionary Force.

Test Bank Questions

Use the cartoon of "The Big Stick..." to answer the following questions.

The Big Stick in the Caribbean Sea

Source: New York Herald, 1905

23. How does the cartoonist portray President Roosevelt?

24. What is the President dragging behind him to enforce his actions?

25. How would you describe President Theodore Roosevelt's approach to foreign policy?

Answer the following questions.

26. How did economic and commercial interests influence U.S. foreign policy decisions in the late 1800s and the nation's involvement in World War I?

27. How did the United States government violate the nation's democratic principles both abroad as an imperialist nation in the late 1800s and at home during World War I?

Test Bank Questions

Answer the following questions.

28. Compare the forces that controlled American public opinion prior to the Spanish-American War with those that controlled public opinion during the early years of World War I.

Match the terms below with the following descriptions. Write the letter of the correct answer. You will not use all the terms.

a. imperialism
b. progressivism
c. muckrakers
d. New Freedom
e. dollar diplomacy
f. Fourteen Points
g. annexation
h. doughboys
i. self-determination
j. direct primary
k. League of Nations
l. arbitration
m. New Nationalism
n. spheres of influence
o. guerrillas

29. addition of a new territory to an existing country

30. peacekeeping organization intended to unite nations after World War I

31. reform movement that sought greater government regulation of economic activity and more social welfare programs

32. principle by which a territorial unit selects its own future political status

33. election in which voters cast ballots to select nominees for upcoming elections

34. President Wilson's peace program to end World War I

35. President Taft's policy of maintaining orderly societies abroad by increasing investment in foreign economies

36. process in which an impartial third party decides on a legally binding solution to a dispute

37. Woodrow Wilson's policy to enforce antitrust laws without threatening free economic competition

38. areas of a country in which foreign nations maintain economic control

39. journalists who exposed corruption in business and politics

40. name for American infantrymen during World War I

Write the letter of the correct answer.

41. In which area was progressivism LEAST effective in the late 1800s and early 1900s?
    A) attacking the political bosses
    B) improving conditions in the workplace
    C) promoting world peace
    D) providing welfare services

Test Bank Questions

Write the letter of the correct answer.

42. What was the purpose of the Roosevelt Corollary?
    A) to free the United States from colonial responsibilities
    B) to prevent foreign governments from interfering in Latin America
    C) to legalize the annexation of foreign territories
    D) to ensure an Open Door policy in China

43. Which of the following was an argument used by anti-imperialists in the late 1800s?
    A) "We have a responsibility to protect these nations from foreign assault."
    B) "Some nations are simply not prepared for democracy."
    C) "The virtues of American civilizations will regenerate the world."
    D) "All people are entitled to life, liberty, and the pursuit of happiness."

44. Why did the United States fight in the Spanish-American War?
    A) to protect United States investments in Asia and Africa
    B) to gain control of the Panama Canal Zone
    C) to protect United States shipping in the Caribbean
    D) to free Cuba and other territories from Spanish rule

45. To which of the following did Florence Kelley make the greatest contribution in the late 1800s and early 1900s?
    A) breaking up holding companies
    B) promoting equal opportunities for women
    C) pushing through prohibition legislation
    D) improving working conditions for women and children

46. Why were business and political leaders in the United States pressured to acquire foreign markets in the late 1800s?
    A) U.S. investments abroad would stem local revolutionary movements.
    B) Industrial production in the United States was slowing down.
    C) Overproduction of industrial and agricultural goods threatened the economy.
    D) It became too expensive to manufacture goods in the United States.

47. Which of the following helped the woman suffrage movement the most?
    A) World War I   B) yellow journalism
    C) the Spanish-American War   D) the League of Nations

Test Bank Questions

Write the letter of the correct answer.

48. Which of the following was a major factor in the outbreak of World War I?

    A) secret alliances among European nations

    B) ethnic diputes in the Austrian-Hungarian Empire

    C) the British naval blockade of Germany

    D) the start of the Russian Revolution

49. Which of the following did NOT encourage the United States to enter World War I?

    A) U.S. investments abroad

    B) unrestricted submarine warfare

    C) the Zimmerman note

    D) Britain's slow starvation of the German people

50. What was the main reason why many policymakers in the United States opposed the Versailles Treaty?

    A) The treaty violated the principle of self-determination.

    B) The Allies' reparations demands were unreasonable.

    C) The treaty would plunge the United States into debt.

    D) The League of Nations threatened to weaken American independence.

Test Bank Questions

Use the cartoon of Roosevelt in Bogotá to answer the following questions.

The News Reaches Bogotá

Source: New York Herald, 1903

51. What event is illustrated in the cartoon? (Bogotá is the capital of Colombia.)

52. What did President Roosevelt use to back up his aggressive approach to foreign policy?

53. How would you describe the cartoonist's point of view?

Answer the following questions.

54. The term <u>jingoism</u> was used to describe the atmosphere in the United States prior to the Spanish-American War. Do you think this term accurately describes the atmosphere in the United States at the beginning of American involvement in World War I? Explain.

55. What impact did World War I have on progressivism?

Test Bank Questions

Answer the following questions.

56. Compare the reasons for United States imperialism in the late 1800s with the nation's reasons for entering World War I in the early 1900s.

Test Bank Answer Key

[1] j

[2] g

[3] n

[4] m

[5] c

[6] b

[7] h

[8] d

[9] f

[10] a

[11] l

[12] e

[13] D

[14] B

[15] C

[16] D

[17] A

[18] D

[19] C

[20] D

[21] A

[22] A

[23] He is shown as a "larger than life" figure marching through the Caribbean Sea.

[24] the United States Navy

[25] He acted independently and used the threat of military force to conduct an aggressive foreign policy.

Test Bank Answer Key

The economy played a major role in both decisions. One of the main reasons the United States embraced imperialism was to secure new markets for American goods. Economic pressure was also behind the nation's foreign policy decisions during World War I. Initially, the nation advocated a policy of neutrality to protect overseas economic interests from the military actions of the Allied nations and the Central Powers. Later, the United States supported the Allies, partly
[26] because commercial ties were strongest with Great Britain.

As an imperialist nation in the late 1800s, the United States violated the basic principle that people everywhere have the right to liberty. Residents living in "unincorporated" territories of the United States were denied the same protections of basic rights as were American citizens. During World War I, the government repressed many civil liberties at home by banning any discussion "disloyal" to the government, by forcing school personnel to sign loyalty oaths,
[27] and by imposing censorship on the press.

Yellow journalists such as Joseph Pulitzer and William Randolph Hearst were largely reponsible for manipulating public opinion prior to the Spanish-American War. They published biased and exaggerated accounts about Spanish atrocities in Cuba, convincing many Americans to urge the government to declare war against Spain. During the early years of World War I, the United States government created a committee on Public Information, the country's first propaganda
[28] machine to control news and information about the war.

[29] g

[30] k

[31] b

[32] i

[33] j

[34] f

[35] e

[36] l

[37] d

[38] n

[39] c

[40] h

[41] C

Test Bank Answer Key

[42] B

[43] D

[44] D

[45] D

[46] C

[47] A

[48] A

[49] D

[50] D

[51] Roosevelt's controversial seizure of the Panama Canal Zone

[52] military force, specifically the United States Navy

[53] The cartoonist viewed the President as a forceful and determined leader who got what he wanted by threatening military force.

[54] While jingoism may have characterized the mood of some Americans who supported U.S. participation in the war effort, it was not the mood of the country. Many Americans were first- or second-generation immigrants who still had close ties to their homelands. Although public opinion favored the Allies, most Americans maintained a neutral but cynical attitude toward European affairs, viewing the war as a great financial boom for U.S. manufacturers. In the end, it was ongoing conflicts between the United States and Germany, particularly over Germany's policy of unrestricted submarine warfare, that led to U.S. entry into World War I.

[55] Because progressives were divided on major issues such as the peace movement, World War I seemed to break up the progressive movement. In addition, important progressive goals, such as more government regulation of business, prohibition, and woman suffrage, were realized during the war. Disillusionment during the postwar years also dimmed the enthusiasm of many reformers.

[56] The United States became an imperialist nation largely because it needed to acquire foreign markets for American goods. In addition, the nation felt pressure to compete with other imperialist nations, such as Great Britain, France, Russia, and Germany, and to spread democratic principles abroad. This desire to defend both democratic ideals and business investments abroad also prompted the United States to enter World War I.

Unit 7

Test Bank Questions

Match the terms below with the following descriptions. Write the letter of the correct answer. You will not use all the terms.

a. Wagner Act
b. welfare capitalism
c. national debt
d. communist
e. Hawley-Smoot tariff
f. Teapot Dome
g. political right
h. Harlem Renaissance

i. red scare
j. speculation
k. Twenty-first Amendment
l. Gross National Product
m. Dow Jones industrial average
n. installment buying
o. Socialist
p. political left

1.   approach to labor relations in which employers provide workers with raises and benefits

2.   fear of communism and other foreign and revolutionary ideas

3.   legislation that legalized such union practices as closed shops and collective bargaining

4.   total amount of money that the federal government has borrowed and has yet to pay back

5.   type of government established after Vladimir I. Lenin seized control of Russia in 1917

6.   total annual value of goods and services a country produces

7.   African American literary movement of the 1920s

8.   method by which consumers pay for expensive items in monthly payments that include interest

9.   highest import tax in United States history

10. people who want to preserve a current system or power structure

11. legislation that repealed the ban on alcoholic beverages

12. scandal that tarnished the reputation of the Harding Administration

Write the letter of the correct ending.

13. Nativism increased after World War I largely as a result of

   A) the Sacco and Vanzetti case.

   B) liberal immigration laws.

   C) the Bonus Army and postwar economic adjustments.

   D) labor strikes and the red scare.

Test Bank Questions

Write the letter of the correct ending.

14. President Calvin Coolidge seemed most concerned with
    A) ending poverty in the United States.
    B) decreasing racial violence.
    C) lowering the national debt.
    D) protecting American business interests.

15. Henry Ford tried to "democratize the automobile" by
    A) applying the assembly line idea to car production.
    B) producing the most fuel-efficient automobile.
    C) allowing auto workers to join unions.
    D) making each car special and unique.

16. In the 1920s, the Scopes trial sparked a national debate over whether public schools should be allowed to teach
    A) fundamentalism.   B) isolationism.
    C) evolution.   D) biology.

17. During the Great Depression, working women generally
    A) earned the same salaries as men performing the same job.
    B) had a better chance of keeping a job if they were married than single.
    C) found new opportunities in jobs that were traditionally open to men.
    D) were fired if they were married.

18. All of the following contributed to the Great Depression EXCEPT
    A) high tariffs.   B) overspeculation.
    C) underproduction.   D) an uneven distribution of wealth.

19. President Herbert Hoover hoped to end the Great Depression through
    A) direct federal relief.
    B) public works programs.
    C) massive government spending.
    D) voluntary controls in business.

20. An American who lived through the Great Depression would most likely
    A) buy on credit.
    B) speculate in the stock market.
    C) pledge stocks as collateral.
    D) pay cash for purchases.

Test Bank Questions

Write the letter of the correct ending.

21. President Franklin Roosevelt received his greatest opposition when he tried to

    A) end discriminatory practices in the North.

    B) tax wealthy Americans.

    C) reshape the Supreme Court.

    D) establish the Tennessee Valley Authority.

22. One important legacy of the New Deal was that it

    A) ended the Great Depression.

    B) encouraged Americans to become more self-reliant.

    C) made the federal government responsible for social welfare.

    D) greatly reduced the national debt.

Use the diagram of Global Economics to answer the following questions.

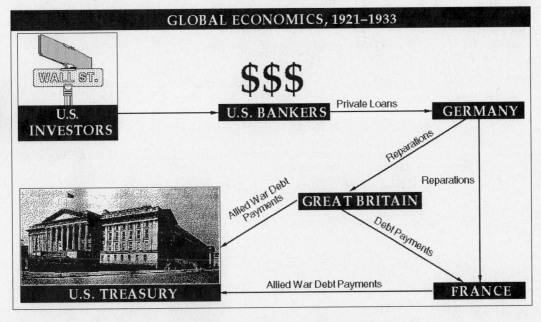

23. Why was Germany dependent on U.S. investments?

24. How were the economies of Great Britain and France dependent on Germany?

25. Why would a severe depression in the United States affect global economics?

Answer the following questions.

26. What personal and political beliefs and principles formed the framework of President Franklin Roosevelt's New Deal programs?

Test Bank Questions

Answer the following questions.

27. Cite evidence to support the following conclusion from your text about the Great Depression: <u>It changed people's feelings about banks, business, government--and money</u>.

28. Compare the Sacco and Vanzetti trial with the trial of the Scottsboro Boys. Whose civil liberties seemed to be at risk in the 1920s and 1930s?

Complete each sentence below by selecting the correct word from the list. You will not use all the words.

a. Warren G. Harding
b. Huey Long
c. F. Scott Fitzgerald
d. Charles A. Lindbergh
e. Nicolo Sacco
f. Marcus Garvey
g. Herbert Hoover

h. Henry Ford
i. John Maynard Keynes
j. Franklin Delano Roosevelt
k. Vladimir I. Lenin
l. Frances Perkins
m. Calvin Coolidge
n. Mary McLeod Bethune

29. President _____ promised the country a "new deal" to relieve the effects of the Great Depression.

30. In 1917 Bolshevik leader _____ helped overthrow the Russian government.

31. President Franklin D. Roosevelt appointed _____ as Secretary of Labor.

32. President _____ believed that voluntary controls in the business world would end the Great Depression.

33. _____ encouraged New Deal programs that aided African Americans.

34. Engineer _____ applied the assembly line idea to automobile production.

35. New Deal critic Senator _____ called his program "Share Our Wealth."

36. President _____ provided uncritical support for American business from 1923 to 1928.

37. Novelist _____ wrote <u>The Great Gatsby</u> to expose the illusions of the Jazz Age culture.

38. _____ was a charismatic Jamaican immigrant who led a movement in the United States to build up black pride.

39. The economist _____ believed that massive government spending could encourage economic growth.

40. Aviator _____ became the first person to fly nonstop from New York to Paris.

Test Bank Questions

Write the letter of the correct answer.

41. Which group most opposed the changes in morals and manners in the 1920s?

    A) communists   B) flappers

    C) progressives   D) fundamentalists

42. What convinced many Americans that the United States was on the brink of a communist revolution after World War I?

    A) bootlegging   B) labor strikes

    C) the Teapot Dome scandal   D) the Scopes trial

43. What was the Harlem Renaissance?

    A) "black pride" movement that encouraged followers to return to "Motherland Africa"

    B) African American musical and literary movement

    C) Father Divine's program to help African Americans in Harlem survive the Depression

    D) migration of African Americans from the South to the North

44. What did NOT contribute to the creation of a national culture?

    A) availability of the automobile

    B) advertising industry

    C) population movements

    D) self-exile of writers and artists

45. Which of the following was a sign in the 1920s of economic trouble ahead?

    A) a decrease in speculation

    B) an increase in installment buying

    C) underproduction in major industries

    D) the rise of small businesses

46. Which statement best describes the overall effect of the Depression?

    A) Most rural and city banks withstood the Depression.

    B) Farmers fared much better than most Americans.

    C) The hardest hit were those at the bottom of the economic ladder.

    D) Big business leaders were hurt the most.

47. Which of the following was most responsible for people's disillusionment with President Hoover?

    A) his failure to protect domestic industries from foreign imports

    B) his program of massive government spending

    C) his endorsement of socialism

    D) his refusal to provide more direct federal relief

Test Bank Questions

Write the letter of the correct answer.

48. After the Great Depression, how did most Americans view the role of the federal government?

    A) The government should take an active role only during a depression.

    B) The government should protect business.

    C) The government should nationalize industry.

    D) The government should ensure citizens' welfare.

49. How did the New Deal try to revive the economy in the 1930s?

    A) by balancing the budget

    B) by enacting public works programs and providing relief

    C) by encouraging voluntary controls in the business world

    D) by encouraging speculation and consumer credit

50. Who benefited most from the Wagner Act?

    A) business leaders   B) labor unions

    C) tenant farmers   D) migrant workers

Use the diagram of Global Economics to answer the following questions.

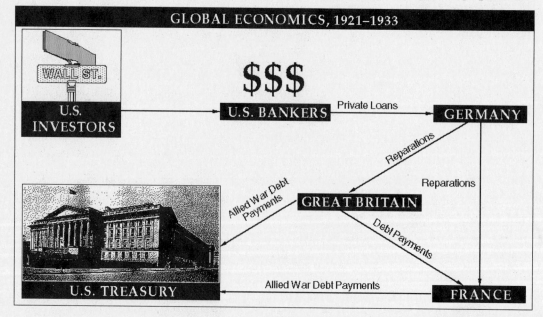

51. What did bankers do with the money they received from U.S. investors?

52. What would happen if Germany could not make reparations payments?

53. In what way was the United States a two-time loser during the Depression?

Test Bank Questions

Answer the following questions.

54. Why do some historians call the political changes that followed the presidential election of 1932 the "Roosevelt Revolution"? Support your answer.

55. Compare how the political right and the political left responded to the Great Depression and the New Deal programs.

56. Discuss three issues with which many Americans struggled during the post-World War I years.

Test Bank Answer Key

[1] b

[2] i

[3] a

[4] c

[5] d

[6] l

[7] h

[8] n

[9] e

[10] g

[11] k

[12] f

[13] D

[14] D

[15] A

[16] C

[17] D

[18] C

[19] D

[20] D

[21] C

[22] C

[23] U.S. investments provided the capital needed to pay reparations.

[24] They depended on reparation payments from Germany in order to pay their war debts.

[25] Not only would a severe depression cause U.S. bankers to suffer investment losses, but foreign nations would not be able to repay their war debts.

Test Bank Answer Key

[26] Roosevelt believed that the federal government was responsible for the general welfare of its citizens, and for narrowing the gap between the nation's wealthy and its poor. He thought that "private economic power" was "a public trust" and that there should be controls on business. He believed in presidential activism and bold experimentation to spur economic recovery and give the nation hope.

[27] Prior to the Depression, most Americans had an unshakeable faith in banks and business. During the Depression, however, many Americans began to support more government interference in the economy and controls on business and industry. The Depression also transformed Americans' attitude toward money, making them aware of money's intrinsic value and the importance of saving and living within their means.

[28] Like the Sacco and Vanzetti trial, the Scottsboro Boys' trial seemed unjust to many Americans. Discrimination played a major role in the conviction of Italian immigrants Sacco and Vanzetti as well as in the conviction of African American boys in Scottsboro. In both cases, the system of justice had ignored the rights and civil liberties of minority groups, specifically African American and south-eastern European immigrants.

[29] j

[30] k

[31] l

[32] g

[33] n

[34] h

[35] b

[36] m

[37] c

[38] f

[39] i

[40] d

[41] D

[42] B

[43] B

Test Bank Answer Key

[44] D

[45] B

[46] C

[47] D

[48] D

[49] B

[50] B

[51] They loaned the money to Germany.

[52] Great Britain and France could not pay their war debts to the United States.

[53] It lost investments on Wall Street as well as foreign war debt payments to the Treasury.

[54] When he became President in 1932, FDR began a bold and experimental program called the New Deal to provide direct federal relief, create jobs, and spur economic recovery. While these programs did not alter the existing structure of government, they did change the social and economic roles of the government as well as the expectations of many Americans. The Roosevelt years marked the beginning of government involvement in the social welfare of all its citizens.

[55] The political left responded by calling for reform movements that promised a fairer distribution of wealth. Communists called for revolutionary changes similar to those taking place in the Soviet Union while Socialists called for more gradual social and economic changes, starting with state-controlled factories and farms. The political right criticized New Deal programs for being socialistic, limiting individual freedom, and discriminating against business. A right-wing group called the American Liberty League urged people to take responsibility for themselves and practice "thrift and self-denial."

[56] Students may discuss the labor strikes and unemployment that resulted when the nation adjusted to a postwar economy; the red scare that permeated society as a result of the Russian revolution and terrorist acts; the rise of nativism and its impact on immigration laws; the desire for renewed isolationism and loss of respect for Europe; continuing racial discrimination; and the cultural and social changes of the Jazz Age.

Unit 8

Test Bank Questions

Match the terms below with the following descriptions. Write the letter of the correct answer. You will not use all the terms.

a. Richard M. Nixon
b. Joseph R. McCarthy
c. Chester Nimitz
d. William J. Levitt
e. Betty Friedan
f. Douglas MacArthur
g. J. Robert Oppenheimer

h. George C. Marshall
i. John L. Lewis
j. Dwight D. Eisenhower
k. Martin Luther King, Jr.
l. Harry S. Truman
m. A. Philip Randolph
n. Rosie the Riveter

1. Republican senator who encouraged a national anticommunist crusade after World War II

2. Baptist minister who became a leader of the African American civil rights movement

3. leader of the United Mine Workers union in the 1940s

4. commander of Allied forces during World War II who became President of the United States in 1952

5. physicist who spearheaded the Manhattan Project

6. Secretary of State who devised a plan to provide American aid for the reconstruction of Europe after World War II

7. developer who pioneered the mass production of houses

8. general who was fired for insubordination during the Korean War.

9. writer who promoted the feminist movement

10. African American leader who proposed a march on Washington in 1941 to demand an end to discrimination

Write the letter of the correct answer.

11. Which of the following best describes the position of the United States during the early years of World War II?

   A) The United States joined France and Britain to fight against the Soviet Union.

   B) The United States supported a policy of appeasement.

   C) The United States provided economic aid to the Axis powers.

   D) The United States, although neutral, became an "arsenal of democracy."

Test Bank Questions

Write the letter of the correct answer.

12.   Which of the following brought the United States into the war?

   A) the bombing of Pearl Harbor

   B) the D-day invasion of Normandy

   C) Germany's invasion of Poland

   D) Japanese attack on Manchuria

13.   To what does the term <u>holocaust</u> refer?

   A) the destruction of London by the German air force during the Battle of Britain

   B) the destruction of Japan during World War II by atomic bombs

   C) the annihilation of six million Jews in Nazi Germany

   D) the internment of Japanese Americans during World War II

14.   Why was rationing necessary during World War II?

   A) to avoid another economic depression

   B) to prevent inflation

   C) to encourage production of goods

   D) to increase the cost of living

15.   How did World War II affect women in the United States?

   A) Working women were transferred to government jobs.

   B) Working women were no longer expected to have complete responsibility for their children and household chores.

   C) The wages of working women decreased significantly during the war.

   D) War made it essential for women of all ages and backgrounds to work.

16.   Which of the following did NOT contribute to economic growth in the 1950s?

   A) The franchise system created thousands of low-paying jobs.

   B) The automobile and computer industries grew rapidly.

   C) Real purchasing power declined steadily.

   D) Many consumers went into debt to purchase items.

17.   Why did Congress pass the Taft-Hartley Act in 1947?

   A) to limit the power of big business

   B) to protect workers against unfair wages and poor conditions

   C) to curb the power of labor unions

   D) to keep the federal government from becoming too big

Test Bank Questions

Write the letter of the correct answer.

18. In which of the following was the African American movement for equal rights most successful in the 1950s?

   A) promoting social equality

   B) combating legal segregation

   C) gaining economic equality

   D) ending job discrimination

19. What was the major goal of U.S. foreign policy in the postwar years?

   A) destroying fascism

   B) appeasing the Soviet Union

   C) preventing the spread of nuclear weapons

   D) containing the spread of communism

20. What did President Truman's Loyalty Program have in common with the organization of NATO?

   A) Both were designed to bolster military morale.

   B) Both sought to improve relations between capitalists and communists.

   C) Both were fueled by a fear of communism.

   D) Both were created to decrease the power of the federal government.

21. Which of the following worsened relations between the United States and the Soviet Union?

   A) all of these answers   B) the Truman Doctrine

   C) the Marshall Plan   D) the Berlin airlift

Test Bank Questions

Use the graph of the National Debt to answer the following questions.

NATIONAL DEBT OF THE UNITED STATES, 1915–1955

22. (a) By about how much did the national debt increase during World War I?
    (b) From 1941 to 1945?

23. Why do you think the national debt increased after Japan surrendered and World War II ended?

24. What appears to be the relationship between war and a country's national debt?

Answer the following questions.

25. How did World War II affect the role of the United States in international affairs?

26. During the postwar years, what economic and social challenges did both Presidents Truman and Eisenhower face?

Complete each sentence below by selecting the correct word from the list. You will not use all the words.

a. agribusiness
b. appeasement
c. holocaust
d. modern republicanism
e. termination policy
f. containment
g. rationing
h. anti-Semitism
i. Taft-Hartley Act
j. Truman Doctrine
k. "Double-V" campaign
l. fascism
m. Marshall Plan

27. In the late 1930s, France and Britain followed a policy of _____ to deal with German aggression.

28. The _____ provided Greece and Turkey with economic and military aid to prevent communism from gaining a foothold in those nations.

29. Discrimination against Jews is referred to as _____.

Test Bank Questions

Complete each sentence below by selecting the correct word from the list. You will not use all the words.

a. agribusiness
b. appeasement
c. holocaust
d. modern republicanism
e. termination policy
f. containment
g. rationing
h. anti-Semitism
i. Taft-Hartley Act
j. Truman Doctrine
k. "Double-V" campaign
l. fascism
m. Marshall Plan

30. The consolidation of small farms into big businesses was known as _____.

31. The Nazis murdered more than six million Jews in the _____.

32. African Americans launched a _____ to win World War II abroad and the fight for equality at home.

33. During World War II, the U.S. government used _____ to prevent high inflation.

34. The United States adopted a policy of _____ following World War II to prevent the spread of communism abroad.

35. The _____ provided American aid for the reconstruction of Europe after World War II.

36. In 1947 Congress passed the _____ to curb the power of labor unions and prevent strikes that might harm the national interest.

Write the letter of the correct ending.

37. The United States entered World War II as a result of
    A) the Battle of Britain.
    B) the German invasion of Czechoslovakia.
    C) Germany's nonaggression pact with the Soviet Union.
    D) the Japanese attack on Pearl Harbor.

38. The Allied strategy during World War II was to first defeat
    A) Japan in Southeast Asia.
    B) the Soviet Union and capture Stalingrad.
    C) the Japanese in the Pacific.
    D) Italy and Germany in Europe and North Africa.

39. The event that finally brought an end to World War II was
    A) the dropping of the atomic bomb on Japan.
    B) General MacArthur's victory in the Philippines.
    C) the Allied invasion of Normandy.
    D) the Battle of the Bulge.

Test Bank Questions

Write the letter of the correct ending.

40. World War II helped end the Great Depression in the United States by
    A) enabling the federal government to lower expenditures.
    B) decreasing the cost of living.
    C) encouraging mass production.
    D) enabling state governments to lower taxes.

41. During World War II, African Americans and Mexican Americans enjoyed
    A) greater job opportunities.
    B) the American dream.
    C) equal rights in the military.
    D) social and economic equality.

42. During World War II, the government encouraged women to
    A) pursue business management.
    B) set up day-care centers for working mothers.
    C) run for political office.
    D) take jobs in defense industries.

43. The American economy in the 1950s could best be described as
    A) government controlled.   B) moderate but steady.
    C) booming.   D) sluggish.

44. In the late 1950s, many Americans began to question their country's status as the strongest world power as a result of
    A) the launching of Sputnik by the Soviet Union.

    B) nationwide labor strikes.
    C) CIA activities in Latin America.
    D) rising unemployment and inflation.

45. All of the following helped the African American movement for civil rights in the 1950s EXCEPT
    A) the termination policy.
    B) Brown v. Board of Education.

    C) the founding of the NAACP.
    D) the Montgomery bus boycott.

46. During the early years of the cold war, most Americans viewed Vietnamese leader Ho Chi Minh and Cuban leader Fidel Castro as
    A) insignificant revolutionaries.   B) trustworthy allies.
    C) dangerous communists.   D) impartial nationalists.

Test Bank Questions

Write the letter of the correct ending.

47. The anticommunist crusade that swept the United States in the postwar years was largely the work of

    A) President Harry S. Truman.

    B) Senator Joseph R. McCarthy.

    C) General Douglas MacArthur.

    D) the Hollywood Ten.

Use the graph of the National Debt to answer the following questions.

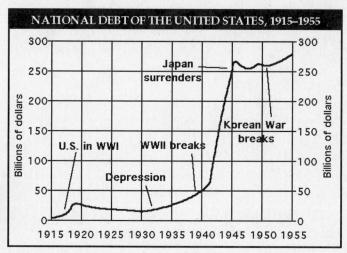

48. During what period shown on the graph did the United States first begin to accumulate debt?

49. About how much debt did the United States accumulate during World War II? During the Korean War?

50. Based on the information presented in the graph, what conclusion can you draw about how war affects government spending and the national debt?

Answer the following questions.

51. Use examples from the post-World War II years to support the following conclusion made by Richard M. Nixon: The governments of the Soviet Union and the United States can never be friends because our goals are different.

52. How did World War II both resolve and create domestic problems in the United States?

Test Bank Answer Key

[1]   b

[2]   k

[3]   i

[4]   j

[5]   g

[6]   h

[7]   d

[8]   f

[9]   e

[10]   m

[11]   D

[12]   A

[13]   C

[14]   B

[15]   D

[16]   C

[17]   C

[18]   B

[19]   D

[20]   C

[21]   A

[22]   (a) by about $20 billion
(b) by about $210 billion

[23]   The United States was providing financial aid for Europe's post-war recovery.

[24]   Government spending, and in turn the national debt, increase significantly during a nation's involvement in war.

Test Bank Answer Key

Because the economies of most European nations were torn apart during World War II, the United States became the most powerful democratic nation economically as well as militarily. As a result, the United States felt compelled to abandon its policy of isolationism and to aggressively defend and promote democracy abroad. Policies such as the Truman Doctrine and the Marshall Plan were implemented to contain [25] the spread of communism.

Both Presidents faced the challenge of converting a wartime economy back to a peacetime economy, determining the proper role of government in the nation's economic and social affairs, and [26] responding to the continuing struggle for equal rights.

[27] b

[28] j

[29] h

[30] a

[31] c

[32] k

[33] g

[34] f

[35] m

[36] i

[37] D

[38] D

[39] A

[40] C

[41] A

[42] D

[43] C

[44] A

[45] A

[46] C

Test Bank Answer Key

[47] B

[48] in 1917 when the United States entered World War I

[49] about $210 billion; about $20 billion

[50] Government spending, and in turn the national debt, increase significantly during wartime.

[51] The Soviet Union was a totalitarian, communist state in which the government controlled society's resources and repressed the civil liberties of its people. By contrast, the United States was a democratic, capitalist nation that valued representative government and private enterprise. After the war, the Soviet Union and the United States both sought to promote their incompatible ideologies. As a result, conflicts broke out over Poland's postwar government, the military and economic status of postwar Germany, and Soviet domination of Eastern Europe.

[52] The social and economic transition from wartime to peacetime resulted in inflation and economic disruptions as millions of workers went out on strike demanding wage increases. The war also breathed new life in the civil rights movement as minorities sought the same rights at home as they had fought for abroad. In the long term, however, the war ended the Depression, created economic opportunities, and brought prosperity to many Americans.

Unit 9

Test Bank Questions

Match the terms below with the following descriptions. Write the letter of the correct answer. You will not use all the terms.

a. Peace Corps
b. de jure segregation
c. New Left
d. Vietnamization
e. Nation of Islam
f. Tet Offensive
g. Medicare

h. Equal Rights Amendment (ERA)
i. (SNCC) Student Nonviolent Coordinating Committee
j. Civil Rights Act of 1964
k. Students for a Democratic Society (SDS)
l. de facto segregation
m. Gulf of Tonkin Resolution
n. Volunteers in Service to America (VISTA)

1. program that provides health care for the elderly

2. legal separation of African Americans and white Americans

3. measure that authorized President Johnson to escalate the United States involvement in Vietnam

4. organization designed to help poor people in the United States

5. Viet Cong military action against South Vietnam

6. program to send American volunteers abroad to help developing nations

7. legislation that banned discrimination in all public facilities

8. militant African American group that promotes separation from white people

9. Nixon's policy to replace American forces with South Vietnamese soldiers

10. political movement that promoted radical change as the only way to solve problems such as poverty and racism

Write the letter of the correct ending.

11. The Great Society provided the most aid to
    A) poor Americans. B) the space program.
    C) small businesses. D) middle-class Americans.

12. The Warren Commission was formed to
    A) protect African American voting rights.
    B) coordinate the Bay of Pigs invasion.
    C) supervise social welfare programs.
    D) investigate the Kennedy assassination.

Test Bank Questions

Write the letter of the correct ending.

13. As a result of the Cuban missile crisis,

    A) the United States built up its nuclear arsenal.

    B) the Alliance for Progress was formed.

    C) President Kennedy regained his prestige and emerged a hero.

    D) the Soviets constructed the Berlin Wall.

14. As a leader in the civil rights movement, Martin Luther King, Jr., is most remembered for promoting

    A) civil disobedience.   B) freedom rides.

    C) militant tactics.   D) teach-ins.

15. Malcolm X encouraged African Americans to

    A) join the "back-to-Africa" movement.

    B) assimilate into white culture.

    C) seek change through political means.

    D) separate themselves from whites.

16. One effect of the civil rights movement was that it

    A) ended de facto discrimination.

    B) united civil rights organizations into a single, powerful group.

    C) inspired women to fight against gender discrimination.

    D) improved living conditions in America's cities.

17. The voice of migratory farm workers in the 1960s was that of

    A) Russell Means.   B) César Chávez.

    C) James Baldwin.   D) Dennis Banks.

18. In her book <u>Silent Spring</u>, Rachel Carson attacked

    A) the building of nuclear power plants.

    B) forest conservation efforts.

    C) the pollution of coal-burning plants.

    D) the use of chemical pesticides.

19. United States policymakers claimed that involvement in the Vietnam War was necessary to protect

    A) U.S. trade with Southeast Asia.

    B) democracy abroad.

    C) American citizens in North Vietnam.

    D) the global economy.

Test Bank Questions

Write the letter of the correct ending.

20. Adherents to the counterculture were most likely to do all of the following EXCEPT

   A) adopt the dress of working-class people.

   B) experiment with psychedelic drugs.

   C) protest U.S. involvement in the Vietnam War.

   D) advocate traditional marriage.

21. President Johnson decided not to run for reelection in 1968 largely because

   A) he disapproved of the escalation measures imposed by Congress.

   B) his Great Society programs had failed.

   C) he had lost the support of the Democratic party.

   D) the antiwar movement had severely damaged his reputation.

Use the graph of American Public Opinion to answer the following questions.

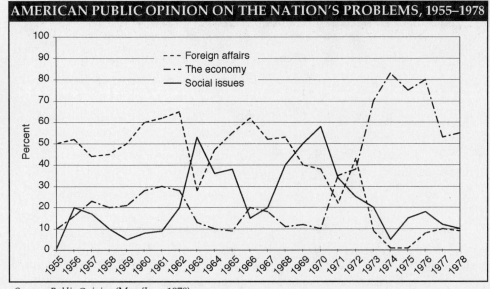

AMERICAN PUBLIC OPINION ON THE NATION'S PROBLEMS, 1955–1978

Source: *Public Opinion* (May/June 1978)

22. When were social issues of greatest concern to most Americans?

23. When did most Americans become more worried about the economy than foreign affairs?

24. Why did over fifty percent of Americans polled consider foreign affairs the country's major problem from 1964 to 1968?

Answer the following questions.

25. This unit is called "The Upheaval of the Sixties." What movements and events would you cite to support this description of the 1960s?

Test Bank Questions

Answer the following questions.

26. What assumptions did President Johnson make about foreign affairs and foreign leaders? How did these assumptions influence his approach to foreign affairs?

27. How did the African American struggle for civil rights in the 1960s affect other ethnic and minority groups in American society?

Match the terms below with the following descriptions. Write the letter of the correct answer. You will not use all the terms.

a. Freedon Rides
b. Civil Rights Act of 1964
c. Environmental Protection Agency (EPA)
d. Black Power
e. new Frontier
f. new Left
g. Gulf of Tonkin Resolution
h. Tet Offensive
i. Immigration Act of 1965
j. Peace Corps
k. Limited Test Ban Treaty
l. March on Washington
m. Volunteers in Service to American (VISTA)

28. The Viet Cong won an important psychological victory during the _____.

29. The _____ banned discrimination in all public facilities.

30. The _____ was the first nuclear agreement signed since the development of the atomic bomb.

31. The _____ was organized to lobby for passage of Kennedy's civil rights bill.

32. Rachel Carson's <u>Silent Spring</u> sparked a debate that led the government to establish the _____.

33. Civil rights activists used _____ to protest segregated bus terminals.

34. President Kennedy's broad reform program was known as the _____.

35. President Kennedy created the _____ to send volunteers abroad to help developing countries.

36. The _____ removed the discriminatory quotas on people from areas outside northern and western Europe.

37. The _____ movement encouraged African Americans to take pride in their culture and heritage.

Write the letter of the correct answer.

38. What was one goal of the Great Society?
    A) to balance the budget
    B) to land a man on the moon
    C) to generate new tax revenues
    D) to end poverty in the United States

Test Bank Questions

Write the letter of the correct answer.

39. Which of the following contributed most to John F. Kennedy's popularity with the American public?
    A) his political experience
    B) his idealism and youth
    C) his religious devotion
    D) his legislative record

40. Which of the following was a major success for President Kennedy?
    A) the creation of an Alliance for Progress
    B) the Bay of Pigs invasion
    C) the Berlin crisis
    D) the Cuban missile crisis

41. What was the main goal of most African American civil rights groups in the 1960s?
    A) to gain citizenship rights
    B) to promote suffrage
    C) to enact social welfare programs
    D) to end segregation

42. What accounts for the success of the Southern Christian Leadership Conference (SCLC)?
    A) Unlike other civil rights groups, the SCLC was not interracial.
    B) The SCLC used more militant tactics than other groups.
    C) The SCLC gave young African Americans a chance to make decisions.
    D) The SCLC relied on economic boycotts and other forms of nonviolent protest.

43. What did the Nation of Islam promote?
    A) a "back-to-Africa" movement
    B) African American integration with white culture
    C) nonviolent confrontation
    D) segregation of whites and African Americans

44. Which of the following groups used the most militant tactics?
    A) American Indian Movement
    B) Japanese American Citizens League
    C) United Farm Workers
    D) National Organization for Women

45. What was the purpose of the Equal Rights Amendment (ERA)?
    A) to outlaw gender discrimination
    B) to ensure the voting rights of African Americans
    C) to protect women's right to personal privacy
    D) to guarantee equal rights for all racial groups

Test Bank Questions

Write the letter of the correct answer.

46. Which of the following enabled President Johnson to escalate United States involvement in the Vietnam War?

   A) Gulf of Tonkin Resolution   B) Tet Offensive

   C) Vietnamization   D) My Lai massacre

47. Which of the following best describes Students for a Democratic Society (SDS)?

   A) They believed that the counterculture threatened democratic principles.

   B) They were deeply committed to containing communism at all costs.

   C) They promoted the Vietnam War as a fight for democracy.

   D) They were disenchanted with American society as a whole.

48. Which of the following was NOT an effect of the antiwar movement in the United States?

   A) Nixon's invasion of Cambodia

   B) Nixon's Vietnamization policy

   C) a reassessment of the global mission of the United States

   D) withdrawal of President Johnson from the presidential race

Use the graph of American Public Opinion to answer the following questions.

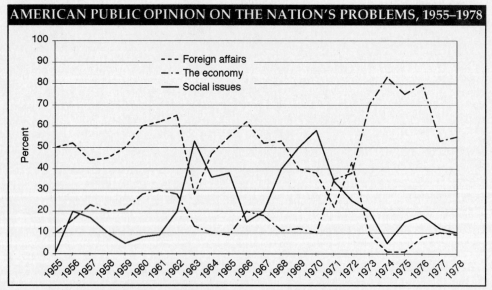

Source: *Public Opinion* (May/June 1978)

49. When were Americans more concerned with social problems than foreign affairs?

Test Bank Questions

Use the graph of American Public Opinion to answer the following questions.

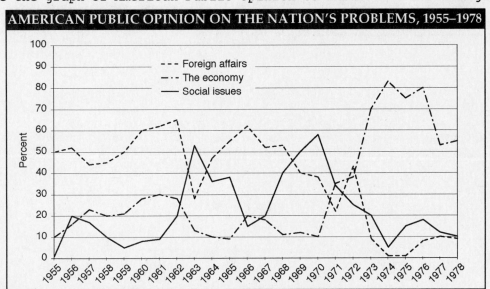

AMERICAN PUBLIC OPINION ON THE NATION'S PROBLEMS, 1955–1978

Source: *Public Opinion* (May/June 1978)

50. What concerned most Americans when John F. Kennedy (1961–1963) was President?

51. Using the information presented in the graph, what conclusions can you draw about the 1970s?

Answer the following questions.

52. What do you think were the main issues that caused division within American society in the 1960s? Choose one issue you have cited and explain how that issue divided society.

53. Dr. Martin Luther King, Jr., and César Chávez both became national heroes as a result of their civil rights efforts. What qualities and achievements made these men "heroes"?

54. How did the social climate in the United States during the 1960s seem to lend itself to the rise of a counterculture?

Test Bank Answer Key

[1] g

[2] b

[3] m

[4] n

[5] f

[6] a

[7] j

[8] e

[9] d

[10] c

[11] A

[12] D

[13] C

[14] A

[15] D

[16] C

[17] B

[18] D

[19] B

[20] D

[21] D

[22] about 1963 and again in the late 1960s

[23] starting about 1973

[24] The war in Vietnam had escalated.

Test Bank Answer Key

American society experienced great social upheaval in the 1960s as a result of the struggle for civil rights, the creation of a youth counterculture that rejected conventional norms, and opposition to the escalating war in Vietnam. Riots in American cities, antiwar demonstrations, teach-ins, and the occupation of Alcatraz are just a [25] few examples of social discontent.

President Johnson assumed that he could deal with foreign leaders in the same way he dealt with policymakers at home. His aggressive stance and dismissive attitude toward smaller nations led to conflict with Panama and the invasion of the Dominican Republic. His policy in Vietnam reflected his determination to do whatever was necessary to [26] win the war.

Encouraged by the gains of the civil rights movement, Latinos, Asian Americans, Native Americans, and women launched their own movements to fight discrimination and promote social, economic, and political equality for their groups. They used the legal tools (1964 Civil Rights Act) and tactics of the civil rights movement to achieve their [27] goals.

[28] h

[29] b

[30] k

[31] l

[32] c

[33] a

[34] e

[35] j

[36] i

[37] d

[38] D

[39] B

[40] D

[41] D

[42] D

[43] D

Test Bank Answer Key

[44] A _____

[45] A _____

[46] A _____

[47] D _____

[48] A _____

[49] around 1963 and again at the end of the 1960s

[50] foreign affairs

[51] Americans were very concerned with the economy, most probably because the country was in a recession.

[52] The struggle for civil rights and racial and gender equality, creation of a youth counterculture, and U.S. involvement in the Vietnam War were issues dividing American society in the 1960s. The women's movement, for example, caused dissension between those who favored women's rights and passage of the ERA and those who argued that a woman's highest purpose in life should be to stay home and raise children. The issue of abortion rights further intensified the division.

[53] Both men gained national recognition and respect for their leadership, social consciousness, and continuous commitment to nonviolent action. In spite of death threats, both leaders devoted their lives to improving conditions for their respective ethnic groups.

[54] In the 1960s, many disillusioned Americans--students, women, and ethnic minorities--began challenging the status quo and establishing movements to correct injustices in society. As the Vietnam War escalated and antiwar sentiment intensified, protest became a way of life, especially at colleges and universities around the country. Social criticism and the challenge to authority created a climate conducive to the creation of a youth counterculture looking for alternatives to traditional patterns of living and a reason for "dropping out."

Unit 10

Test Bank Questions

Complete each of the following sentences by selecting the appropriate term from the choices listed in parentheses.

1. The Democratic nominee for President in 1968 was Lyndon Johnson's Vice President, (George C. Wallace, Hubert Humphrey).

2. The judge who presided over the trial of the Watergate burglars was (Clarence Thomas, John J. Sirica).

3. Top officials in the Nixon White House commited (amnesty, perjury).

4. Nelson Mandela and (Allan Bakke, Frederik W. de Klerk) received the Nobel Peace Prize for their efforts to end apartheid in South Africa.

5. After Vice President Spiro Agnew resigned for accepting bribes, President Nixon appointed (Henry A. Kissinger, Gerald R. Ford) to the position.

6. Anwar el-Sadat of Egypt and Israeli Prime Minister Menachem Begin negotiated the (Helsinki Accords, Camp David Accords).

7. President Reagan remained committed to a missile defense program known as the (Strategic Defense Initiative, Strategic Arms Limitation Talks).

8. In the mid–1980s, United States-Soviet relations improved when (Boris Yeltsin, Mikhail Gorbachev) proposed a program of economic reform and political openness.

9. President Reagan's economic program was based on the theory of (supply-side economics, stagflation).

10. The head of the task force set up to define a new approach to national health care was (Al Gore, Hillary Rodham Clinton).

11. In 1993 PLO head Yasir Arafat and Israeli Prime Minister (Slobodan Milosevic, Yitzhak Rabin) signed a peace agreement.

12. American society in the early 1990s was engaged in a movement toward (multiculturalism, new federalism).

Write the letter of the correct ending.

13. President Nixon took bold steps in

    A) nominating women and minorities.

    B) dealing with the economy.

    C) improving relations with communist nations.

    D) advancing civil rights.

Test Bank Questions

Write the letter of the correct ending.

14. All of the following helped Richard M. Nixon to win the presidential election of 1968 EXCEPT the
    A) disillusionment following the assassinations of King and Kennedy.
    B) rift in the Democratic political coalition.
    C) OPEC oil embargo.
    D) negative reaction to antiwar protests.

15. A significant foreign policy achievement of the Nixon presidency was
    A) United States victory in Vietnam.
    B) détente with the Soviet Union.
    C) establishment of formal diplomatic relations with China.
    D) the fall of the Berlin Wall.

16. During the 1976 presidential campaign, Democrat Jimmy Carter appealed to Americans largely because of his
    A) commitment to truth and honesty.
    B) political experience.
    C) wartime experiences as a naval officer.
    D) strong economic reform.

17. The greatest achievement of President Carter's political career was probably the
    A) negotiation of the release of American hostages in Iran.
    B) SALT II agreements.
    C) reorganization of the Nuclear Regulatory Commission.
    D) Camp David Accords.

18. In general, the New Right coalition formed in the 1980s
    A) encouraged the policy of affirmative action.
    B) wanted to reduce the size of government.
    C) supported broadened social programs.
    D) sought limits to economic competition.

19. President Reagan's program to promote economic recovery included
    A) high tax increases on the most wealthy citizens.
    B) major tax cuts.
    C) the "Whip Inflation Now" campaign.
    D) a drastic reduction in defense spending.

20. President Bush's popularity increased significantly as a result of the
    A) Panama Canal Treaty.   B) Persian Gulf War.
    C) Iran-contra affair.   D) fall of the Soviet Union.

Test Bank Questions

Write the letter of the correct ending.

21. When the American public appeared reluctant to get involved, Clinton reneged on his pledge to

 A) participate in the North American Free Trade Agreement (NAFTA).

 B) impose economic sanctions on South Africa.

 C) support exiled Haitian president Jean-Bertrand Aristide.

 D) send additional U.S. troops to Bosnia.

22. At the beginning of his administration, Clinton made his strongest efforts to tackle the problems of

 A) multiculturalism and aid to education.

 B) health-care reform and the federal deficit.

 C) abortion rights and school prayer.

 D) deregulation and high interest rates.

Use the table of Level of Education to answer the following questions.

LEVEL OF EDUCATION IN THE UNITED STATES LABOR FORCE			
	1969 Percent	1979 Percent	1990 Percent
Total labor force	100.0	100.0	100.0
4 years or more of college	12.6	17.6	23.2
1 to 3 years of college	12.6	17.5	21.3
High school or less	74.8	64.8	55.5
4 years of high school	38.4	40.0	39.4
Less than 4 years of high school	36.4	24.8	16.1

Source: U.S. Department of Labor, Bureau of Labor Statistics, *Occupational Outlook Quarterly* (Summer 1992)

23. What percent of the total labor force had less than 4 years of high school in 1969? In 1990?

24. What trend is shown in the chart?

25. Based on the chart, what conclusions can you draw about jobs in the United States in 1990?

Answer the following questions.

26. Compare the agenda and priorities of the Reagan administration with those of the Clinton administration.

27. How might the New Right have evaluated the Clinton administration in 1993 and early 1994? Give reasons to support your answer.

28. Cite examples to illustrate how the personal beliefs of Presidents and other policymakers can affect foreign and domestic policies.

Complete each of the following sentences by selecting the appropriate term from the choices listed in parentheses.

29. The Democratic presidential candidate assassinated in 1968 was (Robert F. Kennedy, Hubert Humphrey).

Test Bank Questions

Complete each of the following sentences by selecting the appropriate term from the choices listed in parentheses.

30. Secretary of State (John Erlichman, Henry A. Kissinger) was President Nixon's most trusted adviser.

31. President Nixon managed to bring about (détente, realpolitik) in relations between the United States and the Soviet Union.

32. In 1978, President Carter helped negotiate a framework for peace, known as the (Helsinki Accords, Camp David Accords), between Egypt and Israel.

33. President Carter was criticized for allowing (Shah Mohammad Reza Pahlavi, Ayatollah Ruholla Khomeini) to receive medical treatment in the United States.

34. (Cyrus Vance, Nelson Rockefeller) was Secretary of State under President Carter.

35. President Reagan's program to lower taxes in order to increase the money supply was based on the theory of (stagflation, supply-side economics).

36. The nomination hearings of Supreme Court Justice (Clarence Thomas, Sandra Day O'Connor) brought the issue of sexual harassment into the national spotlight.

37. (Hillary Rodham Clinton, Henry Cisneros) led the team whose work resulted in the Clinton administration's health-care reform proposal.

38. Members of the New Right would most likely favor the election of (George Bush, Bill Clinton) as President.

39. In South Africa, Nelson Mandela led the struggle to end the systematic separation of the races, or (apartheid, amnesty).

40. The Clinton administration pledged its support to Russia's president (Boris Yeltsin, Slobodan Milosevic).

Write the letter of the correct answer.

41. Which of the following helped Richard M. Nixon win the presidency in 1968?

A) the oil embargo

B) antiwar demonstrators at the Republican convention

C) disillusioned Democrats who voted for no one

D) the Poor People's Campaign

Test Bank Questions

Write the letter of the correct answer.

42. Which of the following best describes President Nixon's domestic policies?
    A) He increased government outlays on social programs.
    B) His policies controlled spending and slowed inflation.
    C) His policies slowed the advancement of civil rights.
    D) He supported free speech and orderly demonstrations.

43. Which of the following forced President Nixon to resign?
    A) his involvement in the S & L scandals
    B) his presence at the Saturday Night Massacre
    C) his orders to Oliver North in the Iran-contra affair
    D) his involvement in the Watergate scandal

44. Which of the following did NOT harm President Ford's popularity?
    A) the Helsinki Accords
    B) the Nixon pardon
    C) his "Whip Inflation Now" campaign
    D) conflicts with Congress

45. Which of the following objectives was Carter able to achieve?
    A) pushing domestic programs through Congress
    B) assuming the role of peacemaker in foreign affairs
    C) promoting energy conservation
    D) negotiating the release of U.S. hostages in Iran

46. What was the goal of conservative Republicans in the 1980s?
    A) to enact broader social programs
    B) to regulate market forces and free enterprise
    C) to reverse policies of the New Deal and Great Society
    D) to increase the power of government

47. Which of the following best describes the economic conditions during the Reagan years?
    A) The nation experienced an economic recession.
    B) Middle-class citizens enjoyed many new benefits.
    C) The gap widened between rich and poor.
    D) Wealthy citizens were often the targets of high tax increases.

48. Why did Reagan and Bush intervene in Nicaragua and El Salvador?
    A) to stop the flow of illegal arms to Iran
    B) to prevent a Cuban invasion
    C) to protect American investments and trade
    D) to undermine Marxist and left-wing governments

Chapter 45

Test Bank Questions

Write the letter of the correct answer.

49. What was one of President Clinton's main goals at the beginning of his presidency?

A) to eliminate international tariffs

B) to establish a national health-care program

C) to create new guidelines for public schools

D) to prevent the spread of communism

50. Which of the following best describes a trend in American society in the 1990s?

A) The United States moved closer to becoming a biracial democracy.

B) Homosexuals were welcomed

C) Most new immigrants came from Eastern Europe.

D) The nation experienced a significant rise in its minority populations.

Use the table of Level of Education to answer the following questions.

LEVEL OF EDUCATION IN THE UNITED STATES LABOR FORCE	1969 Percent	1979 Percent	1990 Percent
Total labor force	100.0	100.0	100.0
4 years or more of college	12.6	17.6	23.2
1 to 3 years of college	12.6	17.5	21.3
High school or less	74.8	64.8	55.5
4 years of high school	38.4	40.0	39.4
Less than 4 years of high school	36.4	24.8	16.1

Source: U.S. Department of Labor, Bureau of Labor Statistics, *Occupational Outlook Quarterly* (Summer 1992)

51. What percent of the total labor force had 4 years or more of college in 1969? In 1990?

52. How does the percent of workers with a high school education or less in 1990 compare with the percent in 1969?

53. What prediction can you make about the U.S. labor force in the 1990s based on the information in the table?

Answer the following questions.

54. How do the foreign policy challenges the United States faced during the cold war compare with those it faces in the post-cold war period? Give examples to support your answer.

55. How do you think the New Right would have reacted to President Carter's presidency? Explain.

56. In the 1992 presidential race, President Clinton promised to "change" American society. In what way were Clinton's early actions a "change" from the conservative Republican years?

Test Bank Answer Key

[1] Hubert Humphrey

[2] John J. Sirica

[3] perjury

[4] Frederik W. de Klerk

[5] Gerald R. Ford

[6] Camp David Accords

[7] Strategic Defense Initiative

[8] Mikhail Gorbachev

[9] supply-side economics

[10] Hillary Rodham Clinton

[11] Yitzhak Rabin

[12] multiculturalism

[13] C

[14] C

[15] B

[16] A

[17] D

[18] B

[19] B

[20] B

[21] D

[22] B

[23] 36.4 percent; 16.1 percent

[24] More American workers had attained higher levels of education in 1990 than was the case twenty years ago; fewer workers had not completed high school.

[25] A higher percentage of jobs required more highly educated workers in 1990 than was the case twenty years ago.

Test Bank Answer Key

The Reagan administration was very concerned with the cold war and national security. Consequently, high priorities included increasing spending for defense and supporting governments abroad that were sympathetic to the United States. The administration was also intent on reforming tax policy, downsizing government, and shifting social responsibility to the states. Consequently, many federal welfare programs were cut. By contrast, the Clinton administration's domestic priorities were to reduce the federal deficit and to enact a universal health-care plan. Internationally, the Clinton administration had to chart a new direction as it confronted the end of the cold war and increased ethnic tensions in various parts of the world. Foreign priorities included helping formerly communist nations develop democratic, capitalist societies, and participating with [26] international organizations in peacekeeping and humanitarian missions.

The New Right would approve Clinton's spending cuts but would dislike his economic program of tax increases as well as his health-care reform package, arguing that free market forces rather than government-imposed controls were needed to stimulate the economy and reduce the deficit. The New Right conservatives who subscribed to traditional family and religious values would also have objected to [27] Clinton's support of homosexual rights and his pro-choice stand.

Examples include: Secretary of State Henry Kissinger's belief in realpolitik relaxed tensions between the superpowers and changed

the direction of U.S. foreign policy during the Nixon years from

containment to détente. President Ford's belief in limited government led him to veto bills to create a consumer protection agency and to fund programs for education, housing, and health care. President Reagan's conservative philosophy and his steadfast belief in self-reliance resulted in drastic cutbacks in social welfare programs and a greater gap between the "haves" and "have nots" in society. Carter's religious beliefs and his deep sense of morality complicated relations between the United States and the Soviet Union and ultimately hurt his chances for reelection. Both Carter's and Clinton's belief in diversity gave increased numbers of women and [28] minorities political representation.

[29] Robert F. Kennedy

[30] Henry A. Kissinger

[31] détente

[32] Camp David Accords

[33] Shah Mohammad Reza Pahlavi

[34] Cyrus Vance

Test Bank Answer Key

[35] supply-side economics

[36] Clarence Thomas

[37] Hillary Rodham Clinton

[38] George Bush

[39] apartheid

[40] Boris Yeltsin

[41] C

[42] C

[43] D

[44] A

[45] B

[46] C

[47] C

[48] D

[49] B

[50] D

[51] 12.6 percent; 23.2 percent

[52] The percent has dropped from 74.8 percent in 1969 to 55.5 percent in 1990.

[53] Workers with 4 years of high school or less will continue to have trouble finding a job. In the 1990s, more jobs will require a college education.

[54] Foreign policy challenges during the cold war focused on arms limitation, national defense, and containing communism abroad. In the post-cold war era, U.S. foreign policy must focus on the collapse of communism and the creation of new governments in Eastern Europe and in the former Soviet Union. New challenges include how to help formerly communist nations implement economic reforms, make a peaceful transition to a democratic political system, and end ethnic cleansing campaigns within their borders.

Test Bank Answer Key

On a personal level, they probably would have approved of Carter's deep religious faith, devotion to family, and moral commitment. Economically, they would have favored his deregulation policy and his weakened support of social programs, but would have disapproved of

[55] his attempts to balance inflation and economic growth.

Clinton's appointments represented the "face of America" more than the staffs and cabinets appointed by Nixon, Reagan, and Bush. In addition, Clinton brought a new attitude of greater tolerance for controversial issues such as homosexuality and abortion rights. In foreign affairs, the Clinton administration was forced to chart a new course in a changing world brought about by the collapse of communism, the end of the cold war, and an increase in ethnic

[56] tensions.